YOUTH-SERVING
ORGANIZATIONS

YOUTH-SERVING ORGANIZATIONS

National Nongovernmental Associations

BY M. M. CHAMBERS

Second Edition

Prepared for
The American Youth Commission

AMERICAN COUNCIL ON EDUCATION
Washington, D.C., 1941

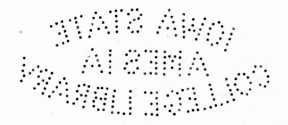

Foreword

FROM the beginning of its existence in 1935 the American Youth Commission has been cognizant of the activities of a large number of national nongovernmental youth-serving organizations of various types and has felt an obligation to keep itself informed as accurately as possible regarding the scope and characteristics of their work.

Officers and directors of some of the leading youth-serving associations have from time to time conferred with members of the staff of the American Youth Commission. With many of them there have been fruitful exchanges of correspondence. The Commission's relations with these organizations have been mutually cordial and helpful.

One of the earliest documents published for the American Youth Commission was the first edition of *Youth-Serving Organizations*, appearing in lithoprinted form in 1937. So great was the demand for this document that the edition was exhausted within approximately a year after its appearance. Continued requests led eventually to the confirmation of a tentative decision to prepare and publish the present second edition, in more attractive and durable form.

The staff member chiefly responsible for this work, M. M. Chambers, is author of the pamphlet, *The Community and Its Young People*, and co-author of several other staff reports. He is widely known as a writer for the educational press, having contributed some 200 articles to national educational journals during the past ten years. He has also contributed articles on youth to the *Social Work Year Book*, the *New International Yearbook*, the *Encyclopedia of Educational Research*, and the *Annals of the American Academy of Political and Social Science*.

Formerly Dr. Chambers was for four years a high school teacher, after which he was successively a teacher of political science in colleges and universities and a research and editorial worker for philanthropic foundations. During recent summer terms he has served as associate professor of education at the Ohio State University.

The American Youth Commission was established in 1935 by the American Council on Education from which it received a mandate to:

1. consider all the needs of youth and appraise the facilities and resources for serving those needs;

2. plan experiments and programs which will be most helpful in solving the problems of youth;

3. popularize and promote desirable plans of action through publications, conferences, and demonstrations.

As in the case of other staff reports prepared for the Commission, the author of the present volume is responsible for the statements which are made; they are not necessarily endorsed by the Commission or by its Director. The Director does take responsibility for the organization of all research projects, the selection of staff, and the approval of staff reports as meriting publication. The Commission is responsible for the determination of the general areas in which research is conducted under its auspices, and from time to time it adopts and publishes statements which represent specifically the conclusions and recommendations of the Commission.

One such statement, entitled "Should Youth Organize?" is reprinted as an appendix to this volume. Another such statement based in part upon the study of youth-serving organizations is *Community Responsibility for Youth*, of which copies will be sent upon request.

FLOYD W. REEVES
Director

Acknowledgments

WITHOUT the cooperation of the officers of the associations named in this book, its making would have been impossible. For their recognition of the possibilities in the undertaking and their voluntary participation in it, let the appreciation of the American Youth Commission and its staff be here recorded.

To Mary P. Eickhoff and to Fredelle Fishburn, both of whom gave faithful and intelligent assistance in assembling and arranging the materials for this edition, conspicuous recognition is due. For errors and other shortcomings, responsibility is mine alone.

M. M. CHAMBERS

Introduction

"TO consider all the needs of American youth between the ages of 12 and 25, and to ascertain by investigation of the agencies concerned with the care and education of youth how effectively these needs are being served" is one of the several purposes of the American Youth Commission of the American Council on Education. In pursuance of this it is necessary to take notice of a large number of voluntary associations of various types, national in scope and nation-wide in influence, whose activities impinge upon the welfare of youth in numerous ways.

Everyone is more or less vaguely familiar with some of these organizations, but many persons are quite unaware that their number runs into the hundreds, and few are acquainted with their precise purposes, the extent of their activities, or their size as measured in terms of men and money.

To provide a convenient catalog of these sorts of information, from which may be gained something of a composite picture of national organizations working with youth in various ways, is the purpose of this book. The data presented have been obtained very largely by correspondence directly with the secretaries of the associations studied. Any evaluation of the purposes or practices of the individual organizations is outside the scope of this report and is expressly disclaimed. There is no intent to set up an "accredited list," and this compilation does not express approval or condemnation of any organization.

The more modest aim is to exhibit brief descriptions of the organizations, largely in the words of their own officers or their own literature. These, it is hoped, will afford much valuable information regarding the influences to which youth are subject, as well as the efforts being made in behalf of youth welfare through a type of social endeavor which plays a considerable part in the current American scene.

It is, of course, in the thousands of local communities that the concrete, immediate problems of youth are dealt with; and a broad-scale review of a large number of national organizations, such as is here presented, cannot purport to offer any direct and specific solutions for local problems. Nevertheless, community leaders in all corners of the land will find it desirable to know in what manner and with what means the various national associations are seeking to influence youth or to advance youth welfare.

This book is designed to supply basic information bearing on such questions as: (1) What are the general purposes and activities of the national youth-serving organizations which have local branches in my community? (2) Are there any national groups not represented in my locality whose aims and policies indicate that a local branch would be an asset to the youth of this community?

Moreover, a knowledge of the organization and work of all the national associations will be a useful prerequisite to the consideration of the coordination of their efforts, either on the national or the local level. All observers seem agreed that there must somehow be brought about, as our social organization grows more complex, a more effective cooperation, not only among nongovernmental agencies but between public and private instrumentalities as well.

Part I of this book presents comments on the place of private associations in American life, suggests further studies, and offers some statistical summaries of data drawn from Part II, which is a descriptive inventory of 320 organizations.

Contents

PART I

SUMMARY PREVIEW

I. The Role of Nongovernmental Associations

Voluntary nongovernmental associations have long been a conspicuous feature of American life. When the French commentator, de Tocqueville, visited the United States a little more than a century ago, he wrote: "The Americans of all ages, all conditions, and all dispositions constantly form associations . . . religious, moral, serious, futile, restricted, enormous, or diminutive. The Americans make associations to give entertainments, to found establishments for education, to send missionaries to the antipodes, and in this manner they found hospitals, prisons, schools. . . . "

Some of these functions have become exclusively or largely governmental since de Tocqueville's time, but the American propensity for private associations still flourishes, as is evidenced by the fact that half of the organizations listed in this report are not more than twenty-one years old.

Services of Voluntary Societies

Nongovernmental associations not only do a great deal to supply the material and spiritual wants of the clientele of their local units; many of them also provide channels of expression through which all who are like-minded concerning particular social problems or other public questions may join in an effective presentation of their views.

Sometimes those engaging in the performance of this latter function have been referred to in terms of opprobrium as "pressure groups," but such services ought not to be too sweepingly condemned. They constitute a part of the machinery of democracy and could not be wholly dispensed with, at least until our political organizations become better adjusted as avenues for the expression of public opinion.

Our two major national political parties notoriously fail to represent the shades of opinion which press for and deserve recognition. They have both embraced adherents of all degrees from extreme conservatism to outspoken progressivism. Real differences between them vanished in startling succession for many years, and they tended to become mere rival engines for political conquest, with no clear-cut division no the real social issues of the day. It is not long since they were cynically but aptly dubbed comparable to Tweedledum and Tweedledee.

The two great national parties extend their influence into half a hundred state and territorial capitals, into three thousand counties, and into scores of thousands of local precincts, where they prevent the development of independent local parties and constantly befog a realistic approach to local problems by confusing them with state and national issues to which they bear no direct relation.

In this situation there is an important field of service for nonpartisan organizations interested in advancing the public welfare in its various phases. It is not to be deplored that we have organized protagonists of public education, public health, public safety, public recreation, and many other essential services which must be improved and expanded as our civilization becomes more complex.

Growth of Cooperation

It is true that mutual jealousies and destructive rivalries among these organizations must be minimized, that mutual understanding must be substituted for suspicion, and cooperation for competitive strife. The broad view of the public welfare as a whole can take precedence over the narrow view of the interests of any one group. This viewpoint is growing gradually.

It is modestly hoped that the arrangement of basic data concerning the membership, purposes, activities, publications, staffs, and finances of more than three hundred organizations in this book may be of some small service in aiding their mutual understanding and in facilitating a broad view of the whole of this area of youth service.

The existence of a multiplicity of national organizations, diverse in purposes and methods, is in itself something of a safeguard against the wholesale regimentation of youth which is a threat to democracy. In so far as these organizations function in the crystallization and expression of opinion on public questions, their diversity is to be expected, and their coalescence or complete harmonization not to be hoped for.

But in so far as they are agencies of social service offering programs of education, recreation, relief, or health building, a growing degree of coordination and cooperation among them may be rightly demanded. In these fields youth and society will long be served by both public and private agencies, and the necessity for weaving their services into a seamless fabric without gaps is now supreme.

RELATIONS BETWEEN SCHOOLS AND OTHER YOUTH-SERVING AGENCIES

The question of techniques of cooperation between the public schools and private associations serving youth is one which this book does not attempt to answer in full. Manifestly any such cooperation must have its limits. The public schools are designed for all young persons and must guard against the intrusion of sectarian, partisan, or commercial propaganda.

On the other hand, schools ought not and cannot insulate their pupils from the currents of public opinion and civic activity, and it would seem that they may profitably permit limited use of their plants and equipment by nonprofit organizations of or for youth, so long as this use does not interfere with the regular public school program.

The growing tendency to develop workable arrangements whereby school buildings and grounds are made available for recreational and other community uses is salutary. The desirability of allowing school buildings to stand unused for many hours even on school days, to be vacant for many whole days during the school year, and to remain closed for weeks or months at a time during vacations, may well be questioned. These conditions tend to diminish as modern schools expand and develop their extracurricular programs for their regular pupils, but it must be admitted that as yet in most places the school plant is not actually operated full time.

The operation of the plant involves costs for such items as heating, lighting, cleaning, and custodianship. In some places these expenses, even when occasioned solely by the presence of a nonschool organization, are borne wholly by the board of education. In other places the use of the buildings is granted only upon payment of fees fixed at different levels and designed to reimburse the board of education for the additional costs entailed.

The protection of the school property from damage is always a factor to be considered, and the services of the school custodian-janitor are sometimes obtained only with difficulty and under circumstances likely to promote friction and resentment. Overtime work in the evenings, even when paid, is often inconvenient or forbidden by labor union rules. Obviously these difficulties can be avoided if the late afternoon and evening use of the plant is planned in advance for a considerable period and made a regularly budgeted and anticipated activity instead of an occasional emergency one.

Cooperation between schools and other youth-serving agencies is being aided by the increasing recognition of ability and experience in the leadership of nonschool associations of boys and girls as a professional asset for a public school teacher; but on no account should such qualifications be accepted as substitutes for the minimum essential combination of scholarship, character, and teaching skill.

The teacher has an obligation to maintain a sympathetic familiarity with the aims and methods of all reputable youth-serving agencies. This obligation is being recognized by institutions for the education of teachers, some of which are taking appropriate action by improving their instruction in health and physical education and by making available new offerings in recreational leadership and social group work. Occasionally a short period of actual field work with some youth-serving agency is made a recognized part of the preparation of a public school teacher.

In their professional relations with youth, teachers are generally handicapped by the burden of numbers, so that in the main their dealings with their pupils must necessarily be in the mass rather than as individuals. A reduction in the pupil-teacher ratio to a point where the teacher has some chance of knowing each pupil more intimately than is now usually possible is much to be desired.

Public school teachers commonly, too, have their time so fully occupied with curricular and extracurricular school duties that little opportunity exists for them to undertake effective work in cooperation with nonschool agencies. For this reason the suggestion is made that the teaching load ought to be reduced, or at least that certain teachers having a taste for work with nonschool agencies and skill in it should be formally relieved of an appropriate fraction of the regular teaching load.

The teacher is a key person in community youth service and can perform important functions in advancing the integration of the efforts of the several agencies if educated to understand and appreciate their services and given reasonable opportunity to cooperate with them.

Further analysis of the problem of the relationships of the schools to nonschool organizations requires extensive consultation with representatives of both fields and careful investigation of its many aspects. This might well be the subject of another study.

WHAT IS A YOUTH-SERVING ORGANIZATION?

By simplest definition, a youth-serving organization is one whose activities are devoted wholly or in substantial part to advancing the welfare of young persons. The associations studied in this report are all thought to come within the meaning of such a definition. Unquestionably not all national nongovernmental societies in this category, especially if the definition be liberally interpreted, have found their way into the present list.

Needless to say, omission of any such organization does not imply any disparagement of its purposes or activities but is to be accounted for by the limitations on the time and other resources available for the assembling of the compilation. For any omission traceable to ignorance or honest error of judgment, the compiler accepts responsibility. In only a negligible number of cases has any organization ignored repeated requests for the minimum essential data or refused outright to furnish any information.

Omissions arising from the foregoing causes could not always be avoided in the present edition, which is at best only a scratch on the surface of a vast mass of valuable social data which will one day be charted, analyzed, assayed, and scrutinized as an indispensable aid to the best thought in planning the welfare of youth and of society.

YOUTH-MEMBERSHIP ORGANIZATIONS

A bifurcate classification of the organizations suggests itself. Some have their membership composed wholly or largely (50 per cent or more) of persons between the ages of 12 and 25. Others have but few if any youthful members but do devote a substantial part of their efforts to enterprises vital to youth welfare. Of the 320 organizations here treated, 81 are deemed to belong to the former class and 239 to the latter.

Within each of these two major divisions are many variations, not only with respect to the proportion of youth membership to total membership, but also with regard to the relationships between youth organizations and the adult organizations by which they may be sponsored or with which they may be affiliated.

Several of the best-known associations for youth stand quite independent, in theory and in fact, from any single national organization of adults outside their own membership. On the other hand, many youth-membership organizations are frankly "feeders" for their respective parent organizations such as churches, fraternal orders, political parties, or other societies. At first one may tend to scorn this latter type as constituting mere sideshows to adult pressure groups, and unworthy of serious consideration as bona fide youth organizations. Such a view is superficial. These organizations must be reckoned an important factor in youth welfare, for good or ill, because they do engage the enthusiasms of millions of young persons for greater or lesser lengths of time, and often profoundly influence the tone of their subsequent careers.

The fact that the motives for their efforts to capture the interest of youth may seem obvious does not go to the essence. Even if the creation and promotion of denominational religious organizations for youth is an enterprise designed for the institutional preservation of the churches, it may at the same time hold as its highest aim the spiritual welfare of individuals and provide for them a service elsewhere unobtainable, but most essential to their best development.

Some who willingly admit the religious groups to the circle of youth organizations will want to exclude certain societies affiliated with adult organizations which have as their sole or principal object the promotion of some particular "cause" such as the abolition of war, the prohibition of the liquor trade, or other species of social reform.

Some of these types are admittedly mere purveyors of propaganda, special pleaders, with an ubiquitous fringe of fanatics. Would youth have a better chance to understand the world if such societies did not exist? No! A stodgy world it would be without the fiery fanatic to harangue, perhaps amuse, perhaps sadden, perhaps convince the young that he possesses the authentic blueprint of Utopia!

At any rate, if the absence of propaganda is to be the test of an acceptable youth organization, none will be acceptable. Even those societies of youth which are ostensibly free of any affiliation with adult pressure groups often conspicuously, though perhaps unintentionally, operate to indoctrinate their suggestible members with definite patterns of social and economic prejudice. In this matter of propaganda, it is plainly appropriate to invite him who is without sin to cast the first stone.

The organizations identified as primarily youth-membership associations are prominently listed in the introductions to the several sections of Part II in which they respectively appear.

Recommendations formally adopted by the American Youth Commission on April 15, 1940 regarding the question "Should youth organize?" are reprinted verbatim as the Appendix, pages 219–21.

ADULT ORGANIZATIONS SERVING YOUTH

The associations largely or wholly composed of persons above the age of 25 require some preliminary consideration. In the first place, some of them are not strictly membership societies at all but federations of other associations. The constituent units are in some instances other national societies, in other cases local or regional institutions or associations, and in still others a combination of these two, with or without the addition of provision for direct individual memberships.

Another distinction which ought not to be overlooked is that between those adult groups which are chiefly professional in character and which serve youth indirectly through research or the advancement of professional standards, and those others which render direct service to their clientele through local service units.

This distinction is patent in the description of each organization in Part II. It will also be observed that some adult organizations are composed largely of interested and sympathetic laymen bound together by purposes relating exclusively to the welfare of youth, while others consist of a lay membership attracted by a program in which youth service forms only a part.

The latter type may recognize the needs of youth and assume a responsibility toward them in various ways, ranging from the mere incidental impact upon youth of a general social service program to more formal and specific devices such as a temporary committee or standing commission on one or more phases of youth welfare, or a distinct department of the headquarters staff devoted to these purposes.

Some adult lay organizations foster well-organized junior auxiliaries enrolling youth as members, while others induct many young persons under the age of 25 into full membership, and still others exclude youth from any type of membership but conduct far-flung and important local youth service, either by dealing directly with individual young people or by actively aiding approved organizations of boys or girls.

These circumstances make it extremely difficult to obtain a comprehensive and accurate statistical picture of the extent of such service on a national scale; but some national organizations are already compiling annual reports of their efforts and achievements, which, though not models of recording in many senses, are commendable beginnings. In any field of social service the fullest effectiveness cannot be reached on a wide scale until facts and figures are available as to what is actually being done. Policies and plans for further advance must grow largely out of experience, and the only way to preserve experience for accurate reference is in periodic records and reports.

THE ORGANIZATIONS CLASSIFIED

A complete alphabetical list of all associations named herein will be found in the general index of this report. Three hundred and twenty of these organizations are included in the descriptive inventory which forms Part II. There they are grouped into twenty sections, as indicated in the table of contents. This twentyfold classification is something of a departure from common practice, adopted for the convenience of those who may wish to consider separately, and with a minimum of searching, any group of organizations devoted to similar purposes or belonging to an easily recognizable characteristic type.

Any classification is to some extent arbitrary, and none is final. But some subdividing of the mass is an essential prerequisite to accurate observation. Probably each organization named herein has more than one sound reason for being regarded as in a class by itself; but few will object to being viewed in proximity to a manageable number of others of comparable or contrasting functions or aims, though in a few instances the justification for the grouping may at first seem obscure.

A strictly logical classification into mutually exclusive groupings is impossible, and effort has been made to mitigate this difficulty by occasional use of cross references from one group to another, as well as by appending a general index.

II. The Information Sought

Social service is not wholly susceptible of measurement in quantitative terms, but it need not be treated as entirely imponderable. The literature of the field tends probably too much toward the vaguely inspirational and hortatory, and too little toward the factual and the specific. Brevity requires that the substance of this report be confined to a few stereotyped categories of facts.

The descriptive inventory of organizations (Part II) treats each by arranging the data under seven headings: (1) identification and address, (2) membership, (3) purpose, (4) activities, (5) publications, (6) headquarters staff, and (7) fiscal support and operations.

IDENTIFICATION AND ADDRESS

The name of the organization, the street and number, city and state in which the headquarters is located, and the name and title of the principal active executive officer are the items usually constituting the identification and address information. A few variations and qualifications may be mentioned. It is not invariably possible to identify one chief executive officer, especially in the more or less amorphous organizations wherein there may be no paid executive and where executive responsibilities are in fact dispersed without reference to any logical or consistent plan. In such cases the name of the titular executive has generally been used, though occasionally two names appear where apparently the two officers are both active and the *de facto* distinctions between their respective ranks and responsibilities are not clear.

In many important organizations the presidency is an unpaid and largely honorary office, with duties limited to infrequent ceremonial occasions and with its incumbency rotated annually or biennially, while the day-to-day executive work is performed by a paid officer known as executive secretary or director, who is in immediate charge of the headquarters staff. In such cases the latter is taken to be the "principal active executive officer," and the name of the president is omitted.

This practice has been adopted on the theory that inquiries concerning the organization should be addressed to the person in charge of the headquarters office and referred by him to his superiors only when in his judgment the matter requires their attention. From this standard type of structure there are occasional variations, however, and here again resort has sometimes been had to the use of the names of two officers in exceptional cases.

The address given is always that of the permanent headquarters, if such an office is maintained. Many small organizations have no headquarters office other than the home or office of the incumbent president or secretary. Hence the address is subject to change at frequent intervals in some instances.

Viewing the organizations as a whole, it appears that the headquarters of somewhat more than a third of the organizations are located in New York City, a fifth in the city of Washington, and a tenth in the city of Chicago. Thus over 70 per cent of all the organizations are maintaining their headquarters in one of these three cities. It is not surprising that the first and second largest cities in the country, the metropolis of the East and the metropolis of the Middle West respectively, should be favored thus; nor is it to be wondered at that the national capital should figure second in the list as the headquarters locale of national youth-serving organizations.

MEMBERSHIP

The aggregate number of individuals reported as members of the national organization or of its local units is recorded first whenever possible. Thereafter appears the number of local and intermediate units and such information regarding their geographic distribution as is obtainable. Whether the organization is a federation of local associations, a council of national bodies, a unitary direct membership aggregation of individuals, a close corporation whose members are in the position of trustees, or a combination of two or more of these types, also appears incidentally.

Any data reported concerning the age and sex of the individual membership is also recorded. Especial effort was made to ascertain the number of members under 25 years of age, but in only a few instances are accurate estimates of this figure obtainable. Hence it is impossible to estimate accurately the aggregate youth membership of all the organizations. At any rate, such an estimate would have to take into account the matter of multiple memberships held by many individuals, regarding which there is little or no reliable evidence on record.

Consequently nothing could be inferred from the grand totals other than that a specified number of organizations reported a certain aggregate number of members under 25 years of age, and that the total is an aggregate of *memberships held* and not of the individuals holding them. The presence of individuals holding multiple memberships makes the aggregate of individuals smaller than the aggregate of memberships held, but to an unknown extent. More accurate conclusions must await the development of better record keeping and reporting—an evolution to which it is hoped this study may contribute some impetus.

PURPOSE

The general objective for which each organization exists, as well as a summary of some of its specific aims, is briefly stated. Sometimes this statement is abstracted directly from the charter or constitution, and sometimes it is couched in the words of the incumbent executive. In either case it has been furnished by the organization as a reliable announcement of its current purposes.

Thoughtful comparison of the aims of different organizations, and of stated aims with evidences of accomplishment in the same organization, will enable the reader to form his own estimates and make his own choices regarding the particular questions or problems he has in mind.

Some critical observers have said that there is a prevalent tendency to use the appeal of youth welfare to attract sympathy and support for purposes vague and ill defined, and in some instances with misguided if not actually fraudulent intent. True, no doubt, and occasionally more or less apparent on the face of the statements of those making such appeals. In the preparation of the present inventory there was no attempt to go behind the report of any organization to verify or discredit it. The rating or accrediting of organizations is no part of this enterprise; and the inclusion or omission of any organization is not to be interpreted as setting upon it any seal of approval or disapproval.

No organization having an admitted purpose to acquire pecuniary profits for any individual is included in this book. This does not, of course, necessarily mean that all the associations described are unaffected by commercial motives. The device of setting up a nonprofit corporation to promote more or less concealed commercial interests is well known. It is not impossible that such an organization may render valuable public service. Concealment of ulterior motives, however, must be regarded as reprehensible.

ACTIVITIES

The principal enterprises in which the organization engages, irrespective of whether these are concerned wholly or partly with youth service or whether they affect the welfare of youth directly or indirectly, are briefly enumerated. Wherever possible this picture is made more vivid by mentioning specific examples of the general activities and by inserting numerical explanations of the scope of each enterprise, wherever such figures are obtainable.

What an organization actually is doing gives a better measure of its worth than does a mere statement of its purposes. Furthermore, a statement of what it is actually doing is of more value to the critical reader than any prospectus of its future plans, however grandiose they may be. With these considerations in mind, every effort has been made to give a fair and accurate picture of what each organization actually does, in as much detail as the space limits will allow.

The facts and figures presented may be profitably analyzed and reflected upon, and to facilitate this process the names of the several activities have been inserted in the alphabetical index. Using this as a key, many interesting studies could be made, disclosing the distribution of a large number of functions among the several organizations, and revealing what types of activities are now uppermost and what types seem to be relatively neglected.

PUBLICATIONS

A periodical bulletin or magazine seems to be almost an indispensable feature of the service of a national organization. Even the smallest and weakest associations often issue regularly a bulletin, even if it be only a mimeographed document. Several of the older and larger organizations publish monthly magazines which have established important places in the periodical literature of the day. A few large associations publish two or more such periodicals simultaneously.

In addition to periodicals, a considerable number of organizations publish also occasional books and pamphlets on subjects related to their major interests. The quality of this output ranges all the way from the most blatantly propagandist pamphlets to substantial books into which go the best scholarly thought of the time upon the topics treated. Even the flimsiest and most transparent of pamphlets are of some value in disclosing the spirit of the organization, if nothing else. Taken together, the total output of publications other than periodicals amounts to a contribution of no mean proportions to the literature of the social sciences.

The lists of books and pamphlets held in stock by some of the older and larger organizations are too extensive for reproduction in the brief descriptive paragraphs which the limits of this book permit. Therefore, a complete enumeration of all such items will not be found herein; but care has been taken to list by title, author, and publisher, as well as date of publication, number of pages, and price, such publications as seem to be among the more important ones in the total program of the organization, and especially such as have a clear bearing upon any particular phase of youth service or youth welfare.

Something more than one thousand separate items will be found listed in this manner, constituting a bibliography which it is hoped may be of frequent use.

HEADQUARTERS STAFF

A key feature of any human enterprise is the personnel engaged. Any description of youth-serving associations would be less than complete if it did not set out at least the total number of persons employed at a given time in the headquarters staffs and in the field forces. The latter expression, as used here, means traveling agents of the national headquarters and not the resident personnel engaged in local or regional subsidiary units. This latter information appears sometimes in the description of the *membership* or *activities* of an association which provides direct service through local units.

With regret that opportunity for a more extensive study of headquarters and field staffs did not present itself, the data presented under that heading are confined to such a form as will disclose a simple classification of the staffs under the following rubrics: full-time paid employees, part-time paid employees, and voluntary unpaid workers. The division of the time of any particular staff member between headquarters and field work is indicated only roughly by placing each under whichever of these captions the major part of his time is recorded as being spent.

Much useful information could no doubt be gathered regarding the age, sex, education, specific training, experience, and remuneration of the staff members, as well as the occasional arrangements regarding such elements in their security as group insurance plans, retirement and pension systems, provision for leaves of absence during illness or for other purposes, annual vacations, and arrangements tending to promote continuity of tenure. Unquestionably such studies should be undertaken, and it was with the utmost reluctance that they were omitted from the present effort. The rudimentary data gathered here would indicate that upward of five thousand persons are continuously engaged in the professional and clerical service of the headquarters of the organizations under observation.

FISCAL SUPPORT AND OPERATIONS

In our present economic order the yardstick which is graduated into dollars and cents constitutes one of the most convenient as well as one of the most significant measures of most social enterprises. It is important to know whether an organization has the secure backing of a permanent endowment fund, what surplus funds it may have invested and temporarily withheld from current use, and what, if any, is the aggregate value of its physical plant and material equipment.

Having observed these items, which may be called a comparatively static part of the financial picture, it is then necessary to perceive the dynamic part, consisting of the flow of income and expenditures during a specified recent fiscal period. Every organization has some sort of accounting system, but exact uniformity in the classification of the sources of income and the purposes of expenditures, affording ready comparability, is rarely found with respect to any two organizations, to say nothing of the hundreds here examined.

Perhaps this is well, for what purport to be exact comparisons are almost invariably misleading to some extent; and it is apprehension concerning invalid comparisons and other possible forms of misinterpretation which causes many fiscal officers to hesitate to release accounts of their fiscal operations in detail.

The present study initiates no crusade for the imposition of uniform accounting methods upon all youth-serving organizations. Any such objective appears naïve in the extreme when one considers the immense variety of the enterprises carried on by the several organizations of diverse types.

Nevertheless a certain degree of consistency among different accounting methods is naturally found, and a considerable minority of the organizations which cooperated in this study have been able and willing to exhibit their annual income and expenditures within a few simple uniform classifications which make it possible for interesting observations to be made. Against hasty comparisons the reader is warned, and implored not to read into the fiscal exhibits any implications or inferences which the data do not support.

III. Statistical Glimpses

There are several factors which make it seem inadvisable to present a grand summation of the statistics in a single, comprehensive table. The fact that many of the organizations are concerned with youth only incidentally to their main purposes, and that their youth membership and youth activitities are generally not statistically separable from their other concerns, means that any gross summation of their reports must be so far short of any true quantitative measure of youth service as to be of very small significance. Too, the membership figures vary in reliability from the results of actual counts in some instances to what are manifestly hazardous estimates in others; it is not possible to eliminate wholly duplications in the reports of federated groups and those of their constituent national associations; and there is nowhere any dependable basis for an estimate of the number of individuals holding multiple memberships. Hence any figure showing the grand aggregate membership of all the organizations would be subject to so many qualifications as to make it of little use.

The other items in the basic tabulations are no doubt more accurately reported on the whole, and very largely free from overlapping, but here again the impossibility of a clean separation of youth service from other enterprises reduces the value of any grand summation and makes it preferable to confine the summary to some 43 of the principal organizations, including 18 of the larger "youth-membership" associations (Table I), 10 of the

TABLE I

STATISTICS OF EIGHTEEN OF THE LARGER YOUTH-MEMBERSHIP ORGANIZATIONS

Organization	Total Membership		Approximate Annual Budget of Headquarters	
	1935–36	1939–40	1935–36	1939–40
American Humane Education Society	6,000,000	7,005,000	$ 18,000	$ 16,800
American Junior Red Cross	8,351,000	8,588,398	225,000	361,000
American Youth Congress	1,600,000a	4,697,915a	17,000	15,500
Baptist Young People's Union of America	325,000	325,000	9,000	10,500
Boy Scouts of America	1,000,000	1,429,622	958,000	1,367,000
Boys' Clubs of America	263,013	295,732	77,000	159,000
Camp Fire Girls	232,058	278,451	88,000	135,100
Catholic Students' Mission Crusade, U.S.A.	500,000	700,000	. . .	20,000
Epworth League	612,119	538,522	39,000	43,700
4-H Clubs	1,060,000	1,528,945	b	b
Future Farmers of America	117,000	230,000	15,100	18,200
Girl Scouts	400,000	636,941	1,131,000	1,459,000
International Society of Christian Endeavor	4,000,000c	4,000,000c	. . .	75,000
National Jewish Welfare Board	350,000a	400,000a	140,000	. . .
National Student Federation of America	225,000d	200,000d	40,000e	15,500
Sodality of Our Lady	500,000	806,800	85,000	75,000
Young Men's Christian Associations	1,061,876	1,316,573	741,000	789,700
Young Women's Christian Associations	407,000	548,000	1,188,000f	958,800f

a Underlying membership of cooperating or constituent bodies.

b None apart from that of the Extension Service of the U. S. Department of Agriculture.

c Includes membership in foreign countries.

d Aggregate number of undergraduates in the student bodies of the universities and colleges members of the federation.

e Includes budget of $13,400 for the American office of the International Student Service.

f Includes work in other countries and contributions to World's Council YWCA.

TABLE II

STATISTICS OF TEN OF THE LARGER ORGANIZATIONS OF ADULTS CONCERNED
IN PART WITH YOUTH

Organization	Total Membership		Approximate Annual Budget of Headquarters	
	1935–36	1939–40	1935–36	1939–40
American National Red Cross	4,137,636[a]	7,139,263[a]	$9,000,000	$15,400,000
American Legion	842,855	1,071,229	409,000	573,500
General Federation of Women's Clubs	2,000,000[b]	2,000,000[b]	...	204,600
National Congress of Parents and Teachers	2,000,000	2,330,000	115,000	160,000
Cooperative League of the United States	750,000	1,041,000	17,500	17,500
American Farm Bureau Federation	1,250,000[c]	1,500,000[c]	200,000	253,900
National Grange	800,000[d]	800,000[d]	110,000	110,000
American Federation of Labor	3,045,347	4,006,354	975,000	1,800,000
Congress of Industrial Organizations	...	4,000,000	...	...
National Women's Trade Union League of America	1,000,000	1,000,000	10,000	10,000

a Exclusive of the membership of the American Junior Red Cross.
b Includes membership of affiliated national organizations.
c Estimated number of individuals in the farm families enrolled in the community organizations.
d Exclusive of membership in Juvenile Granges.

TABLE III

STATISTICS OF FIFTEEN PROFESSIONAL OR QUASI-PROFESSIONAL ORGANIZATIONS
CONCERNED IN PART WITH YOUTH

Organization	Total Membership		Approximate Annual Budget of Headquarters	
	1935–36	1939–40	1935–36	1939–40
National Education Association of the United States	191,000	203,429	$510,000	$800,000[a]
American Federation of Teachers	30,000	35,000	40,000	90,200
Progressive Education Association	10,000	10,000	58,000	43,000
American Library Association	13,000	13,971	289,000	373,200
American Home Economics Association	11,000[b]	15,000[b]	63,000	65,300
American Association of University Women	50,242	68,003	227,000	260,000
National Federation of Business and Professional Women's Clubs	61,005	73,044	136,105	156,700
American Vocational Association	14,340	23,804	24,000	31,500
National Recreation Association	8,027	8,836	243,000	215,300
American Association of Social Workers	9,930	11,500	62,000	65,300
American Public Welfare Association	3,000[c]	3,000[c]	85,000	70,000
National Probation Association	15,000	16,938	87,000	108,200
American Public Health Association	4,900	6,900	115,000	156,300
National Organization for Public Health Nursing	8,000	10,000	101,000	109,000
American Social Hygiene Association	10,000	10,000	100,000	220,000

a Includes about $200,000 attributable to the 27 departments.
b Adult membership only.
c Includes agencies as well as individuals.

larger organizations of adults concerned in part with youth (Table II), and 15 professional or quasi-professional associations whose activities affect the welfare of youth substantially (Table III).

YEAR OF FOUNDING

Three hundred and nineteen organizations reported year of founding. The simplest measure of central tendency—the median—falls in the year 1920. Thus half have been in existence not more than twenty-one years as this report is written. The third quartile division of the range ends in the year 1928, indicating that one-fourth were founded between 1920 and 1928, and that the youngest one-fourth contains no organization more than thirteen years old. It also appears that the birth rate of these national organizations during the early twenties was nearly twice as high as for the period since 1925.

The median years of founding for each of the twenty classes of organizations vary considerably, the extremes being 1896 for the Protestant religious organizations and 1934 for the associations for research and social planning. Other groups whose medians deviate by as much as five years from the median for the whole are the organizations in the field of social work, 1911; the general character-building organizations, 1912; the organizations in the fields of guidance, personnel, and placement, 1927; and the national student associations, 1927. Perhaps these variations may be said to parallel roughly the incidence of certain waves of emphasis in American thought on social problems.

FISCAL MEASURES

Turning attention again to the entire list of 320 organizations, and preserving the distinction between the 81 classified as "youth-membership" societies and the 239 which may be called "adult associations serving youth," we may clarify the picture somewhat by identifying the numbers which fall into specified gradations determined by the size of their endowment funds, if any, and the amounts of the annual budgets reported. The endowment scale, as reported, is displayed in Table IV, and the

distribution of annual budgets in the same class intervals appears in Table V.

TABLE IV
HEADQUARTERS ENDOWMENT FUNDS REPORTED

| | Number of Organizations | |
Class Interval	Youth-Membership Organizations	Adult Organizations
$1,000,000 or more	3	6
$100,000–$999,999	—	8
$10,000–$99,999	3	9
$1–$9,999	3	10
None	23	65
Not reporting	49	141
Total	81	239

TABLE V
APPROXIMATE ANNUAL HEADQUARTERS BUDGETS REPORTED

| | Number of Organizations | |
Class Interval	Youth-Membership Organizations	Adult Organizations
$1,000,000 or more	2	2
$100,000–$999,999	7	43
$10,000–$99,999	25	84
$1–$9,999	15	49
Not reporting	32	61
Total	81	239

More specific statistical material for the organizations in Part II is summarized in a table at the end of each of the twenty sections. In these tabulations, for all organizations reporting such items, data are given for the year of founding, total membership, number of members under the age of 25, number of employees on the headquarters staff, amount of endowment funds, value of headquarters plant and equipment, and approximate annual budget. (See Tables VI to XXV inclusive.)

IV. Other Aspects of the Picture

The historical, legal, and administrative sides of the national panorama of youth-serving organizations receive little attention in this inventory, but they offer rich fields for further study. At this point it is well to recognize some of the limitations of the present effort and to consider some of the more promising avenues for future investigation.

HISTORICAL ASPECTS

The exhibits assembled in Part II of this book record the years in which the respective associations were founded, but usually contain no further historical information prior to the year 1939. The exhibit is a cross section as of a particular date in the case of each organization, and in most instances goes back no further than the course of the preceding fiscal year. Neither the specific dates nor the fiscal years are the same in the cases of all organizations, but it may be said that they fall for the most part between January 1, 1939 and December 31, 1940.

Roughly comparable data for most of the organizations as of approximately four years earlier (1935–36) may be found in the first edition, now available in many libraries, but unfortunately out of print and no longer available for sale. An inkling of some of the changes occurring during the four-year period with respect to forty-three of the larger organizations has already been given herein in Tables I, II, and III, pages 11–12.

The history of the founding of an organization is not adequately indicated by the recording of a single year. Many groups were first organized as local agencies, acquired a national constituency at a much later date, and at a still different date became incorporated. Changes of name, changes of purpose, and important deviations in policy have marked the progress of many organizations more than once. Absorptions, mergers, and dissolutions occur with considerable frequency. All these occurrences have bearings upon the development and future possibilities of national nongovernmental youth service in the United States.

LEGAL ASPECTS

Most of the national associations in this field are nonprofit corporations. Every corporation owes its existence to the granting of a charter or articles of incorporation by the authority of some state or by the Congress of the United States. Each state has its own constitutional and statutory provisions governing the creation and regulation of nonprofit corporations. Scarcely any two charters granted are identical in terms. Not infrequently the provisions of a corporate charter are construed in a decision of a state or federal court in such manner as to affect profoundly the future conduct of the organization's activities.

There are many perennial legal questions which seem constantly to dog the footsteps of nonprofit associations. Prominent among these are (1) the exemption of various types of property or privileges held by these organizations from various forms of federal and state taxation, (2) the question of the pecuniary liability of these associations to individuals who may suffer injuries to person or to property through the negligence of their officers or employees, (3) and the rights and responsibilities of such associations in the role of beneficiaries or trustees of funds or property conveyed to them for charitable purposes by deed of gift or testamentary devise.

Any experienced professional worker who has confronted difficulties arising from legal questions of the foregoing types will attest that there is need for study and clarification of the law governing these subjects, to the end that it may be progressively molded into a more consistent and symmetrical whole, bearing distinctly helpful relationships toward social enterprises of recognized merit. Extensive investigation of the law of nonprofit corporations, especially those phases of it which apply to the type of organizations listed here, is a public service which ought not to be long postponed.

ADMINISTRATIVE ASPECTS

The many details of the management of the affairs of the classes of organizations here treated have never as yet been given comprehensive investigation on a scale comparable to the researches which have been made into the administration of educational corporations, for example, or of the various governmental units and agencies. Scores of questions suggest themselves immediately, whose answers would be of interest and possibly of definite value to those responsible for the administration of these organizations.

14

What conditions or characteristics justify a membership fee, and in what situations is it wise to raise or lower the amount of these fees? What steps may be taken to attract philanthropic gifts successfully without mortgaging the future usefulness of the organization and without indulging in unethical practices? In what circumstances is an expansion of the service of publication indicated, and what are the characteristics in general which make a publication successful both as a source of revenue and as an instrument for increasing the membership and general utility of the organization?

What are the myriad factors which tend to make increasingly effective the annual convention or conference? What devices are generally best for keeping the constitution of an association in step with its growth and with changes in the opportunities for service indicated by changes in the times? What is usually the most satisfactory outline of the structure of central control and administration, including the representative assembly of delegates, if any, the board of directors or other principal policy-forming organ, the executive committee, the executive agent in charge of the headquarters staff, and the division of functions within this staff?

These questions are only partly suggestive of hundreds of others which ought to be dealt with in an investigation of administrative principles now in use or adaptable to the service of this class of organization.

THE PRIMARY UNIT

The problems of administration just mentioned are found in all associations regardless of whether or not they may have subsidiary local units. Several important national organizations perform direct service of kinds which could only be rendered in well-organized local service units. Of the groups listed in this book, about 135 are of this class, of whom approximately one hundred have reported the number of local chapters which they respectively maintain. This number varies from as low as three or four in the case of infant organizations to many thousands, as reported by a few of the older and larger groups.

For example, the International Society of Christian Endeavor reports 80,000 local units; the 4-H Clubs, 78,599; the Boy Scouts of America, 46,733; and the National Congress of Parents and Teachers, 28,000. The size of these local units seems to vary from an average membership of as few as nine persons to an average membership exceeding a thousand.

Generally it may be said that where the average membership of the local unit runs into the hundreds the organization is likely to be one maintaining local institutions, complete with physical plant and other facilities, or one enrolling all or nearly all of the membership of other local institutions such as churches or schools. Obviously, the primary local unit should provide effective face-to-face contacts between all members and the local leaders who labor in their service.

For the majority of the organizations maintaining no permanent physical plants of their own, these effective face-to-face contacts are not likely to occur in a local unit having more than a hundred members. It is therefore not surprising to find that, after the elimination of relatively few groups maintaining larger local units, the size of the local group for the remaining organizations seems to gravitate around fifty as a median figure.

It is also noticeable that some of the largest and admittedly most effective youth-membership organizations regularly maintain units smaller than this. For example, the average enrollment, including leaders, of a local unit of the Boy Scouts of America is 31; of the Sons of the American Legion, 22; of the Camp Fire Girls, 21; and of the 4-H Clubs, 19.

Some associations continuously conduct surveys and studies of the techniques employed in the management of their local units; but no attempt has yet been made to deduce from the total picture a set of general principles regarding the administration of local units, which would be of value not only to existing organizations of many types but also to local as well as national efforts in the future to achieve an advancing degree of community organization for social welfare. A study of the local units of the organizations here briefly mentioned could be productive of such results.

PERSONNEL ASPECTS

In addition to the studies earlier suggested regarding the headquarters and field staffs, much needs to be known concerning three other important classes of persons connected with the work of these agencies: (1) the clientele, (2) the resident staffs (whether paid or voluntary) of the primary local units, and (3) the assembly of influential and socially-minded persons (often including many who are philanthropically inclined) attached to agencies of this type in such capacities as members of boards of trustees, of national or local advisory boards, or of other governing or consultative bodies. It is difficult to designate this group by any one brief caption, but perhaps for convenience they may be referred to as patrons of the organizations they serve.

Regarding the clientele, little is known at present of the actual distribution of young persons by age and sex among the several organizations, and practically nothing definite can be said regarding such features as their status on the economic scale, their family situations, and their educational and employment status.

If given the encouragement afforded by a dependable avenue of publication of such data, many of the organizations would no doubt be able and willing to collect it periodically through their own administrative channels. These data might also well be supplemented by intensive local studies of the same factors, and of the interrelationships among the organizations, made in selected localities by an impartial research agency.

Concerning the local leadership in the agencies maintaining local units, the same kinds of data would be valuable, and special efforts should be made to discover whether the most desirable types of young persons are being drawn into the adult service of the organizations for boys and girls. Ingenuity should be applied to the problem of devising ways and means of making this service attractive to the most suitable persons and making it fruitful of durable satisfactions for them.

In some respects the so-called patron group is the most important element in the whole personnel picture. It is among this group that are found many persons of sufficient local or national influence to enable them to effect speedy and far-reaching improvements in the morale and facilities of their respective organizations, when their interest is sufficiently aroused and their good will effectively mobilized.

In every community it is essential that all these persons, including patrons, professional and volunteer leaders, and representatives of the clientele of the nongovernmental youth-serving agencies cooperate in maintaining liaison among their respective organizations and with the public agencies functioning in the same locality, and participate in progressively planning an inclusive and improved community service.

PART II

DESCRIPTIVE INVENTORY
OF ORGANIZATIONS

V. General Character-Building Organizations for Youth

A small number of large and well-known organizations for boys and girls or young men or young women, offering programs so comprehensive that they can scarcely be designated as less than general character building, form a familiar and important part of the picture of youth welfare in America.

Other organizations for youth, seeking the improvement of morals without advancing any particular religious beliefs, may also be placed within the same classification. Some of these latter are designed to work in immediate and permanent conjunction with the public schools. The desirability of permitting nonschool associations to occupy a portion of the time of the regular school day is doubted by many educators, and the most satisfactory techniques of cooperation between the schools and nonschool organizations remain largely yet to be developed.

All are agreed that the effective character-building organizations perform indispensable functions bearing on the welfare of youth in hundreds of communities throughout the land and that there will long be a place for such agencies to supplement the school and the home in the care of young persons of both sexes during the difficult years when they are emerging from childhood into adolescence, and from adolescence into maturity.

The section which follows is only a brief catalog of some of the general character-building organizations. It presents, however, sources to which the reader may easily refer for fuller information regarding the larger organizations, the record of whose history, accomplishments, and methods would fill many volumes if adequately treated.

The fact that some of the national associations are large and well known should not, however, lead to the erroneous conclusion that a majority, or anywhere near a majority, of American young people are actually reached and served by any organization of this type. For the most part the rural regions are only sparsely covered, and hundreds of communities are as yet untouched.

When the American Youth Commission interrogated 13,500 young people in Maryland, it was found that of those living on farms and in villages more than three-fourths were not members of any club.[1] This finding corresponds closely with the results of similar investigations conducted by the Cooperative Extension Service of the United States Department of Agriculture in rural counties of Arkansas and Oregon, where nearly 80 per cent of the out-of-school youth reported that they had no organization affiliations aside from the church and its societies.[2]

It is therefore apparent that the nonsectarian character-building associations for youth have a vast field for expansion if they are to reach millions of young people to whom their services are not now accessible. Of no less significance is the necessity of effecting a continuing coordination of their respective efforts, both in communities where they now operate side by side and in new territory.

In the present section, organizations whose membership consists chiefly of young persons, as distinguished from those composed wholly or largely of persons above the age of 25, are:

American Junior Red Cross
American Youth Foundation
Boy Rangers of America
Boy Scouts of America
Boys' Clubs of America
Camp Fire Girls
Girl Scouts
Junior Achievement
Order of DeMolay
Pathfinders of America
United Boys' Brigades of America
Young Men's Christian Associations
Young Women's Christian Associations

Cross references: Section VI, pp. 31–44, Section VII, pp. 45–54, and Section VIII, pp. 55–65, for Protestant, Catholic, and Jewish organizations respectively. *See also:* 4-H Clubs, p. 92; Future Farmers of America, p. 93; Future Teachers of America, p. 125; National Association of Student Officers, p. 67.

---

[1] Howard M. Bell, *Youth Tell Their Story* (Washington: American Council on Education, 1938), p. 168.
[2] J. V. Highfill and Barnard D. Joy, *Situations, Problems, and Interests of Unmarried Rural Young People, 16–25 Years of Age,* Extension Circular No. 417 (Little Rock, Ark.: Extension Service, College of Agriculture, University of Arkansas, June 1938), p. 29; Barnard D. Joy and J. R. Beck, *Situations, Problems, and Interests of Unmarried Rural Young People 16–25 Years of Age: Survey of Four Oregon Counties, 1936,* Extension Service Circular 277 (Washington: U.S. Department of Agriculture, Cooperative Extension Work in Agriculture and Home Economics, December 1937), p. 1.

AMERICAN JUNIOR RED CROSS (1917); 18th and D and E Sts., N.W., Washington, D.C.; James T. Nicholson, National Director.

Membership: Individuals, 8,588,398 (June 1940). Membership is through schools only, the unit being each room in an elementary school or each 100 students in a secondary school. In the elementary school the group membership fee is 50¢ a year for every room and in the secondary school $1 a year for every 100, or fraction of 100, students. No individual membership fee is required of any child. The only requirement is a willingness to participate in service.

Purpose: "We believe in service to others, in health of mind and body to fit us for better service, and in worldwide friendship. For this reason we are joining the American Junior Red Cross. We will help to make its work successful in our school and community, and will work together with Juniors everywhere in our own and other lands."

Activities: Carries on a program of local, national, and international service activities in public, parochial, and private elementary and secondary schools. Such activities are designed to apply regular school learning experiences to social planning and service. Gifts may include cookies, jellies, candies, art covers for Brailled stories and holiday menus, greeting cards, calendars, dance programs and favors, checkerboards and other games, layettes and other garments, wooden and stuffed toys. Entertainments are prepared by groups in music, dramatics, literature, and athletics. Social service programs utilize efforts of groups in social studies, science, language, manual and fine arts.

Local activities include making gifts for and taking entertainments to institutions for children, hospitals, old people's homes, and similar institutions; cooperating in family welfare work under the guidance of the local Red Cross chapter or other local welfare organizations; participating in such movements for social and community welfare as making surveys of natural disaster hazards, initiating surveys for the prevention of delinquency, working with public health authorities, and becoming better acquainted with community social and political structures, community needs, and methods for meeting them; and participating in all phases of the program of the American National Red Cross (see p. 186) which have educational value and are appropriate for the age groups.

National activities include gifts and entertainments for United States sailors and for men in government hospitals, gifts for children in schools for the blind, projects of assistance to youth provided by the National Children's Fund, and exchanges of educational materials through intersectional school correspondence.

International activities include carrying on international correspondence through the Junior Red Cross societies in more than 50 other countries, sending approximately 50,000 cartons of good-will gifts abroad every year, and exchanging dolls, handwork, nature study exhibits, and a wide variety of educational materials.

There is no national organization of junior members beyond the senior high school, but high school graduates in a number of cities, including Chicago, Atlanta, Boston, Newark, Syracuse, New Orleans, and Chattanooga, have organized their own Junior Red Cross alumni groups in order to retain their identity as youth groups of Red Cross members. They work in close collaboration with the senior Red Cross chapters of their cities and frequently assume leadership responsibilities for the American Red Cross program in the community. Whatever organization rules they have are decided upon locally in harmony with Red Cross ideals and policies. The alumni groups had their own round table for the first time at the 1936 national convention.

The national staff of the American Junior Red Cross is assisted by an Educational Advisory Committee composed of leaders in the field of educational administration. The national director is also assisted by a National Delegates Advisory Committee composed of 10 representative Junior Red Cross members elected at the annual convention of the American Junior Red Cross.

Publications: *Junior Red Cross News*, 9 issues annually, sent to every enrolled elementary classroom; "A Guide for Teachers" included with each issue. *Junior Red Cross Journal*, for high schools, 9 issues annually, one subscription for every group membership. *An Activities Calendar*, one copy free to each enrolled room in elementary schools; monthly activities supplement included with each issue of the *Junior Red Cross Journal*. Organization pamphlets: *How to Enroll Your School* (ARC 616); *Program of the Junior Red Cross* (ARC 618); *School Correspondence* (ARC 621); *Chapter Organization of Junior Red Cross* (ARC 624); mimeographed toy patterns, plays, and miscellaneous materials free to enrolled schools.

Staff: Full-time paid employees, 26.

Finances: Current operations for the fiscal year July 1, 1939 to June 30, 1940 were as follows:

Income

Allocation from American Red Cross	$144,220.47
Elementary school enrollment	108,068.37
High school enrollment	21,997.18
General contributions and interest	12,501.27*
Contributions for foreign war relief	74,177.02*
	$360,964.31

Expenditures

Service staff	$ 99,764.07
Activities Calendar	19,691.63
Enrollment supplies and services	24,764.77
Junior Red Cross News	96,016.09
Junior Red Cross Journal	19,289.00
Domestic projects	641.84*
Insular and foreign projects	7,521.54*
Foreign war relief	74,177.02*
	$341,865.96

*National Children's Fund.

The American Junior Red Cross maintains a National Children's Fund for the support of projects, national and international in scope, including libraries for rural schools, Brailled stories for blind children, service for children in disaster-stricken areas in the United States, and child welfare and educational activities in foreign countries. Voluntary contributions are received from member groups; the fund is administered by national headquarters and, on foreign projects, in advisement with the League of Red Cross Societies.

Local Junior Red Cross service funds are created through the initiative of the members. It is expected that all contributions to the service fund be earned by the children through the performance of some service or saved through personal choice. Contributions may be called for at the opening of the school year. All money raised in schools in the name of the Red Cross becomes part of the service fund, which is administered, in accordance with Red Cross policies, by a joint committee of local Red Cross officers and school authorities. The junior members are encouraged to take an active part in deciding the welfare projects they support. The group membership fee is usually paid from the service fund.

AMERICAN YOUTH FOUNDATION (1924); 3930 Lindell Blvd., St. Louis, Mo.; Preston G. Orwig, Director.

Membership: Approximately 10,000 persons who have at some time attended one of the camps maintained by the organization are regarded as belonging to its "Founder Fellowship." The membership is distributed in 45 states, several Canadian provinces, Hawaii, the Philippine Islands, Brazil, China, Japan, Singapore, Mesopotamia, and the Belgian Congo. About 7,500 are aged 12 to 24.

Purpose: To discover and train young people for Christian leadership; to do scientific research and experimentation in the field of adolescence; to assist youth through personal contacts and student aids; to give educational and religious service to individuals and organizations; and to promote the wellbeing of youth throughout the world.

Activities: For a three-month period each year two camps are maintained, one near Shelby, Mich., and the other near Ossipee, N. H. The senior leadership camps cover a period of four weeks and are for youth aged 17 to 22. Recreational and character-education camps for boys and girls aged 11 to 17 are conducted for a period of six weeks. During the remaining nine months of the year foundation staff members are available for service to youth and youth leaders in churches, high schools, colleges, businessmen's clubs, women's clubs, youth conferences and conventions. The foundation operates on a nonprofit basis and is nondenominational.

Publications: Three mimeographed quarterlies, free to campers and leaders: *The Founder Fire*, to senior leadership camps; *The Sand-Piper*, to younger girls' camps; and *The Trail*, to younger boys' camps. Also 7-page leaflet, *The American Youth Foundation— Its Program of Leadership Training for Youth*, and small illustrated folders descriptive of the programs of the camps.

Staff: Full-time paid employees, 11, of whom 3 spend major time in field work.

Finances: Value of plant and equipment at headquarters, $150,000. Approximate annual budget of headquarters, $75,000.

BOY RANGERS OF AMERICA, INC. (1913); International Bldg., Rockefeller Center, New York, N. Y.; Emerson Brooks, Founder and National Chief Ranger; Edward W. France, President.

Membership: Boys aged 8 to 12, about 45,000. Local lodges numbering 1,039 in 47 states and 6 foreign countries have been chartered since 1922. There is no denominational test for membership.

Purpose: To fit small boys in character and discipline during the formative period of their lives to take up the scout program to the best advantage, after completing the junior training as a Boy Ranger; to prevent adolescent maladjustment and delinquency.

Activities: Founded on Indian lore and pioneering. Older boys (10 to 11) take up prowess, handicraft, Indian craft, art, accomplishment, nature; intensive character work is begun as soon as a boy enlists. The local lodges have volunteer adult leaders. Helpfulness toward other boys is stressed. The founder lodge has supported a school for Chinese junior boys (in Pautingfu) for nine years. The annual all-Eastern Pow-wow includes a boat ride to West Point, N. Y., as a national shrine, and talks on freedom of speech, freedom of worship, and other civil rights protected by the American form of government. A camp known as Camp Ranger is operated near Dover, N.J.

Publications: *Boy Ranger*, monthly; 10¢ a copy, $1 a year; Arthur Brennt, editor.

Staff: At headquarters, 3 persons.

Finances: Estimated value of equipment at headquarters, $1,200. Approximate annual budget, $2,000.

BOY SCOUTS OF AMERICA (1910); 2 Park Ave., New York, N.Y.; James E. West, Chief Scout Executive.

Membership: Boys and men, 1,429,622, including 884,934 Scouts and Senior Scouts aged 12 to 21 and 178,041 Cubs aged 9 to 11, making a total boy membership of 1,062,975 (June 1940). There are about 350,000 volunteer adult leaders and sponsors and about 1,381 professional paid Scout executives of various ranks. The local units, known as Scout Troops and Cub Packs, number 46,733; these are organized under 544 local councils, which are in turn grouped into 12 regions of the United States. Annual membership fee to national headquarters, 50¢ for Scouts, $1 for adult leaders.

Purpose: To promote, through organization and through cooperation with other agencies, the ability of boys to do things for themselves and others; to train them in Scoutcraft; and to teach them patriotism, courage, self-reliance, and kindred virtues, by placing emphasis upon character development, citizenship training, and physical fitness.

Activities: Nature lore, camping, hiking, woodcraft, handicrafts, and scores of related skills are acquired and enjoyed by different individual members up to prescribed minimum standards, and further as their own tastes and the local facilities permit. Community service activities are stressed and include such enterprises as street patrol duty, caring for church property, cleaning fences and clearing lots, assisting at conventions and fairs, cooperation with the police at the time of parades, shows, or carnivals, assistance to fire departments, service clubs, and veterans' organizations in connection with ceremonies and programs. Relief work in time of fire, flood, or other disaster, and conservation work for the preservation of wild life are also engaged in by many local units as the occasion demands or opportunity offers. Scouts are organized into troops of from 8 to 32 members. In rural communities, neighborhood patrols with as few as two boys may be organized. Each troop is led by a volunteer adult Scoutmaster and sponsored by a troop committee of influential adults who often represent some local institution or organization under whose auspices the troop is established.

Publications: *Boys' Life,* 12 issues annually; $1 a year to members, $1.50 to others; James E. West, editor. *Scouting,* 11 issues annually; 50¢ a year to members, $1 to others. *Cub Leaders' Round Table,* 11 issues annually; 25¢ a year to nonmembers. *The Handbook for Boys* is a comprehensive manual of Scout lore which is revised annually and distributed widely; over 6,300,000 copies have been sold since 1910. The organization publishes and sells many other general and specialized handbooks as well as a great variety of folders, leaflets, and posters.

Staff: Full-time paid employees, 334 (all of national council, including 12 regional offices).

Finances: The local organizations are in part supported by gifts from citizens, community chests, and other local sources. Valuation of local council camp property, buildings, and equipment, $9,559,531. Value of plant and equipment of national headquarters, $56,299. The national council has endowment funds aggregating $1,202,100 and working

capital funds of $729,284. For the calendar year 1939, operations were as follows:

Income

Membership fees	$ 785,924.48
Profit from sales of uniforms, equipment, and advertising	247,839.59
Charter fees and quotas	160,747.60
Interest on investments	72,170.78
Other sources	100,285.49
	$1,366,967.94

Expenditures

Salaries	$ 707,679.29
Travel	117,094.40
Communications	41,889.04
Office supplies	60,439.28
Publications	127,042.89
Rent, insurance, etc.	86,361.95
Other purposes	224,705.34
	$1,365,212.19

BOYS' CLUBS OF AMERICA, INC. (1906); 381 Fourth Ave., New York, N.Y.; David Armstrong, Acting Executive Director.

Membership: Boys, 295,732, in 348 member organizations in 194 cities in 37 states. The Boys' Club Federation of Canada, with 21 member organizations, is also affiliated. The local organizations in the United States include 231 boys' clubs, 106 settlements or community houses (affiliate members), and 11 units of tax-supported public recreation systems (cooperating members). There are 2,195 adult professional leaders and 3,371 adult volunteer workers.

Purpose: To stimulate and promote the Boys' Club movement.

Activities: The national headquarters makes community surveys of boy-life conditions; organizes and conducts training courses for workers with boys; holds an annual convention; maintains a library on boys' work; advises and assists local clubs in solving problems related to publicity, financial appeals, and utilization of personnel and plant. The local clubs have varied programs, among which the following were prominent in 1939: physical education (217 athletic fields, 313 gymnasiums, 58 swimming pools; 15,353 boys were taught to swim, 1,745 passed Junior Red Cross tests, 729 passed Senior Red Cross tests, 115 passed Examiner Red Cross tests), health (74,103 boys were medically examined, 11,151 medically treated, 16,197 treated in 58 dental clinics), musical (51 brass bands, 26 drum and bugle corps, 54 harmonica bands, 122 vocal groups, 60 orchestras), vocational (78,390 boys participated in vocational classes), camping (39,655 boys from 220 clubs attended camps). Of the clubs, 133 have Boy

Scout troops; 125 have club newspapers; 173, dramatic groups; 190, moving picture equipment; and 37, savings banks with 7,936 boy depositors.

Publications: *Boys' Clubs,* 7 issues annually, free; *The Keystone—A Manual of Program Service,* for member organizations, 9 issues annually. Numerous small pamphlets from time to time, among which is *The American Boy in a Democracy,* by Herbert Hoover, 1938, 14 pp. Annual reports.

Staff: Full-time paid employees, 29, of whom 3 are engaged in field work.

Finances: The local clubs own 133 buildings with a net value of $13,784,420.15; 59 camps valued at $1,809,342.46; equipment, $1,115,766.50; camp equipment, $260,814.57; endowment funds, $4,794,-219.37; total net assets, $21,377,157.28. The total annual operating expenses for all clubs in 1939 were $2,629,571.29. Two hundred and three of the clubs were participants in the local community chests.

The national headquarters has an endowment of $9,354.96 and additional invested funds aggregating $101,100.47. Its plant equipment is valued at $5,980.50. For the calendar year 1939, operations for headquarters were as follows:

Income

Gifts for current expenses	$134,505.74
Membership fees	8,984.33
Sale of literature and forms	1,074.34
Reimbursement for services	8,442.55
Invested funds	4,836.54
Other sources	1,238.39
	$159,081.89

Expenditures

Salaries	$106,408.38
Travel	15,553.86
Communications	3,744.00
Rent, insurance, etc.	8,514.18
Office supplies	2,492.25
Printing and publicity	14,215.30
Annual convention	2,152.67
Other purposes	2,994.76
	$156,075.40

CAMP FIRE GIRLS, INC. (1912); 88 Lexington Ave., New York, N.Y.; Lester F. Scott, National Executive.

Membership: Girls and women, 278,451, in 13,190 local groups in 43 states and 8 other countries; of the total membership 219,494 are girls aged 8 to 16, in 1,543 communities in the United States and 49 foreign communities. Annual dues, $1.

Purpose: To provide an opportunity for the personal development of girls through group experience, by means of a program of leisure-time activities de-signed to be fun for the girls; to provide enriching experiences and help them find joy, zest, and adventure in everyday life; to cultivate skills; to give practice in the democratic way of working with others; and to help girls become self-reliant, happy individuals and responsible members of society.

Activities: The program, revised in 1936, is very flexible and offers a wide choice of activities so that each group, under the guidance of its leaders, may have practice in planning and carrying out enterprises suited to its own interests, abilities, and needs. It covers the range of girls' interests, including homemaking, handicraft, camping, nature study, dramatics, music, literature, games, sports, health, personal grooming, social affairs, business, community and world-wide citizenship. The colorful honors, ranks, symbolism, and ritual of Camp Fire appeal to the younger girls, while participation in special projects having community significance is offered the older girls. Local councils sponsor 128 organized camps providing camping experience. The junior organization (Blue Birds) offers a program of creative play activities to girls aged 8 and 9.

From 6 to 20 girls in a church, school, or neighborhood form a Camp Fire group under the leadership of an adult volunteer called the Guardian. Each group has one or more sponsors or a sponsoring committee from the membership of some local adult organization. In the larger towns there are local councils composed of responsible citizens who supervise Camp Fire activities and employ an executive to direct the work in that area, including the Camp Fire camp. Executives are trained at the executives' school conducted in cooperation with New York University. Training courses for volunteers are conducted by executives and national field secretaries. The national headquarters provides guidance through publications, training courses, field service, and correspondence.

Publications: *The Guardian,* a bulletin for leaders with a supplement for girls, monthly except July and August; 75¢ a year; C. Frances Loomis, editor. *The Book of the Camp Fire Girls,* 1940, 247 pp., 50¢; *Handbook for Leaders of Camp Fire Girls,* 1935, 189 pp., $1; numerous other books and pamphlets.

Staff: Full-time paid employees, 43, of whom 6 spend major time in field work; part-time paid employees, 4.

Finances: The national organization aims to be self-sustaining. Local units manage their own finances and, at various times and in various places, have received public or private aid from local sources. In some localities the local executives are paid professional workers employed with funds provided by philanthropic agencies.

Value of equipment at national headquarters, $2,124.02. Cash on hand March 31, 1940, $24,071.88.

For the fiscal year ending on that date, operations were as follows:

Income

Membership fees	$ 97,850.44
Publications, supplies, commissions, etc. (net)	16,017.97
Training courses	5,598.00
Other sources	15,714.67
	$135,181.08

Expenditures

Salaries	$ 78,479.04
Travel	11,819.24
Communications	6,256.97
Office supplies	4,341.08
Publications	11,971.93
Rent, insurance, etc.	8,727.46
Other purposes	8,597.64
	$130,193.36

GIRL SCOUTS, INC. (1912); 14 West 49th St., New York, N.Y.; Mrs. Paul Rittenhouse, National Director.

Membership: Girls and women, 636,941, including 388,945 Girl Scouts aged 10 to 14, 44,154 Senior Girl Scouts aged 15 to 18, 79,757 Brownie Scouts aged 7 to 10, 125 Lone Girl Scouts, and 123,960 adults, distributed in 48 states, in outlying possessions of the United States, and in 4 foreign countries. There are 1,003 local councils, and 5,685 towns have one or more Girl Scout troops. Annual dues to national headquarters, 50¢.

Purpose: To bring to girls a program which will help them to become happy, well-balanced persons and active, responsible citizens; to serve society by helping girls to be good members of their own families and good citizens of their communities, of the nation, and of the world.

Activities: In small groups (16 to 32 girls) operated democratically, girls gain practical information about homemaking, nature, outdoor living, sports and games, music and dancing, literature and dramatics, health and safety, arts and crafts, community life, and international friendship. Girls are encouraged to participate according to their abilities in community affairs and to contribute their services for community needs. Girls aged 15 and over also engage in vocational exploration. The camping program goes on in many large permanent camps as well as in many temporary troop and day camps; 114,585 girls participated in 3,239 such camps in 1939. Each troop has an adult leader and an assistant leader. Each girl is bound by a promise to be helpful to others and to obey the other injunctions embraced in the Girl Scout code; by making the principles effective in practical everyday activities she learns to set character above routine performance and intelligent understanding above material rewards or personal gain.

Senior Girl Scouts sometimes plan and hold conferences under adult guidance. Regional conferences for adults are held in each of the 12 regions of the organization in the United States. The national headquarters arranges for the biennial national convention and for regional meetings, acts as a clearinghouse for information, builds and administers standards, plans program activities, trains adult leaders, carries on the publishing program, and fosters international good will through active participation in the World Association of Girl Guides and Girl Scouts.

Publications: *The American Girl*, monthly, $1.50 a year; *The Girl Scout Leader*, monthly, October through June, 50¢ a year. Subscription to the latter magazine is included in annual membership dues of certain classes of adult leaders and sponsors. Numerous books, manuals, pamphlets, and posters are listed in the catalog of Girl Scout equipment.

Staff: Full-time paid employees, 272, of whom 47 spend major time in field work. NYA worker, 1.

Finances: Local units are financed from local sources, such as gifts from citizens, community chests, or other organizations. Value of plant and equipment of national headquarters, $639,644.42. For the calendar year 1939, operations of national headquarters were as follows:

Income

Contributions	$ 51,894.66
Membership fees	332,335.52
Service fees	124,548.36
Publications	150,965.52
Other sources	799,199.77
	$1,458,943.83

Expenditures

Program material and research	$ 66,213.38
Field services	242,319.33
Adult training and education	94,789.58
Publications	159,038.57
Equipment service	646,618.27
Publicity and information	65,409.55
Registration and statistical services	52,827.23
Camp Andree	19,560.63
General	111,176.23
	$1,457,952.77

JUNIOR ACHIEVEMENT, INC. (1919); 16 East 48th St., New York, N.Y.; J. S. Mendenhall and Marion L. Ober, Codirectors.

Membership: Boys and girls aged 16 to 21, approximately 10,000. Local branches exist in eight states, chiefly east of the Mississippi River.

Purpose: To give young people a practical understanding of the present-day American system of business by having them organize miniature companies, the operations of which, involving purchasing of materials, simple manufacturing, advertising, sales, business management and financing, parallel those of business concerns.

Activities: Boys and girls carry on all advertising, publicity, accounting, recording, and management connected with production and selling in their own miniature companies producing handicraft products. They hold exhibits and demonstrations, participate in local forums, and conduct an annual convention. The national office supplies program suggestions, record forms, and information regarding purchasing of materials, tools, and equipment. The work of the organization is being expanded under two main divisions: the metropolitan area local autonomy plan for large cities; and the state field supervisor plan under which a trained man in charge of an entire state works to develop the program in towns and communities with a population of 2,500 to 50,000.

Publications: Booklets: *Junior Achievement—Plan, Purpose and Scope; How to Organize and Operate a Company; Plastics—How Used in a Junior Achievement Company.* Numerous leaflets and reprints.

Staff: Full-time paid employees, 8.

Finances: Endowment funds, $2,000. Value of equipment at national headquarters, $8,401.83. Balance December 31, 1939, $1,540.66. For the preceding calendar year, operations were as follows:

Income

Gifts and grants	$19,618.00
Endowment and reserve funds	90.00
Other services	131.90
Other sources	2,175.00
	$22,014.90

Expenditures

Salaries	$14,588.32
Travel	604.19
Communications	660.12
Office supplies	763.25
Publications	803.05
Rentals, insurance, etc.	2,607.32
Additions to equipment	458.76
Publicity	245.93
	$20,730.94

NATIONAL SELF-GOVERNMENT COMMITTEE

(1904); 80 Broadway, New York, N.Y.; Richard Welling, Chairman; Sophia Pollack, Secretary.

Membership: A board of directors of 9 members and an associate council of 11 members. There are 5,910 associate members, in 48 states and some foreign countries. These are chiefly high school principals and teachers but include many high school and college student officers. No dues or fees.

Purpose: To stimulate, in teacher training institutions, schools and colleges, and "junior cities" for youth aged 16 to 21 who are no longer in school, the development of student government and the character needed for alert citizens in a democracy; to promote the concept of teaching responsibility by giving responsibility; and to encourage boys and girls to learn the facts about politics through realistic civics teaching in the schools.

Activities: Assists in inaugurating cooperative student self-government in many high schools and colleges throughout the country. Supplies publications to over 5,000 high school teachers and principals interested in student self-government. Directors and members write pamphlets, magazine and newspaper articles; address teacher and student groups; confer with educational authorities. Cooperates with youth groups such as the National Association of Student Officers (see p. 67), the Boys' Brotherhood Republic (290 East Third St., New York, N.Y.), the George Junior Republic (Freeville, N.Y.), and the National Student Federation of America (see p. 68).

Publications: *Civics as It Should Be Taught*, by Richard Welling (first printing 1933, eighth printing 1939), 16 pp., 10¢; *Student Self-Government*, by Richard Welling (Washington, D.C.: National Education Association, 1939), 16 pp., 1¢; numerous leaflets and reprints from national magazines on related subjects by various authors, including Charles W. Eliot, Robert Littell, and Lillian K. Wyman.

Staff: Full-time paid employees, 2; part-time paid employee, 1.

Finances: Endowment fund, $6,937.14. Value of equipment at headquarters, $1,000. Cash balance on hand December 31, 1939, $873.58. For the fiscal year ending on that date, operations were as follows:

Income

Gifts for current expenses	$5,370.00
Publications	51.60
Refund for printing	80.21
Interest on invested funds	136.99
	$5,638.80

Expenditures

Salaries	$3,803.00
Communications	633.00
Office supplies	153.85
Publications	322.62
Rentals, insurance, etc.	624.96
Other purposes	124.62
	$5,662.05

ORDER OF DEMOLAY, GRAND COUNCIL OF THE

(1919); 201 East Armour Blvd., Kansas City, Mo.; Frank S. Land, Founder and Secretary General; Stratton D. Brooks, Executive Director.

Membership: Boys aged 15 to 20 inclusive, 59,465; voluntary adult assistants of all ranks, 14,824. There are approximately 1,000 chapters in 48 states, United States possessions, and Canada. Each chapter is sponsored by some Masonic organization or by a group of Masons. DeMolay, however, is not a Masonic organization, and any youth of suitable age and good character is eligible. The Grand Council consists of 100 members.

Purpose: To establish standards of character and ideals of citizenship among young men as a preparation for future citizenship.

Activities: Emphasizes the virtues of love of parents, reverence, patriotism, cleanness, courtesy, comradeship, fidelity. Stresses the fulfillment of personal obligations and dramatizes Jacques DeMolay as a man who followed that principle even unto death. The awards earned by members for all-round development are based on education, reading, self-expression, current history, nature interests, life work, health education, physical activities, physical fitness, manual skill, home relationships, religious ideals, recreational habits, chapter loyalty, and citizenship. Each member is graduated into adult citizenship with appropriate ceremony upon reaching his twenty-first birthday. Each year special services are required on five "obligatory days": Devotional Day, Sunday nearest March 18; Patriots' Day, May 1; DeMolay Day of Comfort, June 1; Educational Day, in connection with state or national education week; Parents' Day, Sunday preceding November 21. For the development of all-round character and good citizenship, the organization promotes good scholarship, student leadership, vocational selection, athletics, amateur music and dramatics, self-control, and thrift, in addition to numerous other activities pointing toward the ideals it upholds.

Publications: There is no national periodical, but the separate chapters or jurisdictions issue approximately 150 periodicals ranging from multigraphed leaflets to printed magazines. Publications of the Grand Council include: *Constitution, Statutes and Chapter Regulations,* revised 1940, 84 pp.; annual transactions (the 1940 issue is an illustrated booklet of 112 pages); and numerous leaflets and pamphlets.

Staff: Full-time paid employees, 18.

Finances: Value of plant and equipment at national headquarters, $125,340.40. Cash operating balance February 15, 1940, $419.39. For the fiscal year ending on that date, operations were as follows:

Income

Membership fees and dues	$70,411.82
Rituals and certificates	8,652.94
Charters and letters temporary	995.00
Other sources	139.43
	$80,199.19

Expenditures

Salaries	$29,463.64
Travel	1,745.96
Communications	5,800.08
Office supplies	3,950.24
Printing	2,433.13
Plant operation, insurance	1,674.10
Other purposes	9,289.55
Depreciation, capital account, etc.	14,595.09
	$68,951.79

PATHFINDERS OF AMERICA (1914); 4505 Ardendale Rd., South Euclid, Ohio; A. L. Bittikofer, Executive Secretary.

Membership: Children from the fourth grade through high school, probably 20,000, in certain localities in Ohio, Missouri, Tennessee, Montana, and Wyoming.

Purpose: To set up a system of direct character education in order to reduce delinquency and crime by utilizing the facilities of the school system without creating additional tax burdens and without establishing an organization to be supported by charity.

Activities: In each locality specially trained Pathfinder counselors are employed to visit selected schools each month, conducting a period of discussion and instruction based on the Pathfinder lesson for the month. Visits to any given class occur at intervals of four weeks. In the meantime the class president conducts one class period under the supervision of the room teacher. During the year each Pathfinder counselor may reach from 2,000 to 3,000 pupils in this manner. In Cleveland, Ohio, Fairview, Mont., and Wheatland, Wyo., the counselors are paid by the school district. In other localities they contribute part-time service or are paid by some charitable organization. The content of the lessons and the work of the counselors are designed to instill morality, law observance, self-reliance, thrift, and honesty. Sectarian or religious matters are not a part of the program.

Publications: *Pathfinder Lessons,* 1¢ each.

Staff: Full-time paid employee at national headquarters, 1.

Finances: From 1915 to 1930 the late Joseph Boyer, president of the Burroughs Adding-Machine Company, spent approximately $250,000 in demonstrating the program in public and private schools and in correctional institutions and prisons in America and Europe. Since his death in 1930 there has been no regular source of philanthropic support. Approximate annual budget, $1,500.

UNITED BOYS' BRIGADES OF AMERICA (1894); 512 Overbrook Rd., Baltimore, Md.; Gen. Walter A. Koerber, National Commander; Col. J. M. Corame, Adjutant.

Membership: Boys aged 12 and upward who are members of some Christian church, Catholic or Protestant. Local units are functioning in 11 states. A company consists of not fewer than 12 boys. Ten cents for each enrolled member is paid to the national headquarters. Boys 10 to 12 years of age are known as Reserves.

Purpose: To advance Christ's Kingdom among boys and to promote habits of obedience, reverence, discipline, self-respect and all that tends toward a true Christian manliness, and to further such principles as will make the youth of the nation loyal, patriotic, and law-abiding.

Activities: Military drill, physical training, athletics, games, hikes, summer camps, Bible and mission study classes, radio, first aid, and signaling. Merit badges are awarded for the different classes. Biennial national conventions are held in odd-numbered years.

Publications: *Brigader*, national periodical, 2¢ a copy; Capt. J. H. Hilf, editor, 2800 Beechwood Blvd., Pittsburgh, Pa. *Manual*, 1934, 135 pp., 25¢; *Constitution*, 1932, 8 pp., 5¢; numerous leaflets, including *Why Mothers Should Like the Boys' Brigade*, *How to Organize a Company of the Boys' Brigade*, and *Merit Badge Requirements*.

Staff: Part-time unpaid workers, 8.

Finances: Cash operating balance December 31, 1939, $254.35. For the fiscal year ending on that date, operations were as follows:

Income

Membership fees	$108.50
Other fees	14.75
Publications	10.10
Other services	88.88
Other sources	152.60
	$374.83

Expenditures

Communications	$ 13.38
Merit badges and convention expenses	278.27
	$291.65

YOUNG MEN'S CHRISTIAN ASSOCIATIONS OF THE UNITED STATES OF AMERICA, NATIONAL COUNCIL OF (1866); 347 Madison Ave., New York, N.Y.; Eugene E. Barnett, General Secretary.

A national organization formed by the establishment of a national executive body 15 years after the foundation of the first local association in 1851.

Membership: Individuals, 1,316,573, of whom 10.5 per cent are boys under 12, 24 per cent are boys aged 12 to 17, 24 per cent are young men aged 18 to 24, and 31.1 per cent are men aged 25 or over; 3.8 per cent are girls, and 5.6 per cent are women. Local associations (in good standing), 1,187, and area and state committees, 23. Additional registered constituency of 241,892 individuals other than members was reported by 275 associations; additional estimated participating constituency of 945,916 persons not individually registered was reported by 340 associations.

Purpose: "The Young Men's Christian Association we regard as being, in its essential genius, a worldwide fellowship of men and boys united by a common loyalty to Jesus Christ for the purpose of building Christian personality and a Christian Society." Specifically, to advance social education,

leadership and citizenship training, and the welfare of the community; to promote health and physical fitness; to assist men and boys in finding and organizing clean and refreshing social life and recreation; to encourage study of religion and the application of Christian ideals to the rebuilding of a better society; to promote racial and religious tolerance and world peace.

Activities: Much of the program is carried on through informal clubs for boys or young men of congenial age groups. More than 112,000 such clubs, classes, and committee groups were at work in 1939. Those for young men totaled over 23,065 with about 438,000 members, emphasizing all-round club programs, formal and informal educational pursuits, physical and religious activities. Among the clubs for boys were 7,049 high school or Hi-Y clubs, with 200,584 members, and numerous Gra-Y and similar clubs for the grade school groups. An increasing number of neighborhood, church, and employed groups have activity programs which include but slight use of association buildings. Specialized programs are found in associations among rural youth, those in industrial cities, in the Army and Navy, in colleges, and in transportation systems, as well as among colored populations of cities. Over 700 local association buildings are maintained in cities throughout the country, usually equipped with sanitary and pleasant but low-priced dormitory facilities, and in some instances restaurants, as well as gymnasiums, swimming pools, and a large assortment of apparatus for games, sports, and other recreation. Reading rooms, classrooms, and lecture halls are usually a part of the equipment. Some of the local associations maintain recognized schools of high school or college grade, as well as vocational schools.

Publications: *National Council Bulletin*, bimonthly, 10¢ a copy; *Intercollegian and Far Horizons*, by the Student Christian Movement, 7 issues annually. *The Year Book and Official Roster*, a 250-page summary and interpretation of activities. Numerous books and pamphlets are published by the Association Press, including *The Y.M.C.A. and Social Need —A Study of Institutional Adaptation*, by Owen E. Pence, 1939, 360 pp., $2.75; *Youth—Millions Too Many?* by Bruce L. Melvin, 1940, 220 pp.; and such other recent titles as *Group Education for a Democracy*, *Dynamics of Character Education*, *Christian Faith and Democracy*, *From Building to Neighborhood*, *The New Y.M.C.A. Aquatic Program*, *Creative Personalities Series*, and *Guidance in Social Agencies*.

Staff: Full-time paid employees, 155, of whom 50 spend major time in field work. NYA workers, 20.

Finances: Endowment funds for the work of the national headquarters, $3,013,463.13. Equipment at national headquarters, $25,188.60. During the calendar year 1939, operations of the national council were as follows:

Income

Appropriations from local units and contributions from individuals	$309,031.87
Membership fees	5,110.79
Publications	2,656.28
Other services	85,254.64
Interest on investments	100,036.58
Other sources	287,568.78
	$789,658.94

Expenditures

Salaries	$427,499.68
Travel	47,111.51
Communications and supplies	48,111.35
Publications	12,669.80
Rent, insurance, etc.	35,350.28
Other purposes	212,014.65
	$782,757.27

For the aggregate of all local associations and general agencies in the United States: value of plant and equipment, $217,878,300; endowment funds, $37,826,400. Totals of current income and expenditures for all associations reporting in the United States for the calendar year 1939 were as follows:

Income

Membership fees	$ 5,596,800
Program services	5,520,800
Business and club features	22,809,300
Contributions	10,361,200
Other sources	4,983,100
	$49,271,200

Expenditures

General administration	$11,356,200
Program services	10,904,800
Business and club features	14,496,400
Interest on debts	1,323,400
Other purposes	10,907,400
	$48,988,200

YOUNG WOMEN'S CHRISTIAN ASSOCIATIONS OF THE UNITED STATES OF AMERICA, NATIONAL BOARD (1906); 600 Lexington Ave., New York, N.Y.; Emma P. Hirth, General Secretary.

A national organization formed by the union in 1906 of two similar national groups, one having headquarters in the East and the other in Chicago. The earliest local association was the Ladies' Christian Association (1858) in New York.

Membership: Young women, approximately 548,000, a majority of whom are under the age of 25; also 332,799 Girl Reserves, aged 12 to 18. There are 422 community associations (city, town, rural), 590 in student communities, and 478 registered YWCA (Girl Reserve) clubs. The organization reaches and serves many more girls and women than are included in its actual paid membership. It is estimated that during 1938 some 2,866,797 individuals had some kind of continuing relationship with it. Members and clients are largely between the ages of 15 and 35.

Purpose: To advance the physical, social, intellectual, moral, and spiritual interests of young women; to bring young women to such a knowledge of Jesus Christ as Savior and Lord as shall mean for the individual young woman fullness of life and development of character; to make the organization as a whole an effective agency in the bringing in of the Kingdom of God among young women.

Activities: Many of the local YWCA's maintain large buildings containing dormitory and dining facilities, classrooms, lecture rooms, gymnasiums, and rooms for social intercourse. They conduct a great variety of social, cultural, and recreational projects, prominent among which are forums for the discussion of current social, economic, and religious problems. The local secretaries and their staffs give personal and vocational guidance to young women. Some of the efforts of the urban units are devoted to the interests of girls of modest means who are without relatives or friends in the city, and much of the program is directed toward alleviating the condition of underprivileged girls and poorly paid working young women. The Girl Reserve units, located in both urban and rural communities, consist of girls of high school age or thereabouts, with adult leadership and the sponsorship of a local committee of mature women. They provide such programs of social, religious, and educational activities as their local facilities permit and the needs of their membership require.

Publications: *The Womans Press*, 11 issues annually, $1 a year; *The Bookshelf*, 9 issues annually, $1 a year. The latter periodical is largely devoted to the interests of younger girls and serves as a program bulletin for Girl Reserve secretaries. The publication department of the national YWCA, known as the Womans Press and located at headquarters, issues a large number of books and pamphlets on varied subjects germane to the work of the YWCA, which may be found listed in the *Womans Press Catalog*, 1939, 43 pp.

Staff: Full-time paid employees, 210; part-time paid employees, 9.

Finances: On December 31, 1939 the endowment funds of the national board aggregated $5,542,612.84, and its working capital funds were $283,203.54. For the calendar year 1939, income and expenditures, including work in other countries and contributions to World's Council YWCA, were as follows:

Income		*Expenditures*	
General		General	
Income from endowments	$269,017.16	Secretarial retirement fund premiums	$ 19,078.33
Interest received from bank balances, cash discounts, and income from depreciation fund assets	6,176.80	Provision for unemployment insurance	5,200.00
		Fees, legal and other	3,751.57
Operating divisions		Operating divisions	
Laboratory division	42,117.58	Laboratory division	126,663.57
National services division	2,188.87	National services division	103,278.67
Leadership division	12,645.42	Leadership division	121,639.25
National student council	6,350.06	Foreign division	146,223.10
Cooperation and interpretation	854.02	National student council	57,754.77
Regional conferences	4,822.35	General administration and financing	116,814.64
Headquarters services	48,725.50	Cooperation and interpretation	67,065.94
Operating properties	57,801.57	National convention	8,597.74
Contributions (general and special)	448,073.68	Regional conferences	4,044.44
Appropriations		Headquarters services	120,830.81
From Laura Spelman Rockefeller Memorial Endowment	30,025.93	Operating properties	57,856.11
From depreciation fund, Dodge Hotel	30,000.00		
	$958,798.94		$958,798.94

TABLE VI

STATISTICS OF GENERAL CHARACTER-BUILDING ORGANIZATIONS FOR YOUTH

Organization	Year Founded	Approximate Aggregate Membership (individuals)	Number of Members under 25 Years of Age	Total Employees on Headquarters Staff	Aggregate Endowment of National Headquarters	Plant and Equipment (headquarters only)	Approximate Annual Budget (headquarters only)
American Junior Red Cross	1917	8,588,398	8,588,398	26	$	$	$ 361,000
American Youth Foundation	1924	10,000	7,500[a]	11	none	150,000	75,000
Boy Rangers of America	1913	45,000	45,000	3	none	1,200	2,000
Boy Scouts of America	1910	1,429,622	1,062,975	334[b]	1,202,100[c]	56,299	1,367,000[b]
Boys' Clubs of America	1906	295,732	295,732	29	9,355[d]	5,980	159,000
Camp Fire Girls	1912	278,451	219,494	47	none	2,124	135,100
Girl Scouts	1912	636,941	512,981	272	....	639,644	1,459,000
Junior Achievement	1919	10,000	10,000	8	2,000	8,402	22,000
National Self-Government Committee	1904	5,930	....	3	6,937	1,000	5,700
Order of DeMolay, Grand Council of the	1919	74,289	59,465	18	....	125,340	80,200
Pathfinders of America	1914	20,000	20,000	1	none	....	1,500
United Boys' Brigades of America	1894	20,000	....	[e]	....	....	400
Young Men's Christian Associations	1851	1,316,573[f]	820,000	155	3,013,463	25,189	789,700
Young Women's Christian Associations	1858	548,000[g]	400,000[h]	219	5,542,613[i]	....	958,800[j]

a Number of youth between the ages of 12 and 25.
b All of national council, including 12 regional offices.
c Also working capital funds of $729,284.
d Also invested funds of $101,100.
e No paid workers.
f Additional registered constituency reported, 241,892; estimated number of other participants not individually registered, 945,916.

g Paid membership only. The organization estimates that it has continuing relationships with a total of 2,866,797 individuals.
h Exclusive of 332,799 Girl Reserves aged 12 to 18.
i Also working capital funds of $283,204.
j Includes work in other countries and contributions to World's Council YWCA.

VI. Protestant Religious Youth-Serving Organizations

Nearly all Protestant churches devote substantial organized efforts toward enlisting and maintaining the interest of young people. The names of several of the denominational and interdenominational organizations are household words from coast to coast. These groups command the ardent enthusiasm of large numbers of young persons of both sexes for greater or lesser lengths of time and must be counted among the factors influencing their moral and social welfare.

The national picture of Protestant organizations is a complicated one, but lends itself to analysis. There are three important national federations which may be used as focal points: The Federal Council of Churches of Christ in America consists of twenty-two affiliated denominations. The Council of Church Boards of Education represents twenty-two denominational boards of education and five other groups.[1] The International Council of Religious Education is a publication and research agency serving the whole Protestant field.

Each of these national federations maintains committees and divisions devoted wholly or in part to the interests of youth. Recently they have joined with other interdenominational young people's organizations in constituting the United Christian Youth Movement (for a short time known as the Joint Committee on United Youth Program), which has for its central theme the attractive slogan, "Christian Youth Building a New World." This grouping, though relatively new and only loosely federated, represents a step toward coordination of all Protestant efforts in behalf of youth.

Aside from the church boards of education, and apart from the Young Men's and Young Women's Christian Associations (which are treated elsewhere), there remains for our observation here that class of Protestant youth organizations, some denominational and some interdenominational, which is typified by the International Society of Christian Endeavor, the Baptist Young People's Union, the Epworth League, and numerous others.

The varied structure and relations of the different youth-serving activities within a single denomination do not always lend themselves well to uniformity of presentation, and their scope cannot be delimited with statistical precision. These characteristics are accentuated by occasional reorganizations which take place more or less gradually from time to time.

The recent merger of the Methodist Episcopal Church, the Methodist Episcopal Church, South, and the Methodist Protestant Church to form one Methodist Church has set in motion changes which make it difficult either to present a composite picture of the youth activities today or to foretell precisely what form their organization may soon assume.

The difficulty of obtaining a complete and accurate statistical presentation does not obscure the fact that the several Protestant groups collectively enlist millions of youth and play an important part not only in offering them religious inspiration and moral guidance but also in providing means of informal education, healthful recreation, and wholesome social intercourse. The aggregate public welfare value of these activities is not susceptible of calculation; but frequent review of the purposes and programs may serve useful ends.

In the present section, organizations whose membership consists chiefly of young persons, as distinguished from those composed wholly or largely of persons above the age of 25, are:

Baptist Young People's Union of America
Brotherhood of St. Andrew in the United States
Epworth League
Girls' Friendly Society of the U.S.A.
International Society of Christian Endeavor
International Walther League
Junior Daughters of the King
Luther League of America
National Council of Methodist Youth
National Young People's Christian Union of the Universalist Church
Order of the Fleur-de-Lis
Order of Sir Galahad
Pi Christian Fraternal Orders
Pilgrim Fellowship (see Congregational and Christian Churches, Division of Christian Education)
United Christian Youth Movement
Young People's Religious Union
Youth Fellowship of the Reformed Church in America

---

[1] A complete catalog of the constituent boards of the Council of Church Boards of Education, listing headquarters addresses, names of executive officers, functions, publications, and schools and colleges sponsored, is contained in *Christian Higher Education—A Handbook for 1940* (fourth edition), edited by Gould Wickey and Ruth E. Anderson (Washington: Council of Church Boards of Education, 1940).

Cross references: Section V, General Character-Building Organizations for Youth, pp. 19–30, especially American Youth Foundation, p. 21, United Boys' Brigades of America, p. 26, Young Men's Christian Associations, p. 27, and Young Women's Christian Associations, p. 28.

AMERICAN FRIENDS SERVICE COMMITTEE

(1917); 20 South 12th St., Philadelphia, Pa.; Clarence E. Pickett, Executive Secretary.

Membership: Representatives of various Yearly Meetings of Friends (Quakers) in America, and other persons coopted on account of interest and experience. At present there are 125 official members and 200 advisory members. About 2,000 young people, of both sexes, from all parts of the country, and of various religious denominations, have been summer volunteer workers over the past seven years and are retained on the mailing list.

Purpose: To seek to express the Quaker philosophy of life, with its belief in the sacredness of personality and its repudiation of the methods of war and violence, by applying the principles of good will and understanding to social, economic, and international situations of tension and conflict.

Activities: The *Foreign Service Section* conducts international centers in Europe and the Orient, offers scholarships for foreign study, and sponsors various relief projects. Large-scale relief of refugee women and children in France and aid to Spanish refugees in Latin America are notable current activities of the Relief Committee. The Refugee Committee gives aid and counsel to exiles in the United States and abroad; it also conducts a refugee hostel in Cuba and hostels and other retraining services in the United States. The *Social-Industrial Section* has developed a new cooperative community for unemployed coal miners in western Pennsylvania and has established other rehabilitation enterprises. It also conducts summer volunteer work camps and other summer placement efforts for college students. The *Peace Section* carries on a series of Institutes of International Relations and sponsors the Student Peace Service. Jointly the Peace Section and the Social-Industrial Section direct the National Volunteer Service by which young men and women enroll for a year's work in nationally important and constructive service. The *Fellowship Council* draws into closer association scattered groups of Friends and "friends of the Friends." Its purpose is to emphasize the spiritual significance of Quaker service.

In 1940 summer volunteers, aged 18 and over, worked with the following sections: The *Social-Industrial Section* placed 261 young people from 33 states and 3 foreign countries, 21 religious denominations, and 82 colleges and universities in 12 volunteer work camps, and 23 young people in settlements and settlement camps. The *Peace Section* used 119 students, drawn from 26 states and 3 foreign countries, 16 religious denominations, and 55 colleges, in its Student Peace Service in the United States and Mexico, and carried on programs in about 22 communities. The *Refugee Section* used 20 young people as volunteers in refugee hostels.

Publications: *The Quaker Letter* (edited by the Fellowship Council, under Leslie D. Shaffer, secretary), a condensed sheet compiled from Friends' publications and sent four times a year to Friends and "seekers"; *Student Digest* (edited by the Student Peace Service), sent monthly to peace volunteers on college campuses; *Annual Report, 1939*, 52 pp. *Under the Red and Black Star*, 12 pp.; *The Pacifist Handbook*, published jointly with seven other peace organizations; *Student Peace Service*, 12 pp.; *American Friends Fellowship Council*, 33 pp.; *Volunteer Work Camps*, 14 pp.; *A Quaker Contribution toward World Peace*, 6 pp.; *Friendly Service for Refugees*, 8 pp.; *National Volunteer Service*, 4 pp.; *Afserco News*, 8 pp.; relief bulletins; other illustrated leaflets and folders.

Staff: Full-time paid employees at headquarters, 86; field workers in Europe, 50; field workers in the United States, Cuba, and Mexico, 33; part-time employees, 4.

Finances: Balance in the composite fund December 31, 1939, $92,782.55. For the fiscal year ending on that date, income and expenditures were as follows:

Income

General fund	$ 92,593.64
American Friends Fellowship Council	4,774.49
Peace Section	99,684.40
Social-Industrial Section	40,818.66
Friends Service, Inc.	70,162.86
	$308,034.05

Expenditures

General fund	$ 88,231.87
American Friends Fellowship Council	4,773.05
Peace Section	96,873.30
Social-Industrial Section	36,669.90
Friends Service, Inc.	70,162.86
	$296,710.98

BAPTIST YOUNG PEOPLE'S UNION OF AMERICA

(1891); 203 North Wabash Ave., Chicago, Ill.; Edwin Phelps, General Secretary.

Membership: Approximately 5,000 local young people's organizations affiliated with Baptist churches in the territory of the Northern Baptist Convention. Grand aggregate of individual members, 250,000 to 400,000.

Purpose: To promote the devotional life and the development of a sense of stewardship, service, and fellowship among Baptist young people; to develop leadership in the service of the church.

Activities: The local societies carry on a widely varied program of religious, social, and recreational activities and exercises for their members. There are biennial national conventions, and members of the national headquarters staff travel for local and regional conferences and lectures.

Publications: *Baptist Leader*, monthly; $1 a year. Numerous pamphlets and leaflets, and occasional mimeographed documents.

Staff: Full-time paid secretaries at headquarters, 2; part-time paid secretary, 1.

Finances: Balance April 30, 1939, $1,300.64. For the fiscal year ending on that date, operations were as follows:

Income

Northern Baptist Convention	$ 8,670.46
Contributions	280.35
Field reimbursements	431.63
Royalties	577.42
Study courses	89.00
Other sources	488.76
	$10,537.62

Expenditures

Salaries	$ 5,824.00
Travel (board)	514.14
Travel (staff)	927.64
Office expense	1,631.95
Promotion	350.19
Other purposes	233.48
	$ 9,481.40

BROTHERHOOD OF ST. ANDREW IN THE UNITED STATES (1883); 1010 Vermont Ave., Washington, D. C.; Harrison Fiddesof, Executive Secretary.

Membership: Men and boys, 5,000, of whom two-thirds are between the ages of 12 and 24. There are 263 active chapters in the United States and possessions, and national organizations in other countries. Members must be baptized communicants of the Protestant Episcopal Church of the United States or, if outside the United States, of the Anglican Communion. Annual dues to headquarters: $1 for individuals under 21, $2 for others.

Purpose: To spread Christianity throughout the world by developing Christian personalities in men and boys; to promote church attendance and religious education; to train for Christian leadership.

Activities: Annual Corporate Communions on February 22 and the first Sunday after November 30 (St. Andrew's Day). Pilgrimages of young men to historical church points such as Williamsburg and Jamestown in Virginia and Glebe House in Connecticut. Summer camps; annual six-day national convention, divided into conference groups; frequent week-end conference groups in districts. Winter educational programs in large metropolitan areas. Bible classes for young men and adults. Active groups in prisons and schools for delinquent and underprivileged children.

Publications: *St. Andrew's Cross*, 12 issues annually; free to members, $1 a year to others. *Handbook*, and numerous leaflets and bulletins.

Staff: Full-time paid employees, 3; part-time paid employees in field work, 2.

Finances: Endowment fund, $50,000; reserve fund, $1,500. Value of equipment at headquarters, $500. Current balance December 31, 1939, $529.87. For the fiscal year ending on that date, operations were as follows:

Income

Gifts for current expenses	$ 7,391.94
Membership fees	2,812.86
Publications	161.03
Endowment and reserve funds	2,046.76
Other sources	449.70
	$12,862.29

Expenditures

Salaries	$ 3,963.79
Travel	597.27
Office supplies	673.17
Publications	5,172.12
Rent, insurance, etc.	660.00
Other purposes	1,608.93
	$12,675.28

CONGREGATIONAL AND CHRISTIAN CHURCHES, BOARD OF HOME MISSIONS: DIVISION OF CHRISTIAN EDUCATION (1816); 14 Beacon St., Boston, Mass.; Harry Thomas Stock, D.D., General Secretary.

Membership: About 1,600 adults, including the voting delegates to the general council of Congregational and Christian churches and additional members-at-large. The youth organization is the Pilgrim Fellowship, enrolling 189,962 young people aged 12 to 24, with high school ages predominating, and the number of girls probably exceeding that of boys. There are members in 48 states.

Purpose: To help the Congregational and Christian churches to develop an effective program of Christian education in church, home, and school; to make available to these churches the best possible materials, methods, and policies of Christian education for children, young people, and adults—through correspondence, institutes, interviews, and printed literature.

Activities: Develops educational programs for churches; sponsors week-end institutes and summer conferences. The program includes a variety of activities for leaders of children, for young people and their counselors, and for adult groups in churches. The Department of Student Life carries on a program of field work in the colleges, in cooperation with students and pastors related to campus churches. The Department of Young People's Work prepares program suggestions for young people's societies, classes, and clubs. The two staff members of the latter department serve as the field force of the national Pilgrim Fellowship, the youth organization, which elects its own state and associational officers and has its own national council. Approximately 90 summer conferences of the Pilgrim Fellowship are held annually.

Publications: *The Pilgrim Highroad*, published monthly by the Pilgrim Press with the cooperation of the Division of Christian Education and members of the national council of the Pilgrim Fellowship. The staff also edits four pages in *Advance*, the monthly periodical of the churches. Numerous leaflets for workers in local churches, and curriculum materials for workers with children and young people and adults.

Staff: Full-time paid employees, 15, of whom 8 spend at least half-time in field work.

Finances: Aggregate endowment funds, $421,418.70. Value of equipment at headquarters, $3,000. For the fiscal year ending May 31, 1939, operations were as follows:

Income

Gifts for current expenses	$50,657.99
Endowment funds	5,864.75
	$56,522.74

Expenditures

Salaries	$37,162.00
Travel	5,742.90
Communications	2,124.95
Office supplies	2,119.09
Publications	1,050.78
Rent, insurance, etc.	3,727.00
Other purposes	4,596.02
	$56,522.74

In addition, there were unbudgeted receipts and expenditures of $8,700 for student aid.

COUNCIL OF CHURCH BOARDS OF EDUCATION (1911); 744 Jackson Place, N.W., Washington, D.C.; Dr. Gould Wickey, General Secretary.

Membership: Constituent organizations, 27, represented by 111 individuals comprising 15 representatives from the National Conference of Church-Related Colleges, 15 from the National Commission on University Work, 5 from the International Council of Religious Education (see p. 36), 5 from the American Association of Theological Schools, 5 from the Triennial Conference of Church Workers in Colleges and Universities, and 1 to 3 representatives each from the following 22 denominational boards of education:

Board of Education of the Northern Baptist Convention; Education Commission of the Southern Baptist Convention; Seventh Day Baptist Education Society; General Education Board of the Church of the Brethren; Board of Christian Education, Church of the United Brethren in Christ; Division of Christian Education, Congregational and Christian Churches (see p. 33); Board of Higher Education, Disciples of Christ; Department of Religious Education of the Protestant Episcopal Church; Board of Christian Education of the Evangelical Church; Board of Christian Education, Evangelical and Reformed Church; Board of Education of the Five Years Meeting of Friends in America; Board of Christian Education, Norwegian Lutheran Church of America; Board of Education, United Lutheran Church in America; Board of Education, General Conference of the Mennonite Church of North America; Christian Education Department, African Methodist Episcopal Zion Church; General Conference Board of Education, Colored Methodist Episcopal Church; Board of Education of the Methodist Church (see p. 39); Christian Education Board of the Moravian Church (American Province, North); Executive Committee of Christian Education and Ministerial Relief of the Presbyterian Church in the U.S.; Board of Christian Education of the Presbyterian Church in the U.S.A.; Board of Education of the United Presbyterian Church of North America; Board of Education, Reformed Church in America.

Purpose: To promote the cause of Christian education in institutions of learning, including the religious development of students in tax-supported institutions; to strengthen the Christian college; to promote religious instruction therein; to emphasize the permanent necessity of higher education under distinctively Christian auspices.

Activities: Promotes the work and interests of the church-related colleges; stimulates religious work in tax-supported institutions; counsels in Christian life service; holds local, regional, and national conferences; gathers literature on Christian higher education; makes surveys and studies; offers impartial services for the cooperative endeavors of the various denominational boards of education in the field of Christian higher education; develops mutual good will in and understanding of a common cause, Christian higher education. The National Commission on University Work functions through 1,500 local workers with students and holds an annual meeting and a triennial conference of university workers with students. Various denominations hold regional and national conferences for students and student workers, especially the Lutherans, Southern Baptists, Methodists, and Presbyterians. The aggregate number of individual students whom the council seeks to serve is more than 1,000,000.

Publications: *Christian Education*, 5 times annually; $1.50 a year; Gould Wickey, editor. *Christian Higher Education—A Handbook for 1940*, containing lists of denominational foundations and student clubs, lists of religious workers with students in institutions of higher learning, and other data.

Staff: Full-time paid employees, 2; part-time paid employee, 1.

Finances: Value of equipment at national headquarters, $1,223. Balance December 31, 1939, $85. For the preceding calendar year, operations were as follows:

Income

Grants for current expenses	$ 1,097
Membership grants	7,256
Publications	2,374
	$10,727

Expenditures

Salaries	$ 5,883
Travel	503
Communications	706
Office supplies	437
Publications	2,214
Rentals, etc.	994
Other purposes	700
	$11,437

EPWORTH LEAGUE (1889); 810 Broadway, Nashville, Tenn.; Edward D. Staples and Walter Towner, Associate Secretaries.

Membership:* Young people aged 9 to 25, about 538,522. In 1939 Juniors aged 9 to 12 numbered 99,616, Intermediates aged 12 to 14 were 53,834, and Seniors and Young People aged 15 to 25 numbered 385,072. The organization is a division of the Youth Department of the Board of Education of the Methodist Church (see p. 39).

Purpose: To build Christian character; to provide young people a chance for self-expression; to train leaders; to develop friendships; to promote the welfare of the church; and to help build a Christian social order.

Activities: Religious, social, and recreational activities in wide variety are carried on by the local units. District, state, and national conferences and councils are held frequently, and various efforts to enlist the enthusiasm of Methodist youth are launched from time to time. Training conferences, summer institutes, summer camps, and other youth gatherings at various times in the year are sponsored. Planning an

---

* Statistics are for the former Methodist Episcopal Church; the statistics of the former Methodist Episcopal Church, South, and the former Methodist Protestant Church were not available at the time of the report. The three churches were united in 1939.

adequate program for young people and publishing materials to help them carry it into action are among the principal functions of the national staff.

Publications: *The Epworth Herald*, 24 issues annually; $1.25 a year, 75¢ in clubs of ten; W. E. J. Gratz, editor. *The Methodist Youth Leader*, quarterly, for conference, district, subdistrict, and council officers; free to presidents of these organizations, $1 a year to other individuals, $5 for cabinet subscription. *Play*, bulletin for recreation leaders, 10 issues for $1. *Adventures in Christian Leadership*, by Blaine E. Kirkpatrick, 1930, 97 pp., 25¢; *Adventures in Building a Better World*, by Roy E. Burt, revised 1940, 25¢; *Adventures in World Friendship*, by John Irwin, revised 1940, 25¢; *Adventures in Recreation*, by Owen M. Geer, revised 1939, 93 pp., 25¢; *Our Program Builder*, the program planning booklet, 10¢; a large number of other pamphlets and leaflets at nominal prices.

Staff: Full-time paid employees, 17, of whom 8 spend major time in field work.

Finances:* During the fiscal year ending June 30, 1940 total income, consisting of gifts for current expenses from the former Methodist Episcopal Church, was $39,161.72; budget expenditures for the same period aggregated $43,713.

FEDERAL COUNCIL OF CHURCHES OF CHRIST IN AMERICA (1908); 297 Fourth Ave., New York, N. Y.; Samuel M. Cavert, Secretary.

Membership: There are 22 constituent bodies: Northern Baptist Convention (including Free Baptists); National Baptist Convention; Congregational and Christian Churches; Disciples of Christ; Evangelical Church; Evangelical and Reformed Church; Society of Friends; Methodist Church; African M. E. Church; African M. E. Zion Church; Colored M. E. Church in America; Moravian Church; Presbyterian Church in the U.S.A; Protestant Episcopal Church, National Council of the (cooperating agency); Reformed Church in America; Reformed Episcopal Church; Seventh Day Baptist Churches; United Church of Canada (affiliated body); United Brethren Church; United Presbyterian Church; United Lutheran Church (consultative body).

Purpose: To promote the spirit of fellowship, service, and cooperation among the Protestant churches in America; to augment their efficiency; to increase their influence by united action in every department of their operations, at home and abroad.

Activities: Maintains the following agencies: Field Department, the chief work of which is the development of state and local organizations; Department of Evangelism, which carries on its activities by means of conferences, addresses to seminary students, distribution of literature, and visits to churches; Department of Religious Radio, which broadcasts more programs weekly than any other one sponsor; Department of the Church and Social Service; Department of Race Relations, which works for constructive measures to secure justice for Negro workers, farmers, and consumers, and to prevent discrimination against them; Department of International Justice and Good Will; Department of Research and Education, which has made various studies of current conditions and problems; Department of Relations with Churches Abroad; Committee on Worship; and Committee on Financial and Fiduciary Matters.

Publications: *Information Service*, news service of the Department of Research and Education; *The Interracial News Service*. Biennial report in even-numbered years. Numerous pamphlets have been issued by all the departments.

Staff: Full-time paid employees, 60.

Finances: For the calendar year 1939, expenditures aggregated $258,624.35. Income for the same period was as follows:

Denominations and churches	$ 60,387.00
Cooperating and contributing organizations	46,492.68
Individuals	115,875.90
Sales of publications	14,728.09
Other sources	12,414.31
	$249,897.98

GIRLS' FRIENDLY SOCIETY OF THE U.S.A.

(1877); 386 Fourth Ave., New York, N.Y.; Harriett A. Dunn, Executive Secretary.

Membership: Girls and women, 26,000 (membership in the U.S.A.), of whom 12,013 are under 18 years of age; girls aged 5 to 12 are designated as candidates, those over 12 as members. There are 900 local branches in the United States and outlying possessions and in 43 other countries. The organization is sponsored by the Episcopal Church, but membership is open to all creeds.

Purpose: To offer opportunities for friendship, for the development of Christian character, and for the training of leadership in the Episcopal Church.

Activities: Emphasizes the Christian's responsibility for facing world and community issues and for taking action on them. Each parish group is closely related to parish life; the program includes worship, study of the church's mission, service to the church and to the community, recreation, and training in leadership, with definite help given in each of these fields. Program material on special subjects of interest to children and young people is also provided by the national society.

Publications: *The Record*, 5 times annually; 50¢ a year. Program aids are published separately and sold at prices ranging from 5¢ to 50¢ each.

Staff: Full-time paid employees at headquarters, 11.

Finances: Approximate annual budget of headquarters, $35,500.

INTERNATIONAL COUNCIL OF RELIGIOUS EDUCATION

(1922); 203 North Wabash Ave., Chicago, Ill.; Dr. Roy G. Ross, General Secretary; Ivan M. Gould, Director of Young People's Work.

Membership: Constituent membership, embracing the boards of religious education of 42 cooperating Protestant denominations and 30 accredited state councils of religious education. These bodies comprise about 85 per cent of the Protestant church membership of North America and include about 10,000,000 youth. The governing body is the executive committee of 226 members, consisting of representatives of the constituent organizations in proportion to their respective numerical strength, 8 members-at-large, and 20 members elected by the quadrennial convention.

Purpose: To act as an interdenominational agency for the promotion of Christian education in the United States and Canada; to promote the development of Christian individuals in a Christian social order; to promote and execute programs and guidance plans developed interdenominationally.

Activities: Maintains the following departments: (1) Children's Work, (2) Young People's Work, (3) Adult Work, (4) Vacation and Weekday Church Schools, (5) Research, (6) Leadership Education, (7) Radio Education, (8) Visual Education, (9) Curriculum Work, (10) Field Work, and (11) Laymen's Commission. National conventions on religious education are held every four years. Field supervision is given to denominations and state councils of churches and religious education and to denominational and interdenominational youth groups. The Committee on Religious Education of Youth develops standards, guidance materials, and promotional enterprises for young people and their leaders. The director of young people's work serves as executive secretary of the United Christian Youth Movement (see p. 42).

Publications: *International Journal of Religious Education*, monthly; $1.25 a year. *International Council Yearbook*, $1 (the edition for 1940 has 209 pages, paper bound). Numerous pamphlets and leaflets, priced at 1¢ to 80¢.

Staff: Full-time paid employees, 35.

Finances: Value of real estate and equipment December 31, 1939, $75,201.01. Book value of special fund investments, $53,609.54. Cash balances, $9,232.09. For the calendar year 1939, operations were as follows:

Income

Contributions	$ 71,004.03
Conferences	5,161.81
International Journal	23,727.88
General items	25,834.16
Interest	2,438.25
Other sources	3,816.40
	$131,982.53

Expenditures

Departments	$ 97,233.05
Committees and commissions	11,476.06
General supplies and expense	24,606.80
Other purposes	1,828.76
	$135,144.67

INTERNATIONAL ORDER OF THE KING'S DAUGHTERS AND SONS (1886); 144 East 37th St., New York, N.Y.; Kate C. Hall, Executive Secretary.

Membership: Approximately 65,000 persons of all ages, including 2,000 young women aged 18 to 30 in the Young People's Department and 2,500 junior members under 18 years of age. Local units exist in the United States, Canada, and some 15 other countries. "Any person may become a member of the International Order whose purposes and aims are in accord with its objects and who holds herself or himself responsible to The King, our Lord and Savior, Jesus Christ."

Purpose: "The objects of the Order shall be the development of spiritual life and the stimulation of Christian activities."

Activities: Directs 126 institutions in various localities, including, among other types, institutional homes for children, for business girls and students, for nurses, for handicapped persons, and for the aged, as well as clinics, hospitals, and libraries. The Young People's Department contributes toward the maintenance of 12 camps and establishes scholarships and educational projects. It also provides leaders for groups of junior members. The international organization owns a "scholarship house" at Chautauqua, N.Y., and supports 20 scholarships for young women who attend classes in Christian leadership there. Work is undertaken on reservations of North American Indians under a supervisor with cooperative committee members in various branches, and special social service work is carried on in Shanghai, China. In India, Thailand, and elsewhere the activities are largely missionary and educational.

Publications: *The Silver Cross*, monthly, October to June, and vacation issue July-September; $1 a year. Leaflets free on request.

Staff: Full-time paid employees at headquarters, 3; number of part-time paid employees varies.

Finances: The organization owns its headquarters house and the scholarship house in Chautauqua, N.Y. The 126 institutions owned and maintained by the organization have an aggregate property valuation of approximately $4,500,000 and total annual operating budgets of about $1,500,000.

INTERNATIONAL SOCIETY OF CHRISTIAN ENDEAVOR (1881); 41 Mt. Vernon St., Boston, Mass.; Rev. Daniel A. Poling, President; Carroll M. Wright, Executive Secretary and Treasurer.

Membership: Approximately 4,000,000 persons, in about 80,000 local societies affiliated with churches of 87 Christian denominations in all parts of the world. The organization is interdenominational, international, and interracial. Age limits vary widely among the local societies but generally extend from about the ages of 9 to 24 inclusive; some societies extend upward to 35; and some are without upper limit. Usually the local group includes an intermediate (or high school age) society for boys and girls aged about 12 to 17 and a young people's society for those aged about 18 to 24.

Purpose: To promote an earnest Christian life among members; to increase their mutual acquaintance; to train them for work in the church; and in every way to make them more useful in the service of God.

Activities: Holds biennial international conventions and quinquennial world conventions. Gives aid and leadership to the state and provincial unions, which in turn carry on conventions, summer youth conferences, and leadership training institutes. Promotes education in citizenship, world peace, and good will. Encourages the social service work of local societies, including welfare work in prisons, among soldiers and sailors, and among underprivileged children. Each local society has also its social, recreational, and religious programs; meetings of local societies are usually held weekly.

Publications: *The Christian Endeavor World*, monthly; $1 a year in the United States, $1.25 in Canada, $1.50 in other countries; Dr. Daniel A. Poling, editor-in-chief; Dr. Stanley B. Vandersall, editor. Numerous books, booklets, and pamphlets, at prices ranging from 10¢ to $1, among which are: *Christian Endeavor Essentials*, by Wells and Vandersall, 1938, 50¢; *Leadership Through Christian Endeavor*, by Davis, $1; and *Better Meetings for the Young People's Society*, by Stock, 75¢. Also small descriptive folders, some free and some at nominal prices.

Staff: Full-time paid employees, 22; part-time field worker, 1; part-time unpaid workers at headquarters, 23.

Finances: Value of plant and equipment at headquarters, $250,000. Annual expenditures total approximately $75,000, about 50 per cent of which is derived from income-producing services such as building rentals, sales of supplies, etc.

INTERNATIONAL WALTHER LEAGUE (1893); 6438 Eggleston Ave., Chicago, Ill.; Rev. O. P. Kretzmann, Executive Secretary.

Membership: Young persons of both sexes, 80,000, in all states of the United States, with concentration in the Middle West and particularly in Michigan, Ohio, Missouri, and Illinois. The Junior Walther League is for boys and girls aged 12 to 18, and the Senior Walther League for those aged 18 to 24.

Purpose: To assist in keeping Lutheran young people within the church; to promote Bible study; to train well-informed and efficient church workers; to further the cause of home and foreign missions; to foster Christian love, fellowship, and sociability; to encourage charitable endeavors within the church; to promote loyalty to the Christian home.

Activities: A major enterprise is contribution to the support of a very large sanatorium for tubercular youth. This institution is at Wheat Ridge, Colo., and is supported by sales of Christmas seals. Other activities embrace support of foreign and home missionaries, Bible study, maintenance of national committees on Christian knowledge and Christian service, support of gospel radio programs, and maintenance of summer camps throughout the nation for Christian and wholesome recreation and Bible study. There were 40 district conventions in the United States and Canada during the summer of 1940, and 34 summer camps were open.

Publications: At 801 De Mun, St. Louis, Mo.: *The Walther League Messenger*, 11 issues annually; $1 a year; Walter A. Maier, Ph.D., editor. *The Bible Student*, quarterly; Th. Graebner, editor. At 6438 Eggleston Ave., Chicago, Ill.: *The Concordia Messenger*, 12 issues annually; W. F. Weiherman, editor. *The Cresset*, 12 issues annually; $2 a year; O. P. Kretzmann, editor. *Workers' Quarterly*, a magazine for leaders in Walther League work; O. P. Kretzmann, editor. Devotional books and educational materials in printed and mimeographed form are distributed at cost by the Chicago office.

Staff: Full-time paid employees, 19; part-time paid employees, 6.

Finances: Value of equipment at national headquarters, $6,364.60. Cash on hand May 31, 1940, $31,253.68. For the fiscal year ending on that date, operations were as follows:

Income

Membership fees	$ 32,300.75
Publications	64,206.13
Other services	25,240.27
	$121,747.15

Expenditures

Salaries	$ 26,974.80
Travel	7,257.96
Office supplies	4,988.46
Publications	61,762.74
Other purposes	25,452.63
	$126,436.59

JUNIOR DAUGHTERS OF THE KING (1896); Room 305, 150 Fifth Ave., New York, N.Y.; Edna Eastwood, Executive.

Membership: Girls aged 10 to 20, numbering 1,461, in 161 chapters in 25 states of the United States and in China. This is the junior division of the Daughters of the King, an organization of the Protestant Episcopal Church.

Purpose: To spread Christ's Kingdom among girls; to train members to become Senior Daughters of the King and loyal church leaders; to urge girls to pray daily and to take regularly some part in the worship and work of the church.

Activities: Church work, including community social work; evangelistic work in colleges. Representatives attend church camps and conferences, but no institutions or camps are maintained by this organization. Local chapter directresses are subject to the authority of diocesan chairmen, and all are guided by the national junior committee of the national council, which plans the work of the entire organization, junior and senior. Contact with other youth groups of the same church is maintained through delegates to the National Council of Representatives of Youth Organizations, which meets twice or three times a year and advises the National Youth Commission of the Protestant Episcopal Church.

Publications: *The Royal Cross*, including the *Junior Messenger*, 4 issues annually; free to members, 50¢ a year to others; Mrs. W. W. Pedder, editor, 3801 West Seventh St., Los Angeles, Calif. *The Senior Handbook*, 1939, 70 pp., 15¢; *The Junior Handbook*, 1938, 34 pp., 5¢; *Book of Prayers*, 1934, 43 pp., 15¢. Other leaflets.

Staff: Full-time paid employees, 2, of whom 1 is in China; part-time paid employee, 1.

Finances: The following statement applies to the entire organization, junior and senior. Endowment fund, $2,299.12. On August 31, 1939 the cash balance for current expense was $461.70; there was an additional unbudgeted balance of $4,318.57 available for other purposes, such as scholarships, missions, or endowment accumulation. For the fiscal year ending on that date, operations, approximately 10 per cent of which are attributable to the junior division, were as follows:

Income

Gifts for current expenses	$3,031.18
Membership fees	5,397.15
Publications	473.96
Other sources	178.28
	$9,080.57

Expenditures

Salaries	$3,534.00
Travel	156.98
Communications	473.87
Office supplies	70.56
Publications	2,216.29
Rent, insurance, etc.	600.00
Other purposes	1,628.16
	$8,679.86

LUTHER LEAGUE OF AMERICA (1895); 405 Muhlenberg Bldg., Philadelphia, Pa.; Rev. Paul M. Kinports, Executive Secretary.

The official young people's organization of the United Lutheran Church in America.

Membership: Approximately 40,000 young persons aged 12 and upward. There are three departments: Intermediate, for ages 12 to 14; Senior, for ages 15 to 17; and Young People's, for age 18 and above. There are 1,804 local leagues, grouped into district, state, and synodical leagues. Thirty-three state or synodical leagues exist in the United States, Canada, and five other countries.

Purpose: To simulate the Christian faith; to foster loyalty to the church; to give youth an opportunity to realize their desire to render some distinctive service to the church.

Activities: Bible study, discussion groups, study of missions, and social program. Biennial national conventions, yearly state or synodical conventions, and district and conference rallies throughout the year. The work falls chiefly into three divisions of which the titles and functions are: (1) *Educational*, responsible for devotional meetings, selection of reading-course books, and daily Bible-reading promotion; (2) *Missionary*, promoting home, inner, and foreign missions, and adopting biennial projects in that field; (3) *Life Service*, stressing the work of the young people in the church, whether full-time and vocational or part-time and avocational. There are also standing committees on publicity, sustaining membership, and social affairs; special committees are appointed from time to time.

Publications: *Luther League Review*, 11 issues annually, $1.25 a year; *Luther League Topics*, quarterly, 25¢ a year; *Intermediate Quarterly Helps*, 25¢ a year. Numerous pamphlets and leaflets, some free and others at nominal prices.

Staff: Full-time paid employees, 4; part-time paid employee, 1.

METHODIST CHURCH, BOARD OF EDUCATION (1940); 810 Broadway, Nashville, Tenn.; Bishop Adna Wright Leonard, President, Washington, D.C.

Membership: This is an official organ of the newly merged Methodist Church, which embraces the former Methodist Episcopal Church, the former Methodist Episcopal Church, South, and the former Methodist Protestant Church. Probably the number of persons aged 12 to 25 within its constituency exceeds 2,000,000.

Purpose: To carry out the general program and objectives of the Methodist Church through educational institutions, through educational efforts in the local churches, and through educational publications.

Activities: Because of the recent merging of the three components of the Methodist Church, undoubtedly for the time being the general programs of education and other activities in behalf of youth will continue approximately as hitherto. For descriptions, see in this book the Epworth League (p. 35) and National Council of Methodist Youth (p. 39), formerly organs of the Methodist Episcopal Church. In addition, the activities of the former General Board of Christian Education of the Methodist Episcopal Church, South, and of the corresponding agency of the Methodist Protestant Church will be embraced under the present organization. It is known that the work of the present board will fall into three major departments: (1) the Division of Educational Institutions, (2) the Division of the Local Church, which will undoubtedly embrace a youth section, and (3) the Editorial Division. In late 1940 these agencies were in process of becoming established, and precise facts and figures concerning their organization and work could not be had.

Publications: See Epworth League and National Council of Methodist Youth.

Staff: Not reported because in process of organization.

Finances: Not reported because merging is in process and this organization has been in existence less than one complete fiscal year.

NATIONAL COUNCIL OF METHODIST YOUTH (1934); 740 Rush St., Chicago, Ill.; Thomas R. Pendell, Executive Secretary.

Membership: Approximately 100 representatives of the constituent organizations, elected for two-year terms and between the ages of 17 and 25 when elected. There is one representative for each annual or provisional annual conference of the Methodist Church, elected by the Epworth League or other corresponding youth group, and specific provision is made for representatives of students in Methodist colleges and seminaries, Wesley foundations, and the organizations known as Queen Esthers, Standard Bearers, Kappa Phi, Phi Tau Theta, Sigma Epsilon Theta, and Wesley Players, as well as for several ex officio memberships for national officers of Methodist youth organizations and officers of pertinent departments of the Methodist Church. Approximately 1,500,000 youth aged 12 to 25, in the territory served by the former Methodist Episcopal Church prior to its merging with other churches to form the present Methodist Church (see p. 39), participate in the organizations represented.

Purpose: To provide a national medium through which the various organizations of young people in the Methodist Church may form and give expression to their Christian convictions and purposes with reference to the issues affecting the life of young people today.

Activities: Cooperates in developing local church programs and in sponsoring various church-wide endeavors. Provides suggestions and techniques by which local groups may face social situations in the light of Christian gospel, and conducts special projects relating to such fields as world peace, social reconstruction, and devotional life; an active commission for each of these fields, as well as for recreation, rural life, and others, furnishes inspiration to district and local groups. Conducts annual meetings and biennial national conferences of Methodist youth. Provides for the representation of its constituency in the United Christian Youth Movement (see p. 42) and in various other interdenominational and secular youth groups. Sponsors summer work camps and special study conferences.

Publications: *National Council Newsletter* (mimeo.), monthly; 50¢ a year. *Christian Fellowship in a World of Conflict*, edited by T. Otto Nall, 1938, 173 pp., 50¢; *What Is the National Council?* by Hayes Beall, 1937, 30 pp., 10¢; *New Directions*, edited by Thomas R. Pendell, 1939, 34 pp. mimeo., 25¢; *Industrial Conflicts—Strikes*, by Charles C. Webber, revised 1939, 48 pp., 15¢; and other pamphlets.

Staff: Full-time paid employee, 1; part-time paid employee, 1.

Finances: Budget for the calendar year 1940, $4,200.

NATIONAL YOUNG PEOPLE'S CHRISTIAN UNION OF THE UNIVERSALIST CHURCH (1889); 16 Beacon St., Boston, Mass.; post of executive secretary temporarily vacant.

Membership: Approximately 3,000 persons, of whom about 2,500 are between the ages of 12 and 25, in about 200 groups in local churches throughout the country. The financial obligation of a local group to the national organization is 40¢ a member annually.

Purpose: To promote Christian culture, service, and leadership among the young people of the Universalist Church; and to extend the power and influence of liberalism in every way possible.

Activities: Develops program materials for local societies. Holds four summer institutes of one week each at Saco, Me., Forked River, N.J., Marshall, Ind., and Watha, N.C. Holds a national convention annually in July. Maintains affiliation with the International Religious Fellowship, formerly known as the Leyden International Bureau.

Publications: *Onward*, monthly; free to members, 25¢ a year to others. Descriptive folders and program materials.

Staff: Full-time paid employee, 1; part-time paid employee, 1.

Finances: Aggregate endowment, $12,214.42. Value of equipment at national headquarters, $147. For the fiscal year ending June 30, 1940, operations were as follows:

Income

Gifts and grants	$2,123.50
Membership fees	358.03
Service projects	557.74
Endowment and reserve funds	483.37
	$3,522.64

Expenditures

Salaries	$1,627.20
Travel	128.79
Office supplies	243.49
Publications	389.59
Rentals, etc.	420.78
Service projects	557.74
	$3,367.59

ORDER OF THE FLEUR-DE-LIS, INC. (1914); 1 Joy St., Boston, Mass.; Margaret F. Ferguson, Sovereign Queen.

Membership: Girls and young women of the Episcopal Church, 1,500, of whom 1,200 are between the ages of 12 and 25. There are three degrees: Maids, aged 12 to 15; Maidens, aged 16 to 19; Ladies, 20 and over. Members under the age of 12 are known as "Little Sisters." There are about 100 active chapters in the United States, one in Rose Park, South Australia, and one in Liberia, Africa.

Purpose: To provide a church club for church girls; to enlarge their capacity and their desire for efficient church service; to strengthen the bodies, enrich the minds, quicken the ideals, and give expression to the manifold interests of girlhood.

Activities: Programs worked out by the local chapters embrace as far as possible a well-rounded, interesting, varied schedule of religious and community service. Chapter meetings are usually held weekly or biweekly. A typical program includes sports, crafts, dramatics, ceremonials, social activities, and worship. Fleur-de-Lis Camp, Inc., located at Fitzwilliam, N.H., and accommodating 90 campers and a large staff, has been operated during July and August for 11 seasons; registration is not confined to members of the order or to members of the Episcopal Church.

Publications: *Fleur-de-Lis Herald*, 2 issues annually; free; Norah A. Bell, editor; 107 Park St., Lynn, Mass. *The Manual*, 75¢; *The Order of the Fleur-de-Lis, Inc.*, 5 pp. mimeo.

Staff: Part-time unpaid workers, 2.

Finances: Value of equipment at headquarters, $200. Operating balance December 31, 1939, $152.65. For the fiscal year ending on that date, operations were as follows:

Income

Membership fees	$ 28.20
Publications	24.28
Other services	46.75
Other sources	61.09
	$160.32

Expenditures

Travel	$ 40.71
Office supplies	19.69
Publications	13.30
Other purposes	128.66
	$202.36

ORDER OF SIR GALAHAD, INC. (1896); 26 Temple Place, Boston, Mass.; Rev. Arthur O. Phinney, National Director; Hans S. Johnson, Office Executive.

Membership: Boys, approximately 10,000, chiefly between the ages of 9 and 21, with some Counselors above the age of 21. There are four classes below the rank of counselors: Lads, aged 9 and 10; Pages, 11 to 13; Esquires, 14 and 15; Knights, 16 to 20. The entire organization within a parish is known as a Court. Most of these units are adjunct to Episcopal churches, but a few are in churches of other Protestant denominations.

Purpose: To provide a character-building, recreational, and general service organization for boys, and to bring them into contact with the church.

Activities: Recreational, community service, and religious programs as developed by the local courts with the advice and assistance of the national headquarters, diocesan and parish church officers, and local leaders. There is an official Galahad Camp on Lake Sebago in Maine.

Publications: *A Glance at the Order of Sir Galahad*, 8 pp. A series of five handbooks: *Handbook for Leaders of Standard Courts*, 50¢; *Handbook for Boys of Standard Courts*, 35¢; *Initiations*, 50¢; *Ceremonies and Special Occasions*, 50¢; *Crafts*, 10¢.

Staff: Full-time paid employee, 1.

Finances: Approximate annual budget, $2,200.

PI CHRISTIAN FRATERNAL ORDERS (1905); 909 Plum St., Cincinnati, Ohio; David H. Jemison, Grand Chaplain.

Membership: Boys and girls, approximately 2,100, of whom about 1,900 are between the ages of 12 and 25, in Kappa Sigma Pi (boys), Phi Beta Pi (girls), Delta Alpha Pi (college students, men), and Sigma Beta Pi (college students, women). Local units exist in about 100 churches of 21 denominations in all parts of the United States and in other countries. Initiation fee is $1, and local chapter dues vary from 10¢ to 25¢ a month.

Purpose: To unite older boys in a fraternal group, under adult Christian supervision, to insure their moral safety and to train them for Christian leadership and service; to unite the teen-age girls under Christian leadership so that all may develop through earnest endeavor and wholesome pleasure into well-rounded Christian characters and be trained for leadership in church, missionary, and community service.

Activities: Wide range of social, religious, athletic, and recreational exercises. There are several district camps and an annual summer camp. In the fraternal aspects of the organization, members pass from rank to rank in impressive ceremonies. In Kappa Sigma Pi there are: (1) the Order of Tarsus, boys 12 to 14; (2) the Order of Jerusalem, boys at least 15; (3) the Order of Damascus, boys at least 16; and (4) the Order of Rome, boys 17 and over. In Phi Beta Pi there are parallel orders for girls: (1) Order of Palestine, girls 12 to 14; (2) Order of Bethlehem, girls at least 15; (3) Order of Philippi, girls at least 16; and (4) Order of Corinth, girls at least 17. In both organizations the first order (ages 12 to 14) is not prerequisite to the other orders; but the three higher orders are consecutive, admission to each being conditioned upon an acceptable record in the next lower order.

Publications: *The Pi Magazine*, monthly; $1 a year, free to members. Numerous descriptive and promotional folders; a loose-leaf manual for local leaders.

Staff: Full-time paid employees at headquarters, 2; part-time paid employees, 5, of whom 3 spend major time in field work; part-time unpaid workers in field work, 24.

Finances: Kappa Sigma Pi owns a Boys' Home in Clarksburg, W.Va., and a 107-acre farm and campground near Clarksburg, valued at $85,000, governed by a local board of trustees. The Cincinnati headquarters also places boys and girls in boarding homes About 140 dependent children are given temporary residence and kept in public schools through these enterprises, deriving their major support from the community chests. Approximate annual budget, $12,500.

Value of equipment at national headquarters, $1,500. For the fiscal year ending August 31, 1940, income for the national headquarters totaled $3,765; expenditures for the same period aggregated $3,810.

PROTESTANT EPISCOPAL CHURCH, THE NATIONAL COUNCIL: DEPARTMENT OF CHRISTIAN SOCIAL RELATIONS (1919); 281 Fourth Ave., New York, N.Y.; Rev. Almon R. Pepper, Executive Secretary.

Purpose: To stimulate and coordinate the social service work of the 89 dioceses and the provinces of the Episcopal Church; to improve standards of parochial social service; to provide advisory and consultative service to Episcopal social institutions (homes for children and the aged, hospitals, settlements, protective or maternity homes, and guest or rest houses); to direct the Episcopal Social Work Conference and the National Episcopal Conference on Rural Social Work; to conduct conferences on family relations and social and industrial reconstruction.

Activities: Promotes the organization of social relations committees in local parishes for discussion of and work upon individual and social problems through parish house activities, conducted in co-operation with community social institutions and agencies. Approximately 200,000 young people are members of the church and its several young people's organizations. See also Brotherhood of St. Andrew in the United States (p. 33), Junior Daughters of the King (p. 38), Girls' Friendly Society of the U.S.A. (p. 36), Order of the Fleur-de-Lis (p. 40), Order of Sir Galahad (p. 41).

Publications: Proceedings of the Episcopal Social Work Conference, annually. Recent issues bear the following titles: *Episcopal Social Work, 1938; Church and Family Life, 1939; The Parish Church and Its Community,* 1940. These are priced at 50¢ each. Numerous other books and pamphlets on church social work, family relations, rural work, industrial relations, and other subjects, from 5¢ to $1.

Staff: Full-time paid employees, 4.

Finances: Approximate annual budget, $13,500.

See also Protestant Episcopal Church, the National Council: Youth Division (p. 42).

PROTESTANT EPISCOPAL CHURCH, THE NATIONAL COUNCIL: YOUTH DIVISION (1925); 281 Fourth Ave., New York, N.Y.; Rev. Frederick H. Arterton, Secretary for Youth.

Membership: The division sponsors the church's work with youth, assisting prosecution of the work of some 15 national youth organizations as well as hundreds of diocesan and parochial groups. Approximately 200,000 young people are enrolled in one or more of these groups.

Purpose: To advise and assist in the unification, development, and prosecution of work of religious education among the young people of the Protestant Episcopal Church and others.

Activities: Encourages and assists clergymen and leaders of young people's work in local parishes in studying the interests of youth of both sexes, including their personal, social, occupational, and religious problems. See also Girls' Friendly Society of the U.S.A. (p. 36), Order of the Fleur-de-Lis (p. 40), Order of Sir Galahad (p. 41), Brotherhood of St. Andrew in the United States (p. 33), and Junior Daughters of the King (p. 38).

Publications: *The Broadcast,* monthly. *Christianity's*

Answer, 1939, three program units: "Understanding Each Other," "Making Democracy Work," and "Being a World Christian." *A Book Shelf,* revised 1940, 17 pp. mimeo.

Staff: Full-time paid employees, 7.

Finances: Approximate annual budget, $20,000.

See also Protestant Episcopal Church, the National Council: Department of Christian Social Relations (p. 41).

STUDENT VOLUNTEER MOVEMENT (1888); 156 Fifth Ave., New York, N.Y.; R. H. Edwin Espy, General Secretary.

Membership: Students in local units in colleges, universities, and professional schools, about 400, of whom about 150 are under 25 years of age.

Purpose: To enlist students for Christian missionary service, and to encourage them to get the best training possible for that purpose.

Activities: Through literature, correspondence, conferences, and personal interviews, provides information concerning openings in the mission fields under various denominational mission boards, conditions of appointment, and personal qualifications and attitudes essential to successful work. Counsels prospective missionaries regarding choice of fields and types of work, selection of educational institutions and courses of study for specific fields and tasks, and choice of books and pamphlets for individual or group study.

Publications: *Intercollegian,* 7 issues annually; $1.50 a year. Extensive list of books, pamphlets, and folders on the missionary movement, some free and others priced at 5¢ to $2 a copy.

Staff: Full-time paid employees, 9, of whom 4 spend major time in field work.

Finances: Budget for the fiscal year ending September 30, 1939, $16,000.

UNITED CHRISTIAN YOUTH MOVEMENT (1934); 203 North Wabash Ave., Chicago, Ill.; Ivan M. Gould, Executive Secretary.

Membership: Constituent membership, embracing all the denominations and state councils of the International Council of Religious Education (see p. 36), the International Society of Christian Endeavor (see p. 37), the YMCA (see p. 27), the YWCA (see p. 28), the National Intercollegiate Christian Council, the Missionary Education Movement, the National Commission on University Work of the Council of Church Boards of Education (see p. 34), the Student Volunteer Movement (see p. 42), the Home Missions Council, the Federal Council of Churches of Christ in America (see p. 35), and others. About 11,000,000 young people are connected with these agencies.

Purpose: To unite the Protestant youth forces of North America in a common emphasis and program. The theme is "Christian Youth Building a New World."

Activities: Three active organs: (1) the Committee on the United Christian Youth Movement, composed of about 100 individuals, who are representatives of the constituent organizations and of whom over half are young people; (2) the Christian Youth Council of North America, consisting of 250 persons, about 200 of whom are young people; and (3) the Christian Youth Conference of North America, numbering about 1,000 delegates, of whom about 900 are young people. In addition to these activities, six regional youth conferences are held in the United States during the summer. The organization also promotes special day observances in churches and issues a "Statement of Christian Conviction" as a rallying-call for young people of many denominations and churches.

Publications: Occasional pamphlets issued through the International Council of Religious Education.

Staff: None other than volunteer workers. The director of young people's work of the International Council of Religious Education serves as executive secretary.

Finances: The movement has no fiscal operations apart from those of its several constituent bodies.

YOUNG PEOPLE'S RELIGIOUS UNION (1896);
25 Beacon St., Boston, Mass.; Henry V. Atherton, President; Dorothy M. Nugent, Office Secretary.

Membership: Individuals and local societies and federations of Unitarian youth. Aggregate of individuals, about 7,000, including life members ($10 subscription), 175, and contributing members ($1 subscription annually). There are 327 local clubs and 24 federations of clubs.

Purpose: To unite in a general federation, the cardinal principles of which shall be truth, worship, and service, all persons and societies of young people who value those ideals and wish to work together; to foster the religious life; to put into practice such principles of life and duty as tend to uplift mankind.

Activities: Participates in Young People's Sunday (the first Sunday in February) in all Unitarian churches. This inaugurates Young People's Week, during which special stress is placed upon social and educational activities and dramatic performances in all local units. The local federations hold annual conferences, and local clubs operate forums, discussion groups, and dramatic and storytelling organizations. A national conference at Isles of Shoals (10 miles out to sea from Portsmouth, N.H.) is usually held during the last week in June and the first week in July, with an average attendance of 200 young people each week. Regional conferences are also held.

Publications: *Y. P. R. U. News*, monthly, edited by a committee of young people; *Social Action Digest* (mimeo.), monthly, similarly edited. Numerous pamphlets, among which are: *Exploring Liberal Religion*, by James Bissett Pratt, 16 pp., 10¢; *The Art of Being Neighborly*, by Wallace W. Robbins, 16 pp.,10¢; *What Shall I Believe?* by William Brooks Rice, 30 pp., 10¢; *Practical Theatre*, by H. Clarke Pickens, 16 pp., 5¢; *Recreation*, 12 pp., 5¢; *Guide to the Y. P. R. U.*, 20 pp., 10¢; and others.

Staff: Full-time paid employees, 2.

YOUTH FELLOWSHIP OF THE REFORMED CHURCH IN AMERICA (1933); 156 Fifth Ave., New York, N.Y.; Raymond B. Drukker, D.D., Secretary for Young People's Work.

Membership: Young people aged 12 to 25 in the Reformed Church in America.

Purpose: To serve the local church as it serves the youth groups in the church, on the fundamental thesis that the program is not dictated by a denominational agency but is developed on the field by representatives of local congregations.

Activities: Suggests principles and patterns of organization for local youth groups in the Reformed Church in America; suggests topics and source materials for the enrichment of young people's meetings; plans rallies and conferences; sponsors summer regional conferences in the eastern and western parts of the United States; stimulates the young people's organizations to contribute to the support of all the work of all the church.

Publications: Two pages in the *Intelligencer-Leader*, the weekly Reformed Church paper, $2 a year; Rev. Theodore Brinckerhoff, New Brunswick, N.J., is editor of the two pages.

Staff: Full-time paid employees, 2.

Finances: Budget for the fiscal year ending April 30, 1940 was approximately $9,300.

TABLE VII

STATISTICS OF PROTESTANT RELIGIOUS YOUTH-SERVING ORGANIZATIONS

Organization	Year Founded	Approximate Aggregate Membership (individuals)	Number of Members under 25 Years of Age	Total Employees on Headquarters Staff	Aggregate Endowment of National Headquarters	Plant and Equipment (headquarters only)	Approximate Annual Budget (headquarters only)
American Friends Service Committee	1917	125	[a]	173[b]	$ ...	$ ...	$308,000
Baptist Young People's Union of America	1891	325,000	325,000	3	...	...	10,500
Brotherhood of St. Andrew in the United States	1883	5,000	3,500	5	50,000	500	12,900
Cong. and Christ. Churches, Div. of Christ. Educ.	1816	1,600	189,962[c]	15	421,418	3,000	56,500
Council of Church Boards of Education	1911	111[d]	...	3	...	1,223	11,500
Epworth League	1889	538,522[e]	538,522[e]	17	...	...	43,700[e]
Federal Council of Churches of Christ in America	1908	22[f]	none	60	...	...	258,600
Girls' Friendly Society of the U.S.A.	1877	26,000	12,013[g]	11	...	...	35,500
International Council of Religious Education	1922	226[h]	...	35	53,610[i]	75,201	135,100
International Order of the King's Daughters and Sons	1886	65,000	4,500	3	...	...	...
International Society of Christian Endeavor	1881	4,000,000[j]	80,000	23	none	250,000	75,000
International Walther League	1893	80,000	80,000	25	2,299[k]	6,365	126,400
Junior Daughters of the King	1896	1,461	1,461	3	...	...	9,100[k]
Luther League of America	1895	40,000	40,000	5	...	...	...
Methodist Church, Board of Education	1940	...	...	...	...	...	...
National Council of Methodist Youth	1934	100[d]	1,500,000[m]	2	none	...	4,200
National YPCU of the Universalist Church	1889	3,000	2,500	2	12,214	147	3,500
Order of the Fleur-de-Lis	1914	1,500	1,200[n]	[p]	none	200	200
Order of Sir Galahad	1896	10,000	10,000	1	...	...	2,200
Pi Christian Fraternal Orders	1905	2,100	1,900	7	...	1,500	3,800
Protestant Episcopal Church, Department of Christian Social Relations	1919	...[q]	...	4	...	...	13,500
Protestant Episcopal Church, Youth Division	1925	[q]	[q]	7	none	...	20,000
Student Volunteer Movement	1888	400	150	9	...	...	16,000
United Christian Youth Movement	1934	...	...	[p]	none	none	none
Young People's Religious Union	1896	7,000	...	2	...	...	...
Youth Fellowship of the Reformed Church in America	1933	...	...	2	...	...	9,300

a About 2,000 young people have been volunteer workers within the past seven years.
b Includes 50 field workers in Europe and 33 in the United States, Cuba, and Mexico.
c Membership of the Pilgrim Fellowship, youth organization sponsored by the board.
d Individual representatives of the constituent bodies.
e Statistics for the former Methodist Episcopal Church only.
f Number of constituent bodies.
g Number of members under 18 years of age.
h Number of committee members, representatives of the constituent organizations.
i Special fund investments.

k Figure for the entire organization, senior and junior; about 10% attributable to the junior organization.
m Underlying number of youth within the constituency.
n Number of youth between the ages of 12 and 25.
p No paid staff.
q The division serves approximately 200,000 young people enrolled in diocesan and parochial groups and 15 national organizations, including Brotherhood of St. Andrew in the United States, Girls' Friendly Society of the U.S.A., Junior Daughters of the King, Order of the Fleur-de-Lis, and Order of Sir Galahad.

VII. Catholic Organizations Serving Youth

Those who make a study of youth and youth organizations are aware of the active part which the Catholic Church plays in the life of American young people. One-sixth of the population of the United States is Catholic. From coast to coast the spires of the church bear aloft the Cross over smoky industrial districts as well as in the brighter skies of residential suburbs and country towns. Institutions and organizations for youth under the auspices of the church are numerous.

For centuries the Catholic Church has been interested in the welfare and training of children and young people. Willingness to meet the needs of youth is evidenced by religious orders and congregations, schools and other Catholic institutions, the world over. In the United States approximately 2,400,000 children receive their education in Catholic parochial elementary and secondary schools. Some 200 colleges and universities function under Catholic auspices, with a total enrollment of 143,600 students.

The interest of the church in problems centering about youth is also manifest in the existence of many Catholic youth organizations and movements, as well as Catholic youth-serving agencies. Their primary purpose is to train youth in order that they may develop balanced Christian personalities. This is accomplished through a well-rounded program of religious, civic, cultural, social, and recreational activities under the auspices of the leaders of the church.

The parish is the cell of the church, and it is in the parishes that a variety of Catholic youth organizations are found at work. In some instances these youth groups are united on a diocesan basis. Some groups are affiliated with regional or nation-wide youth movements. A few youth organizations which are national in scope are listed and briefly described in the present section. Some of the Catholic youth-serving organizations are also described.

Organizations whose membership consists chiefly of young persons, as distinguished from those composed wholly or largely of persons above the age of 25, are:

Catholic Boys' Brigade of the United States
Catholic Students' Mission Crusade, U.S.A.
Catholic Youth Organization
Columbian Squires (see Knights of Columbus, Boy Life Bureau)
Junior Alumnae of the International Federation of Catholic Alumnae
Junior Catholic Daughters of America
Junior Daughters of Isabella
National Catholic Youth Council
National Federation of Catholic College Students of the United States
Newman Club Federation
Sodality of Our Lady

Cross references: Jesuit Educational Association, p. 126; National Catholic Educational Association, p. 129.

CATHOLIC BOYS' BRIGADE OF THE UNITED STATES (1915); 10 West 76th St., New York, N.Y.; Rev. Kilian J. Hennrich, President and General Director; M. G. Nolan, Director of Organization and Secretary.

Membership: Boys aged 12 to 18, about 40,000, in 325 local branches in 28 states, the Virgin Islands, and Canada. There are about 500 adult leaders. About 1,500 girls are associate members.

Purpose: To bring Catholic boys under the influence of Catholic training, instruction, association, and activities in order that thereby they may become of greater service to God, their country, and their fellow-men; to promote in general the spiritual, moral, mental, physical, social, and civic welfare of all boys irrespective of race or creed.

Activities: Drill, physical exercises, first aid to the injured, music, athletics, instruction in civics, recreation, sports, outings, camps, parades, nature study, hobbies, woodcraft. Weekly meetings of local units are divided into three periods of equal duration, with varied activities under an adult leader. Conferences and seminars are held locally every month; leadership training courses are conducted at the national headquarters, which also conducts annual competitions in various activities and distributes medals and awards. At the annual banquet the medal star "pro juventute" is conferred upon certain benefactors of the organization. The annual convention is held at national headquarters, and a Brigade Summer Camp is operated at Norfolk, Conn.

Publications: *Brigade Bulletin*, free to members. Books and manuals: *Boy Guidance*, 250 pp., $2.50; *Boy Leaders' Primer*, 240 pp., $1; *Brigade Guide*, 84 pp., 75¢; *Play Guidance*, 32 pp., 15¢; *Handbook for Boys*, 50¢.

Staff: Full-time paid employees, 4; part-time paid employees, 8.

Finances: Value of plant and equipment at national headquarters, $65,000. Balance at the conclusion of the fiscal year ending in 1939, $876.74. During that fiscal year expenditures for all purposes totaled $7,496.09. Income for the same period was as follows:

Gifts for current expenses	$ 515.00
Benefit affairs proceeds	6,637.60
	$7,152.60

CATHOLIC STUDENTS' MISSION CRUSADE, U.S.A. (1918); Crusade Castle, Linwood Station, Cincinnati, Ohio; Very Rev. Mgr. Edward A. Freking, Secretary-Treasurer.

Membership: Students and former students in Catholic institutions, 700,000, of whom approximately 500,000 are between the ages of 12 and 24. There are 1,250 senior units (in high schools, colleges, and seminaries), 1,590 junior units (in elementary schools), and 70 veteran units (graduate groups). In the larger centers of population there are local federations, called local conferences.

Purpose: To promote among the Catholic youth of the United States a general knowledge of missionary conditions and activities, both in the homeland and in foreign lands.

Activities: Classroom projects, discussion groups, debates, lectures, dramatics, and interschool educational contests. Under a threefold classification the work is: (1) *spiritual*, including individual and group religious exercises; (2) *educational*, consisting of activities appropriate to the different school levels and embracing interschool rallies and contests of debating and oratory; (3) *missionary aid*, contributing to the support of mission schools, orphanages, and other institutions for child welfare under the direction of Catholic missionaries, both in the United States and in other lands, especially Asia, Africa, and the islands of the Pacific. Members in secondary and higher schools engage in religious training of under-privileged children, conduct religious vacation schools, and take part in various activities for the spread of religious knowledge.

Publications: *The Shield*, monthly, October to May; 60¢ a year (50¢ in bundles of 5). *The Crusade Programmer*, quarterly, in several editions for the various types of units. *The Crusade Leader Book*, for faculty directors in grade schools; books for round tables; numerous plays, pageants, tableaux, and illustrated lectures at prices from 15¢ to $1.50.

Staff: Full-time paid employees, 6; part-time paid employees, 2. There are also 2 part-time unpaid workers at headquarters, and 45 priests in the field, appointed by their respective bishops to direct missionary activities sponsored by the Catholic Students' Mission Crusade.

Finances: For the fiscal year ending May 31, 1939 the budget was $20,000, of which $6,800 was for salaries.

CATHOLIC YOUTH ORGANIZATION (1930); an organization for Roman Catholic youth. The CYO was first established in the Archdiocese of Chicago by the Most Rev. Bernard J. Sheil, Auxiliary Bishop. The Chicago CYO maintains an archdiocesan central office at 31 East Congress St., Chicago, Ill.

The CYO is not organized nationally although the CYO label has been given to an adult-conceived and adult-controlled youth program in several dioceses. Where a CYO is in operation, it is under the control of the local diocesan authorities. The CYO has been effective especially in metropolitan areas such as Chicago, New York, Milwaukee, and San Francisco. Generally speaking, the CYO means a program of activities for youth as distinguished from the traditional type of youth-led organization.

Activities: Emphasis is placed upon leisure-time activities which are usually classified under such headings as religious, social, recreational, guidance, and cultural. Many of these activities are developed on an interparish basis.

Publications: In those dioceses where the organization exists, occasional pamphlets are issued for the constituency. Examples are: *Catholic Youth Organization of Chicago*, 23 pp.; *Catholic Youth Organization of the Archdiocese of San Francisco*, 23 pp.; special folders by Catholic Youth Organization of New York.

CHRIST CHILD SOCIETY (1903); 608 Massachusetts Ave., N.E., Washington, D.C.; Mary V. Merrick, President; Anna J. Keady, Executive Secretary.

A welfare organization pledged to the service of children through relief, health, and character building.

Membership: Approximately 15,000. This includes both senior and junior membership and membership in the college branches. There are 29 local societies and 8 college and academy branches. Members are expected to make annual contributions of $1 or more to the local organization.

Purpose: To aid and instruct poor children and to uplift and brighten their lives; to interest youth in the service of the children of the poor.

Activities: The enterprises of the Washington unit are typical: It provides layettes for new-born infants; maintains a Fresh-Air Farm for convalescent children; supports a free dental clinic at its headquarters; conducts settlement classes and recreational activities in poorer sections of the city; visits children in their homes; pays particular attention to Christmas wants; and instructs children in religion. Through these various services the local organization reaches about 4,500 children annually.

The total number of children reached through settlement houses is approximately 300,000.

Publications: Annual reports of the local units (separate pamphlets); biennial national reports.

Staff: There is no national headquarters staff. The Washington local staff virtually performs the functions of a national headquarters.

Finances: The local branches contribute to the national treasury. Funds are also raised by the sale of Christmas seals. Some of the local units receive support from the community chests. All receive gifts from various sources.

JUNIOR ALUMNAE OF THE INTERNATIONAL FEDERATION OF CATHOLIC ALUMNAE

(1914); 22 East 38th St., New York, N.Y.; Mrs. Mary B. Finan, Chairman of the Youth Program.

Membership: Senior girls in Catholic high schools and colleges and younger members of the International Federation of Catholic Alumnae, probably aggregating about 75,000, in local chapters of the IFCA in 38 states. The membership is restricted to girls doing good work in school and to alumnae interested and active in social or educational service.

Purpose: To offer definite ideals and suitable methods of organization for the preparation of worthy young women for youth leadership and Catholic action; to give inspiration and information to youth; to encourage local efforts at organizing; to promote good morals; to develop good citizenship; and to preserve good health.

Activities: Encourages students to continue their education; stimulates friendly competition among schools and alumnae associations in educational and athletic matters; assists talented pupils pursuing special studies; organizes study clubs; considers vocational guidance; compiles and distributes book lists and motion picture lists. Each of the 500 schools having local chapters furnishes a Federation Sister who assists in the alumnae youth work, and provides free use of auditorium and gymnasium. Many members act as volunteer teachers in settlement houses and in summer schools and vacation schools for underprivileged children.

Publications: *Monthly News Letter.* Space in *Quarterly Bulletin of I.F.C.A.* Occasional publications by the Department of Education of IFCA.

Staff: Full-time paid employee, 1.

JUNIOR CATHOLIC DAUGHTERS OF AMERICA

(1919); 10 West 71st St., New York, N.Y.; Mazie V. Scanlan, National Junior Director, 15 South Rumson Ave., Margate, N.J.

Membership: Catholic girls aged 12 to 18, admitted only on recommendation by a senior order member, approximately 25,000. There are 385 Courts in 37 states, Alaska, Puerto Rico, and the Canal Zone. No national dues.

Purpose: To provide an outlet for the natural desire to "belong to a club"; to furnish opportunities to develop the habit of service to others; and to enjoy recreational, charitable, and spiritual activities under proper leadership.

Activities: Enterprises of the local units include camps, workshops, hiking clubs, dramatics, dancing, athletic tournaments, glee clubs, orchestras, sewing, cooking, and visiting orphanages, veterans' hospitals, and homes for the aged, to cheer and help the less fortunate. State conferences and counselors' training courses are held annually; there is also a biennial convention of state junior chairmen in conjunction with the national convention of the Catholic Daughters of America.

Publications: *Junior Highlights*, bimonthly. Two to four pages monthly in *Women's Voice*, the organ of the senior order. *Junior Booklet; Manual of Tests; Prospectus.*

Staff: Part-time paid employees in field work, 4.

Finances: Local units are self-supporting or financed by senior courts. National expenses are borne by the national court of the Catholic Daughters of America.

JUNIOR DAUGHTERS OF ISABELLA

(1931); 375 Whitney Ave., New Haven, Conn.; Mary F. Riley, National Secretary.

Membership: Catholic girls aged 10 to 22, about 2,200. There are 16 active junior circles located in Illinois, Indiana, Ohio, Maine, Massachusetts, Minnesota, Rhode Island, and the province of Quebec.

Purpose: To promote religious, ethical, cultural, educational, civic, and athletic training of Catholic girls.

Activities: Each local circle holds at least one formal meeting each month and is required to have standing committees on religion, education, social affairs, membership, athletics, and sick members. Each committee consists of five members, if possible, and no member serves concurrently on more than one committee. The committees conduct their respective activities as fully as local conditions permit. Local adult leaders, who serve without pay, are chosen from the local circle of the senior order.

Publications: *News Sheet*, 12 issues annually; free to junior circles, 36¢ a year to individual members. *Constitution Governing Junior Circles*, 1931, 11 pp.; *Ceremonial*, 18 pp.

Staff: National administrative work is carried on by the national secretary of the senior order.

Finances: Local units are locally financed. National headquarters has no budget apart from that of the senior order.

KNIGHTS OF COLUMBUS, SUPREME COUN-CIL: BOY LIFE BUREAU (1923); 45 Wall St., New Haven, Conn.; John J. Contway, Executive Secretary.

Membership: Boys aged 14 to 18, practical Catholics, numbering 21,000, are members of the Columbian Squires, sponsored by the bureau. The organization also has 2,300 adult leaders. There are 380 local units or circles, in 47 states and 5 Canadian provinces.

Purpose: To make available to boys during their leisure time a psychologically sound program under qualified and adequately trained leadership; to cooperate, through the Columbian Squires program, with the home, the church, and the school in the cultural, social, civic, and physical development of the members.

Activities: Conducts summer schools of boy leadership, first established in 1924. In 1939 and 1940 these were held at six key universities and colleges in different parts of the country and consisted of six days of intensive training in the philosophy and techniques of boy guidance and youth programs, with one or two evening sessions at which fundamental principles of boy leadership were presented by professionally trained representatives from national headquarters, under auspices of local councils of the Knights of Columbus. About 18,000 volunteer workers have been thus trained, and at the sponsored professional training course at the University of Notre Dame, Notre Dame, Ind., 211 men have been trained on Knights of Columbus scholarships.

The Columbian Squires program is fivefold: (1) *physical*, stressing participation in athletics for enjoyment and development; (2) *social*, including activities which appeal to this age group in wholesome surroundings and under proper supervision, but with much of the responsibility delegated to the boys; (3) *civic*, embracing participation in public observances, leadership of younger groups, study of local, state, and federal governmental departments, and debates on current civic and social problems; (4) *cultural-educational*, supplementing the school and the home by public speaking, dramatics, music, libraries, and lectures, with some vocational guidance; (5) *religious*, supplementing the spiritual training of the church.

Publications: *Columbian Squires Herald*, monthly, 50¢ a year; one page in *Columbia Magazine*, official organ of the Knights of Columbus, 60¢ a year. Special bulletins for leaders, issued at intervals and on special occasions. Ten pamphlets and leaflets, including *Program of Activities*, 1940, 32 pp., and *How to Organize a Circle of Columbian Squires*, 8 pp.

Staff: Full-time paid employees, 10, of whom 2 spend major time in field work.

NATIONAL CATHOLIC WELFARE CONFER-ENCE (1919); 1312 Massachusetts Ave., N.W., Washington, D.C.; Rt. Rev. Mgr. Michael J. Ready, General Secretary.

The National Catholic Welfare Conference is the agency of the archbishops and bishops of the United States for the promotion of unity in Catholic work.

Membership: The archbishops and bishops (including auxiliaries) of the United States.

Purpose: To serve as the channel for interchange of information and service between the conference and the laity in their common work for the church; to promote, under ecclesiastical supervision, unity and cooperation among clergy and laity in matters that affect the general welfare of the church and the nation; to participate, through Catholic lay representation, in national and international movements involving moral questions; to unify, coordinate, and organize the Catholic people of the United States in works of education, social welfare, immigrant aid, and other activities; to promote locally and nationally "the participation of the laity in the apostolate of the hierarchy."

Activities: Holds an annual meeting in Washington for conference, deliberation, and decision on matters of general public concern on the welfare of the church in the United States. There are eight departments: *Executive*, which maintains bureaus of immigration, information, historical records, publications, business, auditing, and the National Center of the Confraternity of Christian Doctrine; *Education* (see p. 50), with divisions of statistics and information, teachers' registration, and library; *Press*, which serves the Catholic press in the United States and abroad with regular news, features, editorial and pictorial services, and the Catholic news of the world; *Social Action* (see p. 50), which covers the fields of industrial relations, international affairs, civic education, social welfare, family life, and rural life; *Legal*, which serves as a clearinghouse of information on federal, state, and local legislation; *Lay Organizations* (see p. 50), which includes the National Council of Catholic Men and the National Council of Catholic Women; *Catholic Action Study*, devoted to research and reports as to pronouncements, methods, programs, and achievements in the work of Catholic Action at home and abroad; *Youth* (see p. 50), an information center and clearinghouse, also sponsoring the National Catholic Youth Council (see p. 51), a federation of Catholic youth groups.

Publications: *Catholic Action*, monthly, $2 a year; includes a special page called "Catholic Youth's Interests." List of publications, which includes encyclicals, books, pamphlets, and reprints, some of which deal directly with youth, may be obtained on request.

Finances: The departments of the National Catholic Welfare Conference, with the exception of the Department of Lay Organizations, operate by voluntary contributions from the archbishops and bishops of the country. The National Council of Catholic Men and the National Council of Catholic Women meet all their expenses from funds which they receive from their affiliated organizations.

Chart I

YOUTH AGENCIES OF THE NATIONAL CATHOLIC WELFARE CONFERENCE

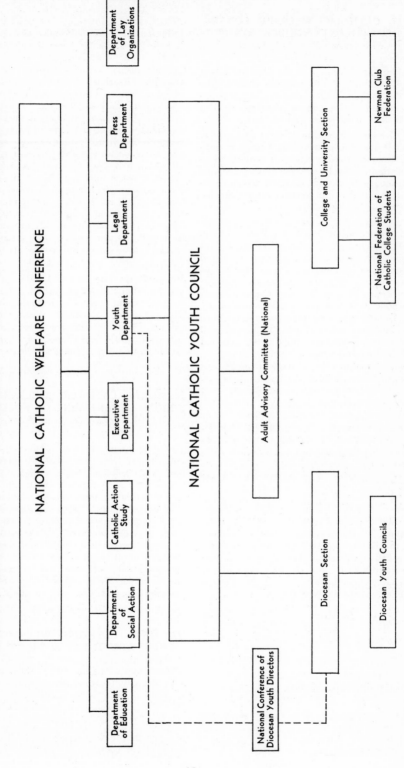

NATIONAL CATHOLIC WELFARE CONFER-ENCE, DEPARTMENT OF EDUCATION (1919); 1312 Massachusetts Ave., N.W., Washington,D.C.; Rev. George Johnson, Ph.D., Director.

Membership: An executive committee of representative Catholic educators from all parts of the country. The chairman of the department is a member of the administrative committee of the National Catholic Welfare Conference (see p. 48).

Purpose: To supply information concerning Catholic education to Catholic educators and the general public; to serve as an advisory agency in the development of Catholic schools and the Catholic school system; to act as a connecting agency between Catholic education activities and governmental education activities; to safeguard the interests of the Catholic school.

Activities: There are four sections: (1) *Information,* which answers queries and collects statistical data relative to Catholic schools; (2) *Research,* which gathers data concerning the past and present status of Catholic schools in the United States and throughout the world; (3) *Teachers' Registration,* which assists Catholic colleges and schools in obtaining lay teachers; (4) *Library,* which prepares bibliographies and lists of books suitable for use in Catholic schools. The department cooperates with the National Catholic Educational Association (see p. 129).

Publications: *Directory of Catholic Colleges and Schools;* a series of pamphlets entitled *Catholic Colleges and Schools in the United States.* See also National Catholic Welfare Conference.

NATIONAL CATHOLIC WELFARE CONFER-ENCE, DEPARTMENT OF LAY ORGANIZA-TIONS (1919); 1312 Massachusetts Ave., N.W., Washington, D.C. *Embraces:*

NATIONAL COUNCIL OF CATHOLIC MEN (1920); Edward Heffron, Executive Secretary;

NATIONAL COUNCIL OF CATHOLIC WOMEN (1920); Agnes C. Regan, Executive Secretary.

Membership: These two councils of the Department of Lay Organizations function through some 4,000 affiliated societies—national, state, diocesan, district, local, and parish—and through units of the councils in many of the dioceses. The several types of units are distributed approximately as follows:

	Nat. Council of Catholic Men	Nat. Council of Catholic Women
National organizations	12	16
Diocesan organizations (councils)	10	63
State organizations	6	2
Knights of Columbus councils	453	—
Other local or parish groups	755	2,800
	1,236	2,881

Activities: These national federations are genuinely interested in youth and render service to youth and to federation affiliates, some of which are engaged in youth work. The National Council of Catholic Women in particular devotes attention to youth through a National Youth Committee, composed of adult women connected with various Diocesan Councils of Catholic Women. This committee, organized in 1920, was originally named Girls' Welfare Committee and at first stressed preventive and protective work. It made a nation-wide survey of housing conditions for Catholic girls. Later, in November 1935, a field worker was added to the staff to specialize in youth work, and National Youth Leaders' Conferences were conducted in Washington in 1935 and 1936 and in Detroit in 1940. The Youth Committee has produced, since March 1937, an annual series of 16 nation-wide weekly broadcasts, "A Call to Youth." It also assists youth groups and youth-serving organizations in the development of leisure-time activities.

Publications: The National Youth Committee of the National Council of Catholic Women prepares pamphlets and booklets, including such titles as *Youth Leaders' Handbook, Youth Today and Tomorrow, Youth Leadership and Catholic Action, General Program for Leisure-Time Activities, Culture for Young People, Handcraft Note Book.*

See also National Catholic Welfare Conf. (p. 48).

NATIONAL CATHOLIC WELFARE CONFER-ENCE, DEPARTMENT OF SOCIAL ACTION; 1312 Massachusetts Ave., N.W., Washington, D.C.; Rt. Rev. John A. Ryan, Director.

The Department of Social Action is concerned with studies and programs dealing particularly with industrial problems, civic obligations, rural life, family life, and in general with subjects affecting social welfare and international relations.

It promotes these purposes through the agency of lay organizations, including youth groups. Particular service is rendered to youth leaders interested in social, international, and family problems, etc. Books, pamphlets, study outlines, and bibliographies are published and circulated. A special Catholic Action Service Program for college and high school students is prepared by staff members.

See also National Catholic Welfare Conf. (p. 48).

NATIONAL CATHOLIC WELFARE CONFER-ENCE, YOUTH DEPARTMENT (1937); 1312 Massachusetts Ave., N.W., Washington, D.C.; Rev. Vincent Mooney, C.S.C., Director; Rev. Paul F. Tanner, Assistant Director.

Purpose: To assist the ordinaries of the dioceses in the promotion of authorized youth organizations; to sponsor the National Catholic Youth Council (see p. 51), unifying agency for all Catholic youth forces of the country; to facilitate exchange of information and programs on youth activities; to assemble information on non-Catholic youth movements and agencies; to interpret this information and make it available for Catholics; to keep in touch with governmental agencies so that Catholic associations and programs may profit from available information and documentation.

Activities: The Youth Department works in close cooperation with the various departments of the National Catholic Welfare Conference (see p. 48), including the Department of Lay Organizations (see p. 50), the Department of Education (see p. 50), the Department of Social Action (see p. 50), the Legal Department, and others. It executes the types of work indicated in the statement of purposes. Its director acts as executive secretary of the National Catholic Youth Council.

NATIONAL CATHOLIC YOUTH COUNCIL

(1937); 1312 Massachusetts Ave., N.W., Washington, D.C.; Rev. Vincent Mooney, C.S.C., Executive Secretary.

An organization of Catholic youth functioning under the Youth Department of the National Catholic Welfare Conference (see p. 50), under the supervision of the administrative board of the National Catholic Welfare Conference (see p. 48).

Membership: There are two major divisions: (1) the *Diocesan Section*, which provides for voluntary affiliation of Diocesan Youth Councils, federations of all existing approved Catholic youth groups in a diocese; and (2) the *College and University Section*, which unites youth on the college level through the two nation-wide student federations—the National Federation of Catholic College Students for students in Catholic institutions (see p. 52) and the Newman Club Federation for Catholic students in nonsectarian institutions (see p. 52).

Direct membership is held only by Diocesan Youth Councils and the two student federations. Through the medium of these unifying organizations, the National Catholic Youth Council serves the organized Catholic youth of the whole nation and reaches all Catholic youth groups. It has an advisory board composed of representatives of nation-wide Catholic youth movements, adult organizations serving youth, and the National Council of Catholic Men (see p. 50) and the National Council of Catholic Women (see p. 50).

Purpose: To federate all Catholic youth groups; to serve as a channel for interchange of experiences and information regarding youth activities and problems; to help Catholic youth groups to understand better and cope with problems of national importance; to train youth leaders in the methods of authentic Catholic Action; to serve as an instrument to represent all Catholic youth organizations in the United States without interfering in any way with the autonomy and the traditional activities of the individual groups.

Activities: The National Catholic Youth Council

works through Diocesan Youth Councils and the two student federations mentioned. The real youth activity is carried on essentially in the parish youth groups and the local units of the different movements in which Catholic youth are organized. The movements provide opportunity to train youth in the application of Catholic principles along the lines of religious work, social and economic life, citizenship, and recreation, including athletics, social life, and arts and crafts. Provision is also made for leadership training for young people and adult youth leaders. Study and discussion clubs and leaders' conferences are organized; conferences on local, deanery, and diocesan bases are held for youth, youth leaders, and youth chaplains. The annual conference of diocesan youth directors provides for similar contacts on a national scale.

Publications: *Catholic Action*, monthly, published by the National Catholic Welfare Conference, carries a special page "Interests of Our Catholic Youth," with information on various problems, manifestations, and publications concerning Catholic youth. The publication of a series of pamphlets dealing with recent methods of Catholic youth work is projected. See also publications of the National Catholic Welfare Conference.

NATIONAL CONFERENCE OF CATHOLIC CHARITIES

(1910); 1317 F St., N.W., Washington, D.C.; Rt. Rev. John O'Grady, Secretary.

Membership: Individuals, 3,500, many of whom are connected with diocesan agencies of Catholic charities throughout the United States. Memberships are of three classes: general, $3 annually; sustaining, $10 annually; subscribing, over $10.

Purpose: To bring about exchange of views among experienced Catholic men and women who are active in social welfare work; to collect and publish information concerning problems and results in Catholic charities, and to encourage further development of a literature in which the religious and social ideals of charity shall find dignified expression; to promote the discussion of general standards in relief and prevention, and to further the organization and development of Catholic welfare work.

Activities: Annual meeting, regional meetings, institutes, surveys, studies, field visits, representation on national committees, research and publication. The conference has assumed leadership in establishing diocesan agencies of Catholic charities in the United States, of which there are now 75 local central agencies with 81 branch offices. The conference has a Committee on Youth Activities which conducts sessions in connection with the annual meeting, with agenda based on studies of the youth organizations and leisure-time programs of various dioceses of the Catholic Church.

Publications: *Catholic Charities Review*, 10 issues annually; $1 a year. Proceedings of annual meetings, $2 each. *Catholic Charities in the United States—*

History and Problems, by John O'Grady, $2, and other books on Catholic social work; monographs of the School of Social Work, Catholic University of America, $1 each. Numerous pamphlets, including *Challenge of Youth Today*, by Most Rev. Bernard J. Sheil, 10¢, and *Mental Health of the Child*, by Henry C. Schumacher, M.D., 10¢. Also *Directory of Diocesan Agencies of Catholic Charities in the United States*, issued annually, 50¢.

Staff: Full-time paid employees, 5, of whom 1 spends major time in field work; full-time unpaid worker, 1.

NATIONAL FEDERATION OF CATHOLIC COL-LEGE STUDENTS OF THE UNITED STATES (1937); c/o Youth Department, National Catholic Welfare Conference, 1312 Massachusetts Ave., N.W., Washington, D.C.; National President, Gertrude Kirk, Dunbarton College, Washington, D.C.

Membership: Open to the student bodies of all Catholic institutions of higher learning in the United States. The local student council or equivalent agency in each institution is the liaison unit with the national federation.

Purpose: To unite the student bodies of the Catholic institutions of higher learning in the United States; to assist both the colleges and the various student groups in order to give energetic and practical application to the teachings of the Holy Father and the church's leaders regarding the formation of a Christian-minded apostolate among the Catholic laity; to contribute to the spreading and deepening of a highly trained Catholic opinion.

Activities: Assists in the development of student councils or analogous bodies in Catholic institutions of higher learning; acts as a medium for the interchange of ideas and experiences on the part of the affiliated units; provides the membership with programs and material in the field of authentic Catholic Action; represents the Catholic student body in national and international life; maintains a permanent central office in the Youth Department of the National Catholic Welfare Conference (see p. 50); organizes national and regional conventions; develops commissions for the accomplishment of particular objectives and special projects, each commission providing documentation, study plans, and literature in its special field of interest.

NEWMAN CLUB FEDERATION (1915); Newman Hall, University of Pennsylvania, 3743 Spruce St., Philadelphia, Pa.; William J. Hurley, President.

Membership: Catholic students attending non-Catholic colleges and universities, about 50,000. There are 307 Newman Clubs in non-Catholic institutions of higher education throughout the country.

Purpose: To organize Catholic students attending secular institutions of higher learning for the purpose of mutual helpfulness and united effort in promoting their religious, intellectual, moral, and social standards; to advance the work of the church.

Activities: Religious instruction programs, retreats, sermons, question boxes; lectures, study groups, library groups; dances, bridge parties, teas, musicales, dramatics; business sessions and club-policy meetings. Local clubs are grouped into intermediate units called provinces. Province conventions and federation conferences are held annually. Divisions of the work include the Bureau of Catholic Action, the Medical Missions Bureau, the Bureau of Publicity, the Junior Newman Club Movement (for secular high schools), the Jewelry Committee, and the John Henry Newman Honorary Society.

Publications: *Newman News*, quarterly; province *Newman News Sheets*, and monthly *News Sheets* issued by local clubs. Pamphlets, including *Newman Club, the Catholic Youth Movement in Secular Colleges* and *Newman Club, a Club of Catholic Culture and Catholic Fellowship*.

Staff: Administrative work is done without pay by the several national officers, two of whom are located in Philadelphia.

Finances: Approximate annual budget, $2,200.

SODALITY OF OUR LADY, THE (1583); 3742 West Pine Blvd., St. Louis, Mo.; Daniel A. Lord, S.J., National Organizer.

Membership: Catholic young people of both sexes, approximately 806,800. There are about 9,626 active units in Catholic parishes, universities, colleges, schools of nursing, and parochial schools in all parts of the United States. Similar organizations exist in every country of the world. In the United States the several types of units are distributed approximately as follows:

	Number of Units	Total Members
Young Men's Parish Sodalities*	600	45,000
Young Ladies' Parish Sodalities*	5,000	500,000
Young Men's and Ladies' Sodalities*	300	15,000
College Sodalities†	235	18,800
High School Sodalities**	1,069	106,900
Grammar School Sodalities‡	2,422	121,100

Purpose: To foster a fuller Catholic life in parish and school; to further Catholic social action; to develop an energetic religious and spiritual life among

* Average age of members, 18 to 30.
† Average age, 17 to 21.
** Average age, 12 to 18.
‡ Average age, 10 to 12.

Catholic young people, expressed in terms of personal faith, loyalty to Christ, imitation of Mary, and constructive Catholic activity.

Activities: Each unit has a priest director, a central committee, and various committees to carry on specific religious and social features. The national headquarters conducts several yearly Summer Schools of Catholic Action in different cities and operates schools of spiritual leadership at regular intervals in several regions. The general program of the organization embraces the following activities: (1) *spiritual*, including training in character and religion; (2) *intellectual*, comprising study of religious, social, economic, and literary subjects, and forums, writing, drama, art work, and speaking practice; (3) *social and recreational*, including some athletics; (4) *Catholic*, such as missionary interest, charity work, cooperation with Catholic social organizations, and participation in social and economic movements among students and young people; (5) annual national and local conventions.

Publications: *The Queen's Work*, 9 issues annually, $1 a year (50¢ in groups of 25); *The Directors' Service*, 9 issues annually, $1 a year; *The Faculty Adviser*, 10 issues annually, $1 a year; *The Sodalist Nurse*, 9 issues annually, free to schools of nursing; *The Sodality Union News*, 9 issues annually, free to groups of sodalities. An extensive list of books and pamphlets on religious topics, morals, conduct and character, biography, social order, and vocations, sold at 2¢ to $2 each, with discounts on quantities.

Staff: Six priests devote full time to national headquarters without salary. Full-time paid employees, 44.

Finances: Value of plant and equipment at headquarters, $45,000. Annual value of unpaid staff services, $20,000. For the fiscal year ending June 30, 1940, operations were approximately as follows:

Income

Publications	$55,000
Other services	20,000
	$75,000

Expenditures

Salaries	$35,000
Travel	10,000
Communications	5,000
Office supplies	5,000
Publications	18,000
Other purposes	2,000
	$75,000

THETA PHI ALPHA FRATERNITY (1912); 216 North 11th St., Mt. Vernon, Ill.; Mrs. F. A. Jettinghoff, Executive Secretary.

Membership: Catholic girl students aged about 16 to 22 and alumnae members of all ages, 2,650. There are 12 active chapters in leading universities, 18 alumnae chapters, and 22 city associations, distributed in 14 states and the District of Columbia.

Purpose: To secure a closer comradeship among Catholic women students in the colleges and universities of North America; to advance their social, educational, and religious interests; and to provide a home atmosphere and environment for them while in attendance at college.

Activities: All the social and educational enterprises common to college fraternities, with the added religious and moral tone resulting from the restriction of membership to Catholic girls and association with Catholic chaperons. The chapters afford supervision and stressing of scholarship, personality development, executive ability, social amenities, and group adaptability, developed through specialized leaders, chapter inspections, regular reports, province conferences, and national conventions.

Publications: *The Compass of Theta Phi Alpha*, quarterly; $1 a year; Dorothy Stephans, editor, 40 The Woodford, Covington, Ky. *Constitution, Pledge Manual, Rushing Manual, Song Book, Chapter Officers' Manual*.

Staff: Full-time paid employee, 1; part-time paid employee, 1.

Finances: Endowment, $375; reserve fund other than endowment, $550. Value of equipment at headquarters, $500. For the fiscal year ending June 30, 1939, income was $7,013.02; expenditures, $5,491.91

Table VIII

STATISTICS OF CATHOLIC ORGANIZATIONS SERVING YOUTH

Organization	Year Founded	Approximate Aggregate Membership (individuals)	Number of Members under 25 Years of Age	Total Employees on Headquarters Staff	Aggregate Endowment of National Headquarters	Plant and Equipment (headquarters only)	Approximate Annual Budget (headquarters only)
Catholic Boys' Brigade of the United States	1915	42,000	41,500	12	$ ...	$65,000	$ 7,500
Catholic Students' Mission Crusade, U.S.A.	1918	700,000	500,000[a]	8	...	...	20,000
Christ Child Society	1903	15,000	...	...	none	...	...
Junior Alumnae of the International Federation of Catholic Alumnae	1914	75,000	...	1	...	...	...
Junior Catholic Daughters of America	1919	25,000	25,000	4	...	...	[b]
Junior Daughters of Isabella	1931	2,200	2,200	[b]	[b]	[b]	[b]
Knights of Columbus, Boy Life Bureau	1923	23,300[c]	21,000[e]	10	...	...	...
National Catholic Welfare Conference	1919	...	...	...	...	...	...
National Catholic Youth Council	1937	...	...	...	...	...	...
National Conference of Catholic Charities	1910	3,500	...	5	...	...	...
Natl. Fed. of Catholic College Students of the U. S.	1937	...	...	[d]	...	...	...
Newman Club Federation	1915	50,000	50,000	...	none	...	2,200
Sodality of Our Lady	1583	806,800	806,800[e]	44	none	45,000	75,000
Theta Phi Alpha Fraternity	1912	2,650	...	2	375[f]	500	7,000

a Number of youth between the ages of 12 and 24.
b None apart from that of the senior organization.
c Membership of the Columbian Squires, youth organization sponsored by the bureau.
d No paid staff.
e Includes members up to 30 years of age.
f Also reserve fund of $550.

VIII. Jewish Organizations Serving Youth

No ethnic or religious group in modern times has so long a history as has the Jewish people. When our ancestors in the north of Europe were roaming the foggy swamps clad in the skins of beasts, the Jews had already behind them thousands of years of civilization; and when the basin of the Mediterranean was under the harsh but orderly sway of the Roman Caesars, to whom the Jews were a vassal people, the Palestinians could rightly look upon their Roman conquerors as upstarts and intruders upon the scene of a Near Eastern civilization which was already ancient.

The Jews in America have always been conspicuously careful to provide effective social service organizations for the care of the unfortunate among their own; and likewise they are diligent in building organizations to preserve among their youth an understanding and appreciation of the best values in the history, literature, and religion of the Hebrew people. This culture is well worth preserving, and it is by no means a discordant or unwelcome element in American civilization.

Among Jewish leaders there are wide variations of social philosophy, but many a rabbi is at the forefront of the most advanced and humane social thought of the day, and many a Jew contributes not only to the care of his own people but also to worthy enterprises for the general social welfare. To some extent the variations of Jewish opinion are reflected in the organizations to be noticed. It will also be observed that several of these groups have been organized to further the world-wide Jewish movement known as Zionism and to contribute to the consummation of the ideal of a Jewish national homeland in Palestine—an aspiration cherished by many Jews in America as well as elsewhere.

In recent years the recrudescence of anti-Semitism in Europe has driven many Jews into exile, some of whom have come to America. Among them are scholars and scientists of international renown who have found welcome places in the faculties of American graduate schools and in research institutes. The privations incident to invasions and conquests during the present war in Europe have also fallen heavily upon the Jewish populations. It is thus natural that many Jewish organizations in the United States find themselves concerned about the relief and adjustment of refugees and solicitous regarding the preservation of racial and religious tolerance in America—an ideal which commands the allegiance of all men of good will.

Of the organizations described in the present section, some are primarily religious, some chiefly fraternal, and some devoted largely to social welfare work. Those whose membership consists chiefly of young persons, as distinguished from those composed wholly or largely of persons above the age of 25, are:

Aleph Zadik Aleph of B'nai B'rith
Avukah, the American Student Zionist Federation
B'nai B'rith Hillel Foundations
Hapoel Hamizrachi of America
Hechalutz Organization of America
Junior Hadassah
Masada, Youth Zionist Organization of America
National Council of Jewish Juniors
National Council of Young Israel
National Federation of Temple Youth
Young Men's Hebrew Associations and Young Women's Hebrew Associations (see National Jewish Welfare Board)
Young Judaea
Young People's League of the United Synagogue of America
Young Poale Zion Alliance

Cross reference: Young Circle League of the English-Speaking Division of the Workmen's Circle, p. 87.

ALEPH ZADIK ALEPH OF B'NAI B'RITH (1924); 1003 K St., N.W., Washington, D.C.; Julius Bisno, Executive Director.

Membership: Jewish young men aged 15 to 21, active members, 10,051 in 383 chapters in 42 states and 5 foreign countries. The number of alumni is about 12,450.

Purpose: To promote patriotism and love of justice; to perpetuate observance of the tenets of Judaism; to advance the ideal of the healthy body, the active mind, and the wholesome spirit; to encourage gentlemanly conduct and the virtues of filial love and charity; to cultivate a spirit of fraternity and good fellowship; to enroll all desirable Jewish young men in a fraternal organization having for its program the mental, moral, and physical development of its members; to strengthen their Jewish affiliations; to abate the pernicious influences of bigotry and race prejudice; and to stimulate interest in humanitarian, educational, and philanthropic endeavors.

Activities: Utilization of the talents of the members in a way that will benefit the individual, the immediate group, and the community. Debates, social affairs, and a great variety of other activities. Oratorical and athletic tournaments, and essay contests in English and Hebrew letter writing. Annual international camp convention. There are three annual international awards to individual members: for the "ideal AZA member"; for the one who does the most "for religious work"; and for the one who does the most "for community service." The organization has a National Scholarship Loan Fund. There is also a free circulating Jewish library, and much work is done on the implementation of a "ten point" Americanization program. Chapters cooperate in sponsoring 175 Boy Scout troops.

Publications: *The Shofar*, 21 issues annually; *The A.Z.A. Monthly Program; Inside Information*, annual member's manual; *The A.Z.A.Leader*, quarterly. All free to members. *A.Z.A. Diary*, annually, 25¢ a copy; Julius Bisno, editor. Forty-seven other booklets and pamphlets ranging in size from 4 pages to 96 pages, free upon request.

Staff: Full-time paid employees, 10, of whom 2 spend major time in the field; part-time paid employees, 15; part-time unpaid workers, 8.

Finances: Endowment fund, $10,500. Value of plant and equipment of national headquarters, $4,000. Balance on hand December 31, 1939, $697.24. For the fiscal year ending on that date, operations were as follows:

Income

Gifts or grants for current expenses	$24,300.00
Membership fees	18,093.11
Other services	524.79
Other sources	1,140.58
	$44,058.48

Expenditures

Salaries	$13,214.16
Travel	2,865.37
Communications	2,816.99
Office supplies	3,093.40
Publications	6,100.73
Rent, insurance, etc.	748.00
Addition to plant and equipment	798.26
Other purposes	12,371.90
	$42,008.81

AMERICAN JEWISH CONGRESS (1917); 330 West 42nd St., New York, N.Y.; Dr. Stephen S. Wise, President.

Membership: The congress is a confederation of national organizations (32 in number), local organizations, and individual members. Community branches and key contacts exist in all the principal cities of the United States. The congress maintains a Youth Division, with members 18 to 35 years of age.

Purpose: To defend the rights of Jews wherever they may be assailed; to strengthen democracy; and to effect the eventual restoration of rights for Jews in countries where they have been denied.

Activities: The program includes political activities with respect to the protection of rights of Jews in Europe, South America, and the United States; combating of discrimination against Jews in employment; exposure of anti-Semitic organizations and the refutation of anti-Semitic libel; strengthening of the law as a means of combating subversive organizations; boycott of the products and services of Nazi Germany; reunion of refugee families; cooperation with other organizations in strengthening the democratic idea and way of life. The Youth Division cooperates in these activities, particularly in the counteraction of anti-Semitic propaganda, the boycott, the combating of economic discrimination, and the strengthening of democratic ties.

Publications: *The Congress Bulletin*, weekly. Pamphlets: *Helping to End Economic Discrimination*, by Rabbi J. X. Cohen, 1937, 15¢; *The Economic Destruction of German Jewry by the Nazi Regime, 1933–1937*, 20¢; and other pamphlets relating to the various interests of the congress.

Staff: Full-time paid employees, 37; part-time paid employees, 4.

AVUKAH, THE AMERICAN STUDENT ZIONIST FEDERATION (1925); 111 Fifth Ave., New York, N.Y.; Alfred J. Kahn, Executive Secretary.

Membership: College students, aged 17 to 24 and of both sexes, 2,000. There are 60 chapters throughout the country. Annual dues, $1.

Purpose: To organize Jewish students to participate along three lines of action: against fascism and imperialist war; for modernizing Jewish institutions in America; for mass immigration to Palestine, for Arab-Jewish cooperation, and against curtailment of land sales.

Activities: Research, pamphlet service, and publications on Zionist questions; discussion groups and activities along the three fronts. Conducts three summer camps in which students from different parts of the country participate. Offers a number of Palestine fellowships and a year of work in Palestine collectives. Supports the Federation of Jewish Labor and the cooperative and collective movement in Palestine.

Publications: *Avukah Student Action*, 13 issues annually; 5¢ a copy; Rosalind B. Schwartz, managing editor. *Short History of Zionism*, by S. H. Sankowsky, 88 pp., 50¢; *Analysis of Zionism*, by Meir Yeari, 5¢; *Associations of American Jews*, by

Adrian Schwartz, 65 pp., 25¢; *Diagram of Zionism*, 5¢. Numerous other booklets and pamphlets on Zionist theory, modern Palestine, the Arab problem, war and fascism, and Jews in America. The prices range from 2¢ to $1.50.

Staff: Full-time paid employee, 1; part-time paid employees, 3, of whom 1 spends major time in field work. There is also unpaid membership assistance.

B'NAI B'RITH HILLEL FOUNDATIONS (1923); 625 East Green St., Champaign, Ill.; Dr. Abram Leon Sachar, National Director.

Membership: Serve approximately 30,000 Jewish students (about 67 per cent men and 33 per cent women) at 44 colleges and universities. Foundations are maintained at the state universities of Illinois, Wisconsin, Ohio, Michigan, California, Texas, Alabama, North Carolina, Indiana, Florida, Georgia, Iowa, Maryland, Minnesota, and Virginia, and at Cornell University, Pennsylvania State College, Northwestern University, University of Chicago, Agricultural and Mechanical College of Texas, and Brooklyn College. Counselors are maintained at the remaining 23 institutions.

Purpose: To provide religious, social, and cultural centers at universities in which there are Jewish students; to stimulate interest among these Jewish students in the survival values of the Jewish heritage; to cooperate with other religious agencies in the cultivation of a moral and spiritual outlook on life.

Activities: Most of the foundations have resident adult directors. Each unit has a student council which is elected by the Jewish student body and which, together with the director, plans and carries through the student program. There are classes, discussion groups, religious services, forums, tournaments, dramatics, socials, and a variety of other enterprises. At the Illinois foundation, courses in Jewish history, comparative religion, and Hebrew and historic outlooks on life are offered for full credit in the university and enroll more than 300 students, of whom nearly half are non-Jews. Similar courses are offered for credit at the universities of Alabama, Iowa, and Missouri.

Publications: *The Hillel Digest*, monthly, summarizing the activities of each foundation; *Hillel Handbook*, annually. *National Jewish Monthly*, with a circulation of 110,000, is published by B'nai B'rith, the Jewish fraternal society which sponsors all of the Hillel Foundations. Each foundation has its own biweekly newspaper.

Staff: The employed personnel of the foundation at the University of Illinois (seven persons) serves as national headquarters staff. Each of the other local foundations has a professionally trained director either in residence or in close proximity to the university.

Finances: The aggregate annual budget is about $165,000, of which $85,000 is supplied by B'nai B'rith. The remainder is contributed by students, parents, B'nai B'rith districts and auxiliaries.

B'NAI B'RITH VOCATIONAL SERVICE BUREAU (1938); 1003 K St., N.W., Washington, D.C.; Max F. Baer, National Director.

Membership: A service agency under the guidance of an administrative committee consisting of: Julius Bisno, executive director of Aleph Zadik Aleph of B'nai B'rith (see p. 55); Maurice Bisgyer, secretary of B'nai B'rith; Richard E. Gutstadt, director of the B'nai B'rith Anti-Defamation League; and Dr. Abram Leon Sachar, national director of B'nai B'rith Hillel Foundations (see p. 57).

Purpose: To conduct a program of group vocational guidance for the Jewish youth of America.

Activities: Disseminates occupational information, chiefly through publication of occupational literature; holds regional and national conferences, including a national joint fraternity and sorority conference on vocational guidance; sponsors forums, speakers, and showing of films. The bureau carries its educational program to parents as well as to youth, particularly through an open letter to parents on the vocational problems of children.

Publications: *Vocational Notes* (mimeo.), monthly. B'nai B'rith Vocational Series, 10¢ each, including: *Professional Opportunities for Jewish Youth; Chart Supplement to Professional Opportunities for Jewish Youth*, 22 pp.; *How to Plan Your Life-Work*, by J. Anthony Humphreys, published in cooperation with Science Research Associates, 1939, 48 pp.; *The "Which?" Book*, a guide indicating the vocational relationship of school subjects, 19 pp.; *Careers in the Skilled Trades*, by I. David Cohen, 1940, 48 pp. One hundred *Occupational Outlines of American Major Occupations*, published in cooperation with Science Research Associates, 10¢ each or $6.15 for the set. Also other pamphlets, including several published jointly with other interested organizations.

Staff: Full-time paid employees, 2.

Finances: Financial support is derived from grants.

COUNCIL OF JEWISH FEDERATIONS AND WELFARE FUNDS (1932); 165 West 46th St., New York, N.Y.; H. L. Lurie, Executive Director.

An association of local communal agencies for the development of Jewish social services.

Membership: Jewish federations, welfare funds, and community councils, 195, in 160 cities in 39 states, the District of Columbia, and 4 Canadian provinces.

Purpose: To organize Jewish community resources to serve Jewish group needs locally, regionally, nationally, and abroad; to determine methods and practices in the welfare fields and to establish standards and principles to guide members.

Activities: Maintains a staff of field workers to advise and encourage organized and unorganized Jewish communities. Maintains a research staff. Advises local communities on methods of raising and allocating funds for local and nonlocal needs and on the work of national and overseas agencies and their relationships to the local communities. Regional conferences are held at intervals during the year. A national conference, called the General Assembly, is held once a year. Youth activities include collection of statistics on the work of Jewish agencies for child care and vocational services, studies of centralized community programs of Jewish education, and advisory services to communities on family welfare and other community youth needs. The council has published a survey of the organization and activities of the youth divisions of 28 federations, welfare funds, and community councils, and arranged a meeting of youth division leaders at the annual General Assembly.

Publications: *Notes and News*, bimonthly, $1 a year. A complete list of numerous publications is contained in a bulletin issued January 17, 1940.

Staff: Full-time paid employees, 24, of whom 4 spend major time in the field; part-time paid employees, 3, of whom 2 spend major time in the field.

Finances: Balance on hand December 31, 1939, $24,638.92. For the fiscal year ending on that date, operations were as follows:

Income

Gifts or grants	$ 35,120.00
Membership fees	71,418.87
Publications	197.53
Studies	1,755.73
Other sources	468.00
	$108,960.13

Expenditures

Salaries	$ 73,330.32
Travel	7,438.53
Communications	4,045.23
Office supplies	1,803.82
Publications	2,574.12
Rent, insurance, etc.	4,075.00
Addition to plant and equipment	370.91
Other purposes	2,832.74
	$ 96.470.67

HAPOEL HAMIZRACHI OF AMERICA (1921); 1123 Broadway, New York, N.Y.; Rabbi Ben Zion L. Rosenbloom, President.

Membership: Jewish young persons, approximately 10,900, organized in 106 branches in 15 states; affiliates exist in 23 other countries. There are two subsidiary organizations: Hashomer Hadati, a scout educational system for youth between the ages of 9 and 18, with 2,200 members in 60 branches in 14 states; and Zeire Hapoel Hamizrachi, an organization for youth between the ages of 18 and 21, with 1,000 members in 7 states.

Purpose: To establish in Palestine a Jewish national homeland based on the principles of Jewish tradition and social equality; to propagate and stimulate interest in the Jewish nation and its religious ideas; to observe the principles of traditional Judaism.

Activities: Holds an annual convention; conducts religious, educational, and social programs designed to further the aims of the organization; and maintains a farm for the purpose of affording members contact with agricultural life. Youth activities consist of educational programs, scout training, athletics, and agricultural preparation for Palestine.

Publications: *Horizon*, 10 issues annually; *Yedioth*, 10 issues annually.

Staff: Full-time paid employees, 8.

Finances: The administrative budget of the national organization for 1940 was appproximately $10,000.

HECHALUTZ ORGANIZATION OF AMERICA (1932); 1140 Broadway, New York, N.Y.; Bialik Margolis and Harry Sosewitz, Associate Secretaries.

Membership: Young men and women, aged 18 to 25, 500. There are 20 branches in the United States and Canada.

Purpose: To provide agricultural and other vocational training for Jewish young men and women who will carry technical proficiency to the Jewish national homeland in Palestine; to prepare them culturally for participation in the Hebrew life of the country.

Activities: Maintains two training farms, at Cream Ridge, N.J., and Liberty, N.Y., where the residents receive two years of experience in agricultural work, after having had a year of training in Hebrew culture and physical education at some local branch of Hechalutz. The entire period of training, covering two to three years, is in preparation for departure for Palestine, where the members become agricultural pioneers.

Publications: *Jews and Arabs in Palestine*, by Enzo Sereni and R. E. Ashery, 400 pp., 95¢; *Arab Movement in Palestine*, by Michael Assaf, 73 pp., 25¢; *Hechalutz: Tel Hai Memorial Edition*, 20 pp., 15¢; *Story of Tel Hai*, 76 pp., 10¢; *A Call to Jewish Youth*, 4 pp., free.

Staff: Full-time paid employees, 3, of whom 1 spends major time in the field; part-time unpaid worker, 1.

Finances: Value of equipment at national headquarters, $500. Balance on hand August 31, 1939, $1,032.04. For the fiscal year ending on that date, operations were as follows:

Income

Gifts or grants	$ 5,126.04
Membership fees	66.03
Publications	117.29
Other services	359.45
Other sources	5,599.93
	$11,268.74

Expenditures

Salaries	$ 1,288.00
Travel	97.00
Office supplies	672.54
Publications	575.59
Rent, insurance, etc.	1,072.50
Other purposes	6,861.92
	$10,567.55

JEWISH AGRICULTURAL SOCIETY, INC.

(1900); 301 East 14th St., New York, N.Y.; Dr. Gabriel Davidson, General Manager.

Purpose: To encourage and direct Jewish residents of the United States in the vocation of agriculture.

Activities: Gives advice to prospective purchasers of farms; makes loans available; maintains a field staff and Rural Sanitation Department; and sponsors agricultural cooperatives. The society maintains an Agricultural Education and Extension Department and a Farm Employment Department, the purpose of which is to try to find farm employment for Jewish youth. It has also awarded scholarships and granted loans to agricultural students.

Publications: Annual reports.

Staff: Full-time paid employees, 29.

Finances: Approximate budget for the calendar year 1940, $100,000.

JEWISH OCCUPATIONAL COUNCIL, INC.

(1938); 1819 Broadway, New York, N.Y.; Eli E. Cohen, Executive Director.

Membership: Participating national organizations, 11: American Jewish Committee, American Jewish Congress (see p. 56), B'nai B'rith, including B'nai B'rith Vocational Service Bureau (see p. 57), Conference on Jewish Relations, Hebrew Sheltering and Immigrant Aid Society, Jewish Agricultural Society (see p. 59), Jewish Labor Committee, National Council of Jewish Women, National Jewish Welfare Board (see p. 62), National Refugee Service, Union of American Hebrew Congregations (see p. 62). Local Jewish vocational services, 16, in Baltimore, Boston, Chicago, Cincinnati, Cleveland, Detroit, Kansas City, Los Angeles, Milwaukee, Minneapolis, Newark, New York, Philadelphia, Pittsburgh, San Francisco, and St. Louis.

Purpose: To act as a clearinghouse for all national and local Jewish organizations engaged in occupational guidance, placement, and training; to provide these agencies with occupational information and to cooperate with them in research projects; and to guide Jewish communities or organizations that may request assistance in establishing or improving occupational services.

Activities: Relations with national agencies: offers assistance to national groups interested in vocational problems; attempts to make available to these groups the contributions of general economic research, to introduce as much order as possible into the occasionally overlapping and conflicting activities of the individual organizations, and to meet any reasonable demands and suggestions that may be made; suggests research projects, acts as consultant on material in prepublication stage, and prevents duplication of research activity.

Relations with local vocational agencies: by mail and by personal visits of the director, has provided assistance to local Jewish vocational services throughout the country on problems in personnel, administration, forms and procedure, programs, promotion, and requests for information. A more formal system of clearance of administrative and functional material is now being undertaken by these agencies.

Publications: *Annual Report of the Executive Director*, 1940, 22 pp. Six special reports: *Occupational Research and Informational Activities of Leading Jewish Agencies*, 1940, 23 pp. mimeo.; *Some Aspects of the Jewish Economic Problem*, 1940, 23 pp.; *A Bibliography for Jewish Vocational Agencies*, 1940, 23 pp.; *Some Characteristics of 408 Baltimore Jewish Youth*, an experimental study based on a survey conducted by the American Youth Commission in 1937 (see p. 72), 1940, 20 pp. mimeo.; *A Guide to General Vocational Services*, 1940, 23 pp.; *Patterns of Jewish Occupational Distribution in the United States and Canada*, 1940, 31 pp.

Staff: Full-time paid employees, 3; part-time paid employee, 1.

Finances: Estimated annual value of space, heat, light, and similar services received without charge, $300. Balance June 15, 1940, $1,917.68. For the fiscal year ending on that date, operations were as follows:

Total Income

Gifts and grants for current expenses	$14,500.00

Expenditures

Salaries	$10,247.25
Travel	479.20
Office supplies	188.05
Publications	1,414.36
Rentals, insurance, etc.	204.16
Other purposes	49.30
	$12,582.32

JUNIOR HADASSAH (1921); 1860 Broadway, New York, N.Y.; Mrs. Alice B. Jacobson, Executive Secretary.

The young women's Zionist organization of America.

Membership: Young Jewish women aged 18 to 25, 20,000, in 253 local units. Affiliated with the senior Jewish women's organization known as Hadassah. There are 17 regional headquarters in the United States, intermediary between the national headquarters and the local units. The individual membership fee is $2 a year.

Purpose: To foster Zionist ideals, which are centered on the upbuilding of a Jewish homeland in Palestine; to develop an appreciation of Jewish culture; to bring to its members an understanding of Jewish life, past and present; to interpret Jewish problems; to support Zionist enterprises in Palestine; to contribute to the social service enterprises in Palestine mentioned below.

Activities: In America: conducts an extensive educational program for the study of Hebrew, Jewish history, literature, religion, and art; conducts year-round social affairs to raise funds for Palestinian work; maintains a service for presenting and analyzing American problems in order to guide members in the support of or opposition to movements, issues, and legislation in respect to their effect on the preservation of democracy.

In Palestine: maintains Meier Shfeyah, a children's village which now has 165 underprivileged and refugee children, Pardess Anna, a citrus farm for specialized training of graduates of Meier Shfeyah, and the Henrietta Szold School of Nursing (the last with the aid of senior Hadassah); participates in the Youth Aliyah movement, which has transported thousands of European refugee children to Palestine and settled them in agricultural colonies and trade centers; and assists the Jewish National Fund in its land reclamation and reforestation programs.

Publications: *Hadassah Newsletter*, monthly, carrying a Junior Hadassah section. *Junior Hadassah Year Book*, annually; the 1940 issue contains 72 pages with many illustrations. *Junior Hadassah*, descriptive pamphlet; *Youth Aliyah*, descriptive booklet; *Meier Shfeyah: Story of a Self-Governing Children's Village*, an account of the development of the village; *The Nurse: Guardian of Health*, story of the origin and work of the Henrietta Szold School of Nursing.

Staff: Full-time paid employees, 3; part-time paid employees, 11; part-time unpaid workers, 2.

Finances: The society maintains six general relief funds and five special trust funds, of which the aggregate unexpended balance as of June 30, 1939 was $42,454.92. On the same date the administration (current operation) fund had an unexpended balance of $5,899.95. Operations for the fiscal year ending June 30, 1939 were as follows:

Income	
Dues from members	$11,746.49
Shekel fund	784.51
Administration quota fund	6,990.31
Pavilion tickets receipts	151.38
	$19,672.69

Expenditures	
Salaries	$ 8,777.13
Newsletter	2,400.00
Rent	504.00
Convention expenses	284.02
Other purposes	6,682.23
	$18,647.38

MASADA, YOUTH ZIONIST ORGANIZATION OF AMERICA (1933); 111 Fifth Ave., New York, N.Y.; Natanel Cohen, Executive Director.

The official senior youth section of the Zionist organization.

Membership: Young persons, mostly men, between the ages of 18 and 30, 1,500 in 60 active chapters located in 20 states. About 75 per cent of the members are between the ages of 18 and 24.

Purpose: To aid in the establishment of an autonomous Jewish commonwealth in Palestine; to strengthen Jewish community life in America; to aid in the furtherance of the Hebrew renascence; to aid in the defense of Jewish rights.

Activities: Annual national convention; regional conferences from time to time; annual summer camp (established 1936). The national office furnishes material for the cultural programs of the local units. There is a sports program, and classes are sponsored in Hebrew language, literature, and history.

Publications: *Masada News*, biweekly; free to members, $1 a year to others; David Romanoff, managing editor. *Folk Songs of the New Palestine* (30 songs in 12 folders), subscription $3. *New Songs from the Land of Israel*, 25¢; *Auto-Emancipation*, by Leo Pinsker, 15¢; *Examination of Jewish Problem*, 15¢; *Masada, Its Aims, Principles and Program*; *Arab Movement in Palestine*, by Michael Assaf, 25¢.

Staff: Full-time paid employees, 2. The national president and the executive committee serve without pay.

NATIONAL COUNCIL OF JEWISH JUNIORS (1919); 1819 Broadway, New York, N.Y.; Caroline B. Lourie, Executive Secretary; Vera Teplitz, President, 451 Melrose St., Chicago, Ill.

The auxiliary to the National Council of Jewish Women.

Membership: Jewish youth, 8,600, in 137 local sections in the United States and Canada. Of this number 8,000 are juniors aged 18 to 30, and 600 are subjuniors aged 14 to 18.

Purpose: To work in the fields of religion, social welfare, civics, education, and peace; to cement the bonds of good fellowship among the junior sections of the National Council of Jewish Women; and to provide a medium for the interchange of ideas.

Activities: Biennial national conventions. In alternate years state conference meetings are held. The social welfare activities are based upon community needs. The council sponsors summer camps, toy-lending libraries, and dental clinics, and renders service and cooperation to all endeavors which have for their goal the furtherance of faith and humanity. Numerous activities are carried on in behalf of newcomers to this country. Among these are naturalization and Americanization classes, financial support to the international case work of the national organization and to the Port and Dock Service. Through the Hannah G. Solomon Scholarship Fund, the council awards scholarships each year to students for graduate study in social service in various universities. Study programs are conducted in the fields of religion and Jewish affairs, education, peace and international relations, and social legislation.

Publications: *The Council Woman*, published jointly by the National Council of Jewish Women and the National Council of Jewish Juniors; $1 a year or 35¢ a copy, included in membership dues; Viola Paradise, editor. Guides for each department and for study group leaders.

Staff: Full-time paid employee, 1; part-time paid employee, 1. The services of the professional staff of the National Council of Jewish Women and of a number of volunteer workers are also available.

Finances: Balance April 30, 1940, $1,100. For the fiscal year ending on that date, operations were approximately as follows:

Income

Gifts or grants for current purposes	$ 100
Membership fees	2,700
Other sources	200
	$3,000

Expenditures

Salaries	$1,600
Travel	50
Communications	400
Office supplies	170
Additions to equipment	35
Other purposes	45
	$2,300

NATIONAL COUNCIL OF YOUNG ISRAEL (1912); 200 West 40th St., New York, N.Y.; Samuel H. Fromberg, President.

An American Jewish youth movement devoted to the furtherance of the cause of Jewish orthodoxy.

Affiliated with the American Jewish Congress (see p. 56).

Membership: Model synagogues, 70, throughout the United States, Canada, and Palestine, but chiefly in New York and vicinity.

Purpose: To bridge the gap between the older and younger generations of Orthodox Jews; to arouse and intensify the loyalty and consciousness of Jewish youth; to perpetuate the traditions of Judaism in America; and to teach and prove that true Americanism and true Judaism are compatible and go harmoniously hand in hand.

Activities: The central organization maintains a Sabbath Committee, Palestine Committee, and food laboratory; sponsors Young Israel School of Adult Education; makes contributions to institutions of Jewish learning; and maintains an employment bureau, including a department for unemployed German refugees. A national convention is held in June, and regional conferences at other times during the year. The local branches conduct forums on current Jewish problems and study Jewish history, Jewish philosophy, Bible, Talmud, and the spoken Hebrew language. The branches organize junior and intermediate clubs for boys and girls under the supervision of competent Jewish leaders, and some of them sponsor Boy Scout troops; the clubs strive to offer their members a well-rounded program of athletics, handicrafts, hobby pursuits, and clean recreational and social activities; training courses are conducted for leaders of boys' and girls' work.

Publications: *Young Israel Viewpoint*, monthly; $1 a year; Moses H. Hoenig, editor. *Why Young Israel —How Young Israel*, pamphlet.

Staff: Full-time paid employees, 6; special directors in field, 2; part-time unpaid workers, 8.

Finances: Balance May 31, 1940, $623.67. For the fiscal year ending on that date, gross operations were as follows:

Income

Contributions	$ 56.59
Per capita tax	565.09
Viewpoint	748.81
Junior and Intermediate Committee	1,091.28
1939 convention	3,984.79
Other sources	27,196.58
	$33,643.14

Expenditures

Salaries	$ 7,736.00
Communications and printing	2,911.75
Viewpoint	570.00
Junior and Intermediate Committee	1,753.51
1939 convention	3,886.56
Rental	1,000.00
Other purposes	15,981.87
	$33,839.69

NATIONAL FEDERATION OF TEMPLE YOUTH
(1939); 34 West Sixth St., Cincinnati, Ohio; Richard N. Bluestein, President, Boston, Mass.

The youth organization of the Union of American Hebrew Congregations (see p. 62).

Membership: Young men and women aged approximately 18 to 30, 10,000, in 79 groups located throughout the United States. Annual dues, 15¢ a member.

Purpose: To promote the cause of the synagogue as the ideal center for Jewish life and thought; to prepare Jewish youth to lead richer lives through a fuller knowledge of their Jewish religious and cultural heritage; to cooperate with other youth organizations in promoting the ideals of religion, good citizenship, peace, and good will.

Activities: Biennial national conference. National committees on interfaith, Jewish needs, vocational guidance, social justice, and college activities. These committees devise methods of implementing their programs so that each youth group may be served.

Publications: The federation acts as a distributing agency of the publications of the Commission on Jewish Education of the Union of American Hebrew Congregations.

Staff: The director of youth activities of the Union of American Hebrew Congregations acts as executive director of the National Federation of Temple Youth.

NATIONAL JEWISH WELFARE BOARD (1917);
220 Fifth Ave., New York, N.Y.; Frank L. Weil, President; Louis Kraft, Executive Director.

The national organization of Young Men's Hebrew Associations, Young Women's Hebrew Associations, and Jewish Community Centers.

Membership: Constituent local societies, 317, in the United States and Canada, embracing an aggregate individual membership of about 400,000 persons of both sexes, of whom approximately 200,000 are estimated to be between the ages of 12 and 25. There are seven regional federations of local centers.

Purpose: To promote the social welfare of soldiers, sailors, and marines in the Army and Navy of the United States, disabled veterans, and young men in Civilian Conservation Corps camps, and especially to provide them with adequate opportunity for religious worship, education, devotion, solace, and improvement; to promote the religious, intellectual, physical, and social well-being and development of Jews, especially young men and women, and to that end to stimulate the organization of Jewish Centers, YMHA's, YWHA's, and other kindred societies; to assist, advise, and encourage such societies; to further and correlate their activities; to promote the interchange of advantages which they afford; and to cooperate with other organizations for the development of Judaism and good citizenship.

Activities: Two timely enterprises are Aid to New Immigrants and the Vocational Guidance Department. Older regular departments include Jewish Center Administration, Surveys and Studies, Jewish Extension Education, Leadership Training, Jewish Center Lecture Bureau, Personnel, Field Service, Health and Camping, Jewish Center Publications and Periodicals, Army and Navy Service, Campaign and Fund Raising, Public Relations, and Community Organization.

Publications: *The Jewish Center*, quarterly, $2 a year; *Metropolitan Leaders Association Review*, quarterly; *News Service*, biweekly; *Program Aids*, bimonthly. A number of bulletins under the following categories: Jewish center—administration and special problems; activities and projects; civic and Jewish holidays; biographical material; the current Jewish scene; training; camps and health activities; special publications and proceedings; plays and pageants; lists; program service.

Staff: Full-time paid employees, 21 professional, of whom 9 spend major time in field work, and 17 clerical. Part-time paid employees for army and navy welfare work, 9; volunteer workers in same services, 120.

Finances: Of the local centers, 238 own buildings having an aggregate value of approximately $37,-000,000. Annual expenditures of Jewish centers in the aggregate are about $4,700,000.

UNION OF AMERICAN HEBREW CONGREGATIONS, DEPARTMENT OF YOUTH ACTIVITIES
(1931); 34 West Sixth St., Cincinnati, Ohio; Rabbi Selwyn D. Ruslander, Director of Youth Activities.

The department is a service agency established by the organization's Commission on Jewish Education.

Membership: This department serves some 300 Reform Jewish congregations, as well as many youth groups either not connected with Reform Jewish congregations or connected with synagogues which request help or information. There are between 10,000 and 20,000 Jewish youth connected with the Reform synagogues.

Purpose: To act as a youth-serving agency for the Temple Youth groups (see National Federation of Temple Youth, p. 62) of the Reform Jewish congregations in the United States.

Activities: Supplies material for youth work; lectures on problems of youth; and stimulates interest in youth work throughout the congregations.

Publications: The department acts as a distributing agency for the publications issued under the auspices of the Youth Committee of the Commission on Jewish Education (Dr. Emanuel Gamoran, educational director). These publications include: *The Youth Leader* (mimeo.), quarterly, $1 a year, Rabbi Selwyn D. Ruslander, editor; *Arts-Crafts for the*

Jewish Club, by Dr. Harry L. Comins and Reuben Leaf, 362 pp., $2.50; *The Quest for Peace*, by Dr. Abraham Cronbach, 223 pp., $1.50; *The Rise and Destiny of the German Jew*, by Dr. Jacob R. Marcus, 365 pp., $1; *The Jewish Festivals*, by Hayyim Schauss, 320 pp., $2.50; and numerous other books and pamphlets relating to similar subjects.

Staff: Full-time paid employees, 2.

YOUNG JUDAEA (1909); 111 Fifth Ave., New York, N.Y.; Louis P. Rocker, President; Sonia Dingol Wexler, Vice President.

Membership: Boys and girls aged 10 to 18, 20,000, in 750 clubs. About 80 per cent of the members are girls.

Purpose: To advance the cause of Zionism; to promote Jewish culture and ideals in accordance with Jewish tradition; to further the mental, moral, and physical development of the Jewish youth; to emphasize anew the ideal of democracy, a vital part of the Jewish heritage.

Activities: Annual national and regional conventions; Jewish holy day programs; dramatics, discussion and debates on Jewish history; educational, recreational, and social programs of great variety and interest. The organization raises funds for the Jewish National Fund and for Keren Hanoar— the Jewish Scouting Fund of Young Judaea for the Jewish scouts in Palestine. The different regions sponsor camps for their own members.

Publications: *Young Judaean*, 9 issues annually; $1 a year, included in 50¢ membership. *The Leader*, 9 issues annually; $1 a year, included in $1 leader's fee. Numerous booklets and pamphlets on Jewish history and on recreational and cultural activities.

Staff: Full-time paid employees, 2; part-time paid employees, 2.

Finances: Operations for the fiscal year ending May 31, 1939 were as follows:

Income	
Gifts or grants	$11,003.50
Membership fees	854.50
Publications	4,298.77
Other services	555.90
Other sources	72.05
	$16,784.72

Expenditures	
Salaries	$ 7,302.59
Travel	201.54
Communications	1,790.44
Office supplies	2,639.85
Publications	5,888.85
Other purposes	712.74
	$18,536.01

YOUNG PEOPLE'S LEAGUE OF THE UNITED SYNAGOGUE OF AMERICA (1923); 3080 Broadway, New York, N.Y.; Rabbi Samuel M. Cohen, Executive Director; Ella Lichtman, Executive Secretary.

Membership: There are 397 groups in the United States and Canada which are affiliated and associated with the Young People's League.

Purpose: To advance the culture and religion of American Jewry; to unify youthful Israel for the advancement of education and philanthropy, and break down race prejudice; to offer an inclusive program in behalf of youth for the promotion of social, cultural, educational, religious, and civic welfare.

Activities: Sponsors programs of intellectual, cultural, and spiritual content in each local unit, such as lectures, essays, debates, panel discussions, dramatics, athletics, and radio programs. The national headquarters maintains a speakers bureau and has organized speakers training courses; it also offers training courses for leaders in adolescent activities. Annual national conventions include seminars, panel discussions, and symposia with scholarly and distinguished leaders.

Publications: *Jewish Youth Journal*, 75¢ a year. *Guiding Jewish Youth*, a manual for club leaders and workers with adolescents, by Rabbi Samuel M. Cohen, $2. Booklets on various phases of religious, cultural, and educational subjects, ranging in price from 10¢ to 25¢.

Staff: Full-time paid employees, 2; part-time paid employees, 2; part-time unpaid workers, 6.

YOUNG POALE ZION ALLIANCE (1920); 275 Seventh Ave., New York, N.Y.; Kieve Skidell, Executive Secretary.

Membership: Young men and women aged 17 to 21, 1,500, in 30 chapters in the United States and 3 chapters in Canada.

Purpose: To advance the cause of a socialist cooperative commonwealth, in Palestine as well as in America and throughout the world; to aid the Zionist movement in the rebuilding of Palestine as the Jewish national homeland; to aid young American Jews in keeping the great traditions of Judaism and in taking a suitable part in American life.

Activities: Study of the history and problems of socialism, the Hebrew and Yiddish languages and literature, and the history, achievements, and problems of the upbuilding of Palestine and its labor movement. Local clubs organize cultural circles, dramatic circles, debating teams, sport teams, choirs, orchestras, and social gatherings. Yiddish and Hebrew folk songs, labor songs, and the dancing of the Palestine Hora have a place in the musical and artistic programs. The organization cooperates with labor unions and with numerous other Jewish organizations connected with the world-wide Zionist movement. There are an annual convention, periodical educational seminars usually over Labor Day week end, and other midwinter functions. A national camp committee is in charge of nine cooperative camps situated in the vicinity of New Haven, Philadelphia, Baltimore, Chicago, Detroit, Rochester, Los Angeles, Montreal, and Toronto. A special committee is in charge of the educational program directed for those interested in training for pioneering in Palestine; the seat of this committee is at the Hechalutz Farm, Cream Ridge, N.J. (see Hechalutz Organization of America, p. 58).

Publications: *News and Views*, 20 issues annually; Kieve Skidell, editor-in-chief. *Nationalism and the Class Struggle*, by Ber Borochov; *Essays on Socialist Zionism*, by Dr. Nachman Syrkin; *Revolutionary Constructivism*, by Berl Katznelson; *Labor Zionism* (a brief summary); *Pesach Book; The Balance Sheet of Stalinism*, by Willi Schlamm; *The Leader and Democratic Socialism*, by Shalom Wurm; *Towards Unity of Youth*, by Liebenstein; *Assimilation*, by Shalom Wurm.

Staff: Full-time paid employees, 6, of whom 3 spend major time in the field; part-time paid employees, 4, of whom 2 spend major time in the field.

Table IX

STATISTICS OF JEWISH ORGANIZATIONS SERVING YOUTH

Organization	Year Founded	Approximate Aggregate Membership (individuals)	Number of Members under 25 Years of Age	Total Employees on Headquarters Staff	Aggregate Endowment of National Headquarters	Plant and Equipment (headquarters only)	Approximate Annual Budget (headquarters only)
Aleph Zadik Aleph of B'nai B'rith	1924	22,501	10,051	25	$10,500	$ 4,000	$ 44,000
American Jewish Congress	1917	2,000	...	41	...	...	...
Avukah, the American Student Zionist Federation	1925	30,000a	2,000	4	...	...	160,000
B'nai B'rith Hillel Foundations	1923	none	30,000a	7	...	...	...
B'nai B'rith Vocational Service Bureau	1938	...	...	2	...	...	...
Council of Jewish Federations and Welfare Funds	1932	195b	...	27	...	...	109,000
Hapoel Hamizrachi of America	1921	10,900	3,200c	8	...	...	10,000
Hechalutz Organization of America	1932	500	500	3	...	500	11,300
Jewish Agricultural Society	1900	...	...	29	...	...	100,000
Jewish Occupational Council	1938	27b	...	4	...	...	14,500
Junior Hadassah	1921	20,000	20,000	14	noned	...	19,700
Masada, Youth Zionist Organization of America	1933	1,500	1,100	2	...	...	...
National Council of Jewish Juniors	1919	8,600	8,600e	2	...	...	3,000
National Council of Young Israel	1912	70b	...	6	...	...	33,800
National Federation of Temple Youth	1939	10,000	10,000e	1	...	...	...
National Jewish Welfare Board	1917	400,000f	200,000g	47	...	37,000,000h	4,700,000h
Union of Am. Hebrew Cong., Dept. of Youth Activities	1931	...	...	2	...	...	...
Young Judea	1909	20,000	20,000	4	...	...	18,500
Young People's League of the United Synagogue of Am.	1923	397b	...	4	...	...	...
Young Poale Zion Alliance	1920	1,500	1,500	10	...	...	...

a Number of Jewish students served in 44 institutions of higher education.
b Number of constituent bodies.
c Number of members under 21 years of age.
d The organization has general relief funds and special trust funds totaling $42,455.
e Includes members up to 30 years of age.
f Underlying membership of 317 constituent bodies.
g Number of youth between the ages of 12 and 25.
h Total for all Jewish Centers.

IX. Student Associations

In the school year 1940–41 there are 1,425,000 students enrolled in all institutions of higher education in the United States. This number has more than trebled within twenty-five years, and there is reason to believe that in the future larger and larger numbers of our young people will find a way to avail themselves of facilities for higher education.

Public and private high schools now enroll 7,160,000 boys and girls. For the past quarter of a century this number has been increasing at the phenomenal rate of about one million every five years. Already three-fourths of our population aged 14 to 17 inclusive are in attendance at school. Unfortunately this percentage varies widely from state to state and is far lower for the rural population as a whole than for the urban population.

Nevertheless it is possible to envision the day when we shall achieve the admirable and distinctively American ideal of secondary education for all. Even at present we have more pupils in secondary schools than has all the rest of the world combined. For the first time in all history we begin to approach a situation in which a great democratic nation will have a citizenry most of whom have had the benefit of schooling beyond the elementary level.

American students have not generally exhibited the propensities for political organization and agitation which characterize their brethren in Latin America and in many parts of Europe and Asia. In the main, their voluntary organizations tend to be either social or religious. The American college fraternity is everywhere known and exists in a hundred varieties having national headquarters with local chapters on many campuses. Fraternities are omitted from this section, because they have been made the subject of a well-known and comprehensive manual already available from another source.[1]

The national student organizations selected for inclusion here are limited to a small number, for the most part consisting of those expressly concerned with the development of leadership among students and the focusing of their attention upon important public problems. The statement of the American Youth Commission entitled "Should Youth Organize?" reprinted as an appendix to this book (pages 219–21), is germane to the subject of youth organizations.

Associations whose membership consists chiefly of young persons, as distinguished from those composed wholly or largely of persons above the age of 25, are:

American Student Union
National Association of Student Officers
National Honor Society of Secondary Schools
National Junior Honor Society
National Student Federation of America

Cross references: Avukah, the American Student Zionist Federation, p. 56; B'nai B'rith Hillel Foundations, p. 57; Catholic Students' Mission Crusade, p. 46; National Federation of Catholic College Students, p. 52; Newman Club Federation, p. 52; Pi Christian Fraternal Orders, p. 41; Sodality of Our Lady, p. 52; Student Volunteer Movement, p. 42; Theta Phi Alpha Fraternity, p. 53.

AMERICAN STUDENT UNION (1935); 381 Fourth Ave., New York, N.Y.; Herbert Witt, Executive Secretary.

Membership: Students of both sexes between the ages of 15 and 24, approximately 22,000, in 200 colleges and 100 high schools in 42 states.

Purpose: To educate and organize students to keep America out of war; to obtain economic security and employment opportunity; to insure religious, racial, and political liberty; and to maintain civil liberty and academic freedom.

Activities: Campaigns in behalf of expansion of the National Youth Administration and passage of the American Youth Act (see American Youth Congress, p. 82); participates in organization of student peace strike, annually in April, as demonstration against war; combats retrenchment in educational budgets and advocates federal aid to education; combats racial discrimination and violations of academic freedom; sends occasional deputations to legislative and administrative authorities. Holds annual national convention (Christmas week); conducts semiannual conferences in the New England, New York, Middle Atlantic, Ohio, Midwest, and California districts. Sponsors annual student tour, which in 1940 was to Mexico. Conducts summer leadership institute for chapter officers.

---

[1] *Baird's Manual of American College Fraternities* (Menasha Wis.: George Banta Publishing Co.).

Publications: *The Student Advocate*, monthly during school year; 75¢ a year (publication suspended from 1938 to October 1940). Pamphlets and folders: *Students Serve Democracy*, 1939, 32 pp., 5¢; *Not in Your Textbooks*, 1940, 4 pp., free in quantities under 10, 5 for 1¢ for larger orders; *Academic Epidemic*, 1940, 20 pp., 5¢.

Staff: Full-time paid employees at headquarters, 2; part-time unpaid workers, 6. There are 6 full-time paid district secretaries, financed locally and not on payroll of national headquarters.

Finances: Value of equipment at headquarters, $600. Estimated annual value of unpaid staff services, $2,500. For the fiscal year ending November 30, 1939 the budget was approximately $12,000.

INTERNATIONAL STUDENT SERVICE IN THE UNITED STATES (1920); 8 West 40th St., New York, N.Y.; Robert G. Spivack, Acting Secretary.

Membership: A committee of approximately 30 educators and leaders of youth organizations in the United States. There are corresponding committees in 23 countries, reporting to André de Blonay, general secretary, 13 rue Calvin, Geneva, Switzerland. The constituency in the United States is composed in part of student refugees from Germany, Czechoslovakia, Poland, Finland, Spain, and other countries affected by war or persecution, of whom the service interviews some 1,500 annually. There are also some 1,000 to 3,000 American students and faculty members assisting the service.

Purpose: To stimulate social, cultural, and political intercourse between the students of all nations by conferences, refugee and relief assistance, publications, work camps, and similar intellectual pursuits.

Activities: The organization has placed or assisted over 800 refugee students since 1933. With the National Intercollegiate Christian Council, it sponsors the World Student Service Fund, which is attempting to raise $100,000 for relief of war victims in China and Europe. The committee cooperates with Work Camps for America (see p. 139) by recommending refugees for scholarships. The Geneva office, with the aid of the Rockefeller Foundation, carries on research into such questions affecting university people as graduate unemployment, health conditions, and academic freedom. Conferences in Europe are financed with the aid of the Carnegie Endowment for International Peace. During 1939 two conferences were held in the United States on "The Bases of a Durable Peace."

Publications: *I.S.S. Bulletin*, 9 issues annually; published at 13 rue Calvin, Geneva, Switzerland. Pamphlets: *The Bases of a Durable Peace; A Statement of Fact* (mimeo.), relative to the program of the European Student Service Fund; *Europe's Blackout of Education*.

Staff: Full-time paid employees, 6, of whom 1 spends major time in field work; part-time paid employees, 3.

Finances: Operating balance August 31, 1939, $746.89. For the fiscal year ending on that date, operations were as follows:

Income

Gifts for current expenses	$ 6,196.83
Cash for refugees	2,233.00
For Chinese fund	1,239.00
Scholarships and grants for 1938–39	26,073.50
Other sources	82.09
	$35,824.42

Expenditures

Salaries	$ 3,120.70
Travel	812.11
Communications	379.48
Office supplies	313.18
Rent, insurance, etc.	515.20
Scholarships and grants for 1938–39	26,073.50
Other purposes	3,863.36
	$35,077.53

NATIONAL ASSOCIATION OF STUDENT OFFICERS (1930); Grover Cleveland High School, Ridgewood, Queens, N.Y.; Grace M. Anderson, President of the National Conference on Student Participation.

Membership: Boys and girls of secondary school age, about 50, officers of major student organizations in junior high schools, senior high schools, and junior colleges. Annual dues, $1.50.

Purpose: To train young people in realistic citizenship through participation in school activities.

Activities: Holds an annual meeting in connection with the summer convention of the National Education Association (see p. 131). Local projects sponsored include a great variety of enterprises related to school morale and the improvement of school citizenship.

Publications: *Service Bulletin*, issued 3 times during the school year 1939–40.

Staff: No paid employees.

Finances: Income and expenditures for the fiscal year ending June 30, 1940 were approximately $100.

NATIONAL HONOR SOCIETY OF SECONDARY SCHOOLS (1921) and NATIONAL JUNIOR HONOR SOCIETY (1929); 5835 Kimbark Ave., Chicago, Ill.; H. V. Church, Secretary.

Membership: Chapters of the National Honor Society, in high schools throughout the United States and possessions, 2,500. Chapters of the Junior Honor Society, in junior high schools and the lower years of senior and four-year high schools, 300.

Purpose: To stimulate the scholarship, leadership, service, and character of the students in secondary schools of the country; to raise the secondary schools of the United States to a higher plane of more effective service.

Activities: More than half of the local chapters sponsor service undertakings in their schools. Other chapters are purely honorary, with members usually elected at the time of graduation from the school. All members of all chapters become impressed with an obligation for further activities in behalf of the improvement of secondary schools after they have been graduated. In 1937 a revolving scholarship loan fund designed to provide 40 or more scholarship loans to members of the society who are in their upper three years in college or university was authorized by the national council. It is hoped that each local chapter will eventually provide minimum essential financial assistance to one of its own promising but needy members who is in his first year in college or university.

Publications: *Student Life*, 8 issues annually; 50¢ to clubs of three or more persons, to individuals who are student officers or faculty sponsors of student councils, or to members of the National Association of Secondary-School Principals (see p. 128), $1 to others.

Staff: Employees, 2.

Finances: Expenses are borne by the National Association of Secondary-School Principals.

NATIONAL STUDENT FEDERATION OF AMERICA (1925); 1410 H St., N.W., Washington, D.C.; John Darnell, President.

Membership: The organized student bodies of 130 universities and colleges, serving 200,000 undergraduates.

Purpose: To achieve a spirit of cooperation among the students of the United States and to consider questions affecting students' interests; to develop intelligent student opinion on questions of national and international importance; to promote international amity among students as a means of furthering permanent peace.

Activities: Holds annual congresses and district conferences; surveys such student problems as self-government, honor systems, fraternities, and cooperatives, and makes the results available through its general information service. In 1936 the Intercollegiate Council on Public Affairs merged with the National Student Federation in order to devote the combined resources of the two organizations to awakening students to the need for the preservation of democracy, the improvement of social standards in America, and the stabilization of world peace; the NSFA Public Affairs Council carries on the resulting program—the discussion of public affairs through interest groups and nonpartisan forums, and active preparation for the obligations of citizenship through First Voter Forums. The federation assists foreign refugee students in this country, and cooperates with the Open Road (see p. 137), an organization conducting educational tours for American students in Europe and South America. It also sponsors international debates and cooperates with the National Peace Conference (see p. 216), the United Student Peace Committee, and the American Youth Congress (see p. 82). Curtailment of the international activities is being necessitated by the present European war.

Publications: *N.S.F.A. Reporter*, weekly news release; *N.S.F.A. Notes*, weekly column. *Proceedings of 15th Annual Congress*, 1940, 33 pp., 15¢; *Proceedings of 14th Annual Congress*, 1939, 38 pp., 15¢. *Survey of Women's Social Regulations*, 1939, 17 pp., 25¢; mimeographed sheets on specific topics, such as honor systems, orientation, and others, free to members.

Staff: Full-time paid employees, 3, of whom 1 spends part time in field work.

Finances: Value of equipment at headquarters, $727.20. Operating balance December 15, 1939, $891.07. For the fiscal year ending on that date, operations were as follows:

Income

Gifts for current expenses	$ 490.00
Membership fees	2,995.76
Publications	11.00
Student travel	4,339.78
Debate	4,755.21
Student identity cards	228.77
Annual congress	449.80
Subrentals	269.63
Other sources	1,956.87
	$15,496.82

Expenditures

Salaries	$ 3,409.10
Travel	3,761.79
Communications	541.58
Office supplies	902.62
Publications	1,707.01
Rent, insurance, etc.	685.95
Food, lodging, sight-seeing, entertainment	960.50
Other purposes	2,637.20
	$14,605.75

TABLE X

STATISTICS OF STUDENT ASSOCIATIONS

Organization	Year Founded	Approximate Aggregate Membership (individuals)	Number of Members under 25 Years of Age	Total Employees on Headquarters Staff	Aggregate Endowment of National Headquarters	Plant and Equipment (headquarters only)	Approximate Annual Budget (headquarters only)
American Student Union	1935	22,000	22,000	2	none	$600	$12,000
International Student Service in the United States	1920	30[a]	none	9	...	...	35,800
National Association of Student Officers	1930	...	...	[b]	...	...	...
National Honor Society of Secondary Schools	1921	2,500[c] }	...		...	...	[d]
National Junior Honor Society	1929	300[c] }	...	2	...	...	
National Student Federation of America	1925	200,000[e]	200,000	3	none	727	15,500

a Number of committee members.
b No paid staff.
c Number of chapters.

d Expenses are borne by the National Association of Secondary-School Principals.
e Aggregate number of undergraduates in the student bodies of the 110 universities and colleges members of the federation.

X. Organizations for Research and Social Planning

The extraordinary accomplishments resulting from patient research in technological fields encourages many to believe that the application of the same impartial and persistent curiosity to the study of social problems may be expected to lead to equally fortunate results in the field of social science.

Admittedly social science research lags behind at the present moment, and its development will necessarily have to contend with certain prejudices, taboos, and superstitions which are not easily overthrown. The expansion of free public education is a powerful aid in dispersing the fogs which becloud the approach to social problems, however, and it is encouraging to note that year by year social research seems to attract to its banner greater resources in men and money.

There are in the United States about one hundred great philanthropic foundations, some devoted in part to financing or conducting research. Some of their activities ramify into all the social science fields. The foundations are excluded from the present section, because a volume would be required to treat them adequately, and more than one volume treating various aspects of the subject has appeared in recent years.[1]

Hence this section is limited largely to research organizations maintained by or in connection with associations representing the several professions or other national groups interested in national and community research and social planning. Usually the organizations listed have relatively small financial resources in their own right, but they are sometimes generously aided on specific projects for limited periods by the philanthropic foundations.

The salutary tendency toward coordination of multifarious impulses and activities in research is evidenced in the work of four great national research councils, which came into existence between 1916 and 1923. These are the National Research Council, the American Council of Learned Societies, the American Council on Education, and the Social Science Research Council. The National Research Council and the Social Science Research Council are described in the present section. The American Council on Education appears below in Section XVI in juxtaposition with other national educational organizations but is represented here by two of its major temporary research undertakings, the American Youth Commission and the Commission on Teacher Education.

The welfare of youth, as a research problem, is scarcely narrower in scope than the entire cosmos of the social welfare. For this reason any listing of research organizations working in behalf of youth must include not only those restricted to youth welfare alone but also those engaged in the several social science fields, a large part of whose advances, if any, will result in benefit to young persons.

Cross references: Section XVI, Educational Associations, pp. 112–41, especially American Council on Education, p. 117; Section XVIII, Leisure and Recreational Associations, pp. 151–69, especially Motion Picture Research Council, p. 160, and organizations concerned with conservation. *See also:* Association for the Study of Negro Life and History, p. 97; Psychological Corporation, p. 148.

AMERICAN EDUCATIONAL RESEARCH ASSOCIATION (1930); 525 West 120th St., New York, N.Y.; Helen M. Walker, Secretary-Treasurer.

A department of the National Education Association (see p. 131).

Membership: Active members, individuals elected on proof of good ability and sound training in educational research, 499. Additional affiliated members (through a state research association), 40. Annual dues for active members, $5.

Purpose: To encourage and promote the investigation of educational problems through research, publications, meetings, and like means of cooperative endeavor.

Activities: Appoints special committees to prepare each bimonthly number of the *Review of Educational Research* and the annual official report; confers annual awards for outstanding research studies; cooperates in sponsoring an *Encyclopedia of Educational Research* (to be published in 1941); holds an annual meeting in February in conjunction with

---

[1] See bibliography, pp. 222–24, particularly the entries following the names of E. C. Lindeman, H. C. Coffman, and Raymond Rich Associates.

that of the American Association of School Administrators (see p. 114) and a summer program at the June meeting of the National Education Association. The research activities serve youth by helping to improve the educational system and to increase knowledge of the physical, psychological, and educational development of young people.

Publications: *Review of Educational Research,* 5 issues annually; free to members, $4 a year to others (single copies, $1). Titles of recent numbers include "Mental and Physical Development," "Pupil Personnel, Guidance, and Counseling," "The Language Arts," "School Organization and Administration," and "Physical and Mental Health." Douglas E. Scates, Duke University, Durham, N.C., is chairman of the editorial board. The annual official report is a volume of approximately 200 pages containing the papers read at the annual meeting.

Staff: Part-time paid employee, 1.

Finances: Value of equipment at headquarters, $100. Balance on hand December 31, 1939, $6,917.36. For the fiscal year ending on that date, operations were as follows:

Income	
Membership fees	$2,351.00
Publications	3,983.43
Annual banquet	261.00
Reserve funds	760.90
	$7,356.33

Expenditures	
Salaries	$ 905.14
Committee expenses	534.49
Communications and supplies	976.89
Publications	4,404.73
Annual banquet	311.13
Other purposes	223.94
	$7,356.32

AMERICAN PLANNING AND CIVIC ASSOCIATION (1935); 901 Union Trust Bldg., Washington, D.C.; Miss Harlean James, Executive Secretary.

Formerly American Civic Association and National Conference on City Planning.

Membership: Individuals and associations, 1,800, including a number of libraries and governmental bureaus. Dues are as follows: annual, $5; sustaining, $10; contributing, $25 to $100; patron, $200 to $1,000.

Purpose: To create a better physical environment which will conserve and develop the health, happiness, and culture of the American people.

Activities: Promotes public understanding and support of national, regional, state, and local planning for the best use of urban and rural land, water, and other natural resources; the advancing of higher ideals of civic life and beauty in America; the safeguarding and developing, for the largest good to the people, of natural wonders and scenic possessions and of national and other parks and recreational facilities. Furnishes its members with information on which to build local planning, park, and civic improvement programs. Through publications the members are informed of current developments in outdoor physical improvement throughout the country. A watch service is maintained to keep members posted on federal legislation and executive action in the field of planning, parks, and civic improvement. An annual meeting provides members with an opportunity to study, under expert guidance, the application of planning principles.

Publications: *Planning and Civic Comment,* quarterly; Dora A. Padgett, managing editor. *American Planning and Civic Annual;* Harlean James, editor. Various civic bulletins. All publications are free to holders of the minimum annual membership.

Staff: Full-time paid employees, 6.

Finances: Approximate annual budget, $40,000.

AMERICAN SOCIETY OF PLANNING OFFICIALS (1934); 1313 East 60th St., Chicago, Ill.; Walter H. Blucher, Executive Director.

Membership: Individuals, 750. Annual fee, $5.

Purpose: To promote efficiency of public administration in land and community planning through the association of officials engaged in the making or administration of national, state, regional, or local plans, by exchanging information, improving administrative standards and practices, engaging in research, publishing the results of studies, cooperating and collaborating with other public and private agencies and associations, and in all proper ways furthering the usefulness of public agencies in the field.

Activities: Serves as a clearinghouse for planning information; arranges regional or sectional planning meetings; aids in perfecting legislation for state planning, regional planning, local planning, rural and local zoning; assists in the establishment of official planning agencies. Furnishes consultation, inquiry service, and field service.

Publications: *News Letter,* 12 issues annually; free to members. *Proceedings of the National Conference on Planning,* annually since 1935, ranging from 166 pp. to 210 pp., $2 each; *Proceedings of the First Conference on State Planning Administration,* 1936, 103 pp., $1; *Proceedings of the Conference on City Planning Administration,* 1937, 136 pp., $1. *Planning in Europe,* 1935, 12 pp.; *Planning in Europe,* 1939, 8 pp.; *A Mayor Has His Troubles,* 1940, 8 pp.; *Planning Bibliography,* 1939, 13 pp., 25¢; *The Airport Dilemma,* 1938, 46 pp., $1; *The Parking Problem in Central Business Districts,* 1938, 28 pp., $1.

Staff: Full-time paid employees, 8, of whom 1 spends major time in field work; part-time paid employees, 10.

Finances: Endowment fund, $22,000. Value of equipment at headquarters, $1,000. For the fiscal year ending December 31, 1939, the budget was approximately $35,000, including $10,000 for field service.

AMERICAN SOCIETY FOR PUBLIC ADMINISTRATION (1939); 1313 East 60th St., Chicago, Ill.; Robert M. Paige, Secretary-Treasurer.

Membership: Individuals, about 1,000. Classes of members and annual dues: regular, $5; sustaining, $10; junior (aged 28 or less), $3.

Purpose: To stimulate more extensive discussion, research, and experimentation in administrative policies and practices involved in the management of public services; to encourage the collection, compilation, and dissemination of information on matters relating to public administration; to advance generally the science, processes, and art of public administration.

Activities: Conducts an annual meeting; encourages the organization of local chapters; produces a scholarly journal.

Publications: *Public Administration Review*, quarterly; free to members, $5 a year to others; Leonard D. White, editor-in-chief.

Staff: Part-time services of various persons contributed.

Finances: The society's sole source of income is membership fees. Because of its rapid growth and the fact that the first fiscal year had not expired at the time of this report, no financial statement is practicable.

AMERICAN YOUTH COMMISSION OF THE AMERICAN COUNCIL ON EDUCATION (1935); 744 Jackson Place, Washington, D.C.; Floyd W. Reeves, Director.

Membership: Individuals, 15: Owen D. Young, *chairman;* Henry I. Harriman, *vice chairman;* Miriam Van Waters, *secretary;* Will W. Alexander, Clarence A. Dykstra, Dorothy Canfield Fisher, Willard E. Givens, Rev. George Johnson, Mordecai W. Johnson, Chester H. Rowell, William F. Russell, John W. Studebaker, Henry C. Taylor, Matthew Woll, George F. Zook.

Purpose: To consider all the needs of American youth between the ages of 12 and 25; to develop a comprehensive program for their care and education; to ascertain by investigation of the agencies concerned with the care and education of youth how effectively these needs are being served; to recommend procedures and practices which seem to be most effective in solving the problems of youth.

Activities: Conducts investigations of (1) the employment and vocational adjustment of youth, (2) the expansion and reorganization of general secondary education, (3) the equalization of educational opportunity, (4) the significance of recreation and recreational facilities, (5) health as a factor in the welfare of youth, (6) the situation and prospects of rural youth, (7) the status and outlook of Negro youth, and (8) community organization to improve youth services and utilize youth resources.

Among major studies recently completed or nearing completion are: surveys of youth in the state of Maryland and in the cities of Muncie, Ind., and Dallas, Tex., involving interviews with about 20,000 young people aged 16 to 24; a study of the CCC, broadened to embrace also observation of NYA resident training centers and work camps under private auspices; an inspection and demonstration of the coordination of local agencies for the occupational adjustment of youth, carried on in eight centers with the cooperation of the U. S. Employment Service Division; and a study, conducted by white and Negro sociologists and psychologists in several centers in the South and North, of the effect of caste and class restrictions upon the developing personality of Negro adolescents.

Other enterprises in progress include a project, involving cooperation with local agencies in several localities in different states, to implement the findings of the commission in rural areas. The commission maintains contacts with other agencies of research and youth service, national and local, governmental and private. It implements its recommendations by means of publications and radio broadcasts, as well as by conferences, consultations, and other cooperative techniques.

Publications: *Bulletin of the American Youth Commission*, occasionally. Free pamphlets: *A Program of Action for American Youth*, 20 pp.; *Youth—Their Jobs, Their Health, Their Schooling*, 12 pp.; *The Occupational Adjustment of Youth*, 16 pp.; *Community Responsibility for Youth*, 12 pp.; *Should Youth Organize?* 8 pp.; *Youth, Defense, and the National Welfare*, 12 pp.; *Finding the Facts about Youth*, 16 pp.; *New Strength for America*, 12 pp.; *Rallying Resources for Youth*, 20 pp. Books: *How Fare American Youth?* by Homer P. Rainey and others, 1937, 186 pp., $1.50; *Secondary Education for Youth in Modern America*, by Harl R. Douglass, 1937, 137 pp., $1; *Youth Tell Their Story*, by Howard M. Bell, 1938, 273 pp., $1.50; *American Youth—An Annotated Bibliography*, by Louise Arnold Menefee and M. M. Chambers, 1938, 492 pp., $3; *Equal Educational Opportunity for Youth—A National Responsibility*, by Newton Edwards, 1939, 189 pp., $2; *The Health of College Students*, by Harold S. Diehl and Charles E. Shepard, 1939, 169 pp., $1.50; *Youth in European Labor Camps*, by Kenneth Holland, 1939, 303 pp., $2.50; *How to Make a Community Youth Survey*, by M. M. Chambers and Howard M. Bell, 1939, 45 pp., 25¢; *In a Minor Key—Negro Youth in Story and Fact*, by Ira DeA. Reid, 1940, 134 pp., $1.25; *Children of*

Bondage, by Allison Davis and John Dollard, 1940, 299 pp., $2.25; *The Community and Its Young People*, by M. M. Chambers, 1940, 36 pp., 25¢; *What the High Schools Ought to Teach*, 1940, 36 pp., 25¢ (paper) and 50¢ (board); *Matching Youth and Jobs*, by Howard M. Bell, 1940, 278 pp., $2; *Guideposts for Rural Youth*, by E. L. Kirkpatrick, 1940, 167 pp., $1; *Negro Youth at the Crossways*, by E. Franklin Frazier, 1940, 301 pp., $2.25; *Growing Up in the Black Belt*, by C. S. Johnson, 1941, 360 pp., $2.25; *Youth, Family, and Education*, by J. K. Folsom, 1941, 299 pp., $1.75; *Color and Human Nature*, by W. L. Warner and others, 1941, 300 pp., $2.25; *Work Camps for High School Youth*, by Kenneth Holland and G. L. Bickel, 1941, 27 pp., 25¢.

Forthcoming books are: *Thus Be Their Destiny*, by Donald Wyatt and others; *Youth Labor Programs*, by Lewis L. Lorwin; *Youth in American Labor Camps*, by Kenneth Holland; *Leisure, Youth, and Recreation*, by C. Gilbert Wrenn and D. L. Harley; *400 CCC Boys*, by Ruth S. Cavan; *Color, Class, and Personality*, by Robert L. Sutherland; *Youth Employment and Unemployment*, by T. L. Norton and others; final report of the American Youth Commission.

Staff: Full-time paid employees, 26; part-time paid employees, 9.

Finances: The General Education Board made an appropriation of $500,000 for the general support of the commission over a period of five years beginning September 1935. In December 1939, the General Education Board made an additional appropriation of $150,000 for general support for an 18-month period ending June 30, 1941. These grants are exclusive of special projects for which supplementary grants were made from time to time. For the fiscal year ending June 30, 1940, total expenditures, including special projects, were $243,139.72. For the same period operations for general support and for publications were as follows:

Income

Grants for general support	$105,866.37
Sale of publications	11,166.97
	$117,033.34

Expenditures

Salaries	$ 71,295.05
Travel	5,440.62
Communications	3,104.71
Office supplies	2,484.47
Publications (for free distribution)	8,277.05
Rent, insurance, etc.	7,739.11
Furniture and equipment	987.49
Expenses of commission members	4,697.80
Radio programs	1,512.61
Miscellaneous	327.46
Printing of books and reports	10,809.53
	$116,675.90

See also American Council on Education (p. 117).

COMMISSION ON TEACHER EDUCATION OF THE AMERICAN COUNCIL ON EDUCATION

(1938); 744 Jackson Place, N.W., Washington, D.C.; Karl W. Bigelow, Director.

Membership: Individuals, 15: Payson Smith, *chairman;* E. S. Evenden, *vice chairman;* Harold Benjamin, Mildred English, Harry M. Gage, Helen Hay Heyl, Charles W. Hunt, Harold E. Jones, Fred J. Kelly, Lewis Mumford, Shelton Phelps, W. Carson Ryan, Alexander J. Stoddard, Frank W. Thomas, Ralph W. Tyler; *ex officio*, George F. Zook.

Purpose: To conduct a nation-wide study of teacher education in such a way as to work directly with and through already existing agencies; to put into use and test in practice the best available knowledge regarding problems in the field; to be concerned with all experiences of educational significance to teachers from their first training to retirement; to stimulate cooperative and experimental attack on relevant problems but especially on those of widest and deepest significance; and to encourage continuous evaluation of teacher education programs wherever they occur.

Activities: Conducts (1) a cooperative study of teacher education with 34 universities, liberal arts and teachers colleges, and public school systems of differing size, representing all parts of the country, and (2) state-wide programs in Michigan, New York, and Georgia that are jointly financed and administered with local bodies of state-wide competence. Extensive consultant services are provided in the fields of child growth, teacher personnel, and evaluation; a collaboration center on child development in Chicago offers training in this area, at the postdoctoral level, with special emphasis on collating the contributions of various disciplines such as human biology, cultural anthropology, psychology, and pedagogical research. A clearinghouse and information service are maintained at the Washington office. The latest project to be launched is an inquiry into the special problems connected with the education of college teachers. The commission promotes intervisitation and study, especially among the institutions participating in its activities, and secures consultant services as needed for fields other than those already described and continuously provided.

During the summer of 1940, the commission conducted a workshop on teacher education for representatives of the cooperative study at the University of Chicago. In cooperation with the Progressive Education Association (see p. 137) similar workshops were promoted for public school teachers in Denver, Des Moines, Greenville, Houston, Los Angeles, and Milwaukee. Evaluation services and two scholarships for teachers were furnished to the Open Road (see p. 137) for each of three of that organization's regular field seminars.

Publications: Free pamphlets: *Cooperation in the Improvement of Teacher Education*, 19 pp.; *Cultural and Social Elements in the Education of Teachers,*

51 pp.; and numerous reprints. Mimeographed documents: *Bennington Planning Conference* (report), 1939, 961 pp., 80¢; *The Teacher, the School and the Community*, by Stephen E. Epler, 1940, 66 pp., 10¢; *Workshop in Teacher Education, Chicago 1940*, 36 pp., 10¢.

Staff: Full-time paid employees, 23.

Finances: The work of the commission is financed by grants from the General Education Board. For the fiscal year July 1, 1939 to June 30, 1940, income for the commission and its projects totaled $187,-126.52; expenditures for the same period aggregated $182,916.75. The budget for 1940–41, including the headquarters office and various types of field work in cooperation with institutions for the education of teachers, is $400,000.

See also American Council on Education (p. 117).

COORDINATING COUNCILS, INC. (1938); 145 West 12th St., Los Angeles, Calif.; Kenneth S. Beam, Executive Secretary.

Membership: Individuals, 234; organizations, 54. Approximately 650 autonomous coordinating, neighborhood, and community councils are located in 30 states and Australia. In some counties there are also Junior Coordinating Councils; the junior council in Los Angeles County enrolls a total membership of 250.

Purpose: To conduct studies, surveys, and conferences in order to assemble information regarding the problems met and methods used by various types of coordinating councils; to disseminate the foregoing information; to maintain a reference bureau and clearinghouse at headquarters; and to provide consultant service relative to the organization and operation of councils and relative to means of preventing delinquency and crime through the elimination or control of the basic conditioning factors.

Activities: The local councils promote cooperation between public departments, private agencies, and civic organizations; conduct surveys of community resources, needs, and conditions influencing children and youth; provide or improve community services to all age groups in fields of health, education, mental hygiene, probation, recreation, police service, and others; secure new ordinances and support for both local and state measures involving the welfare of children and youth. Indicative of the activities for youth is the following summary of work carried on by the 72 councils in Los Angeles County: 42 assisted in establishing community dances; 34 established special employment bureaus for youth; 63 assisted in setting up vacation church schools; 18 established young married people's groups in churches; 51 worked for the community recreation bill which was passed by the state legislature; 60 assisted summer camps, mostly by raising money to send underprivileged boys and girls to camp; 56 had committees on salacious literature; practically all worked to control undesirable influences such as the sale of liquor to minors and the location of gambling devices near schools; through the efforts of the central office and many councils, 97,107 boys and girls from 8 to 20 years of age were provided free admission and transportation to radio broadcasts, baseball games, county fair, and other events.

Publications: *Community Coordination*, 6 issues annually; 50¢ a year. *The First Eighteen Months*, 1939, 10 pp., free; *Outline for Self-Study of Coordinating Councils*, 10 pp. mimeo., free. Various other pamphlets.

Staff: Full-time paid employees, 2, of whom 1 spends part time in field work.

Finances: Estimated annual value of space, heat, light, and similar services received without charge, $500. Balance July 15, 1939, $61.06. For the fiscal year ending on that date, operations were as follows:

Income

Gifts and grants	$8,050.00
Membership fees	157.00
Publications	222.68
Other services	104.95
	$8,534.63

Expenditures

Salaries	$5,959.48
Travel	1,362.54
Communications	100.49
Office supplies	267.70
Publications	645.50
Rentals, insurance, etc.	137.86
	$8,473.57

EDUCATIONAL POLICIES COMMISSION (1935); 1201 16th St., N.W., Washington, D.C.; William G. Carr, Secretary.

Membership: Twenty distinguished educators appointed jointly by the National Education Association (see p. 131) and the American Association of School Administrators (see p. 114): *chairman*, Alexander J. Stoddard; *members*, Cornelia S. Adair, George S. Counts, Edmund E. Day, J. B. Edmonson, Frederick M. Hunter, John K. Norton, Agnes Samuelson, John A. Sexson, Payson Smith, George D. Strayer, Willis A. Sutton, Emily A. Tarbell; *ex officio members*, Willard E. Givens, Carroll R. Reed, Donald DuShane, S. D. Shankland, Mary D. Barnes; *advisory members*, John W. Studebaker, George F. Zook.

Purpose: To make the best practices and procedures known throughout the country and bring about desirable changes in the content and method of education; to stimulate thoughtful, realistic, and long-term planning both by the profession and by the lay public, looking toward the continuous adaptation of education to social need.

Activities: Has prepared pronouncements of policy in the following fields: (1) the unique function, the structure and administration, and the purposes of education in American democracy; (2) education and economic well-being in American democracy; (3) the relation between education and social services; (4) the present and future school population; (5) study of citizenship education in secondary schools and publication of a report of the findings, undertaken during 1939–40 with the aid of a supplemental grant of funds; (6) three reports on educational problems related to the war situation.

Publications: *The Unique Function of Education in American Democracy*, 1937, 129 pp., 50¢; *Structure and Administration of Education in American Democracy*, 1938, 128 pp., 50¢; *Purposes of Education in American Democracy*, 1938, 157 pp., 50¢; *Education and Economic Well-Being in American Democracy*, 1940, 227 pp., 50¢; *Learning the Ways of Democracy: A Case Book of Civic Education*, 1940, 486 pp., $1; *Education and the Defense of American Democracy*, 1940, 23 pp., 10¢; *For These Americas*, 1940, 15 pp., 10¢; *American Education and the War in Europe*, 1939, 11 pp., 10¢; *Deliberative Committee Reports of 1939*, 54 pp., 50¢ (also published for 1936 and 1938).

Staff: Full-time paid employees, 9.

Finances: A grant of $250,000 for the five-year period 1936–40 provided for the initial support of the commission. Subsequently the General Education Board made available a supplemental grant of $26,000 for a study of citizenship education in secondary schools, CCC camps, and NYA resident centers. Income for the calendar year 1939 was $50,000, derived from grants; there was some additional income from the sale of publications. The commission has been continued for another four years (January 1, 1941 through December 31, 1944) with an annual budget of approximately $35,000.

INSTITUTE OF PUBLIC ADMINISTRATION
(1906); 261 Broadway, New York, N.Y.; Luther Gulick, Director.

Membership: Trustees, 12: Richard S. Childs, *chairman;* Henry Bruere, *treasurer;* F. Trubee Davidson, Harold W. Dodds, William Tudor Gardiner, E. Roland Harriman, Herbert Hoover, Frank O. Lowden, Carl H. Pforzheimer, George S. Van Schaick, Delos Walker, and Lucius Wilmerding, Jr.

Purpose: To carry on impartial research in public administration; to make the results of experience known to public administrators and others; to train for public service; to advise public officials with regard to administrative problems.

Activities: Research, publication, conferences, educational work, and consultative service in public administration. A limited number of college and postgraduate young men and young women espe-cially interested in public administration obtain practical experience and training on projects prosecuted by the institute. Others of the same group are benefited by the publications of the institute. All youth are served indirectly through the improvement of public administration, especially in connection with health, welfare, education, recreation, crime prevention, and other national, state, and local services.

Publications: *National Institute of Public Administration—An Adventure in Democracy*, by Luther Gulick, 1928, 106 pp., $1.25; *City Health Administration*, by Carl E. McCombs, M.D., 1927, 524 pp., $5.50; *Better Government Personnel*, 182 pp., $2, and seven other monographs of the Commission of Inquiry on Public Service Personnel, priced from $2 to $6 each; *Reorganization of State Governments in the United States*, by A. E. Buck, 1938, $2.50. Numerous other books and pamphlets on various phases of public administration. List on request.

Staff: Full-time paid employees, 11.

Finances: Endowment, $1,207,301. Value of equipment at headquarters, $20,248.33. For the fiscal year ending June 30, 1939, operations were as follows:

Income

Endowment investments, etc.	$65,443.39
Publications	1,404.85
Other services	6,553.65
Other sources	5,739.22
	$79,141.11

Expenditures

Salaries	$66,563.79
Travel	869.54
Communications	930.14
Office supplies	436.65
Publications	324.22
Rentals, etc.	5,017.59
Special research	5,318.34
Other purposes	6,226.11
	$85,686.38

LABOR RESEARCH ASSOCIATION (1927); 80
East 11th St., New York, N.Y.; Robert W. Dunn, Executive Secretary.

Membership: Individuals, 100, including the directors and persons in the research field closely associated with the work of the organization.

Purpose: To conduct studies of social, economic, and political questions in the interest of the labor and progressive movement and to issue its findings in the form of bulletins, pamphlets, and books.

Activities: Research, writing, and publication, as evidenced in the following list. Special services to labor unions and workers' organizations.

Publications: *Economic Notes*, monthly, 65¢ a year; *Labor Notes*, monthly, 65¢ a year; *Railroad Notes*, monthly, 50¢ a year. *Labor Fact Books*, issued in 1931, 1934, 1936, and the latest in 1938 (224 pp., $1); *Arsenal of Facts*, 1938; *Youth Arsenal of Facts*, 1939; *Shoes: The Workers and the Industry*, by Horace B. Davis, 1940, 256 pp., $1.50; *The South in Progress*, by Katharine DuPre Lumpkin, 1940, 256 pp., $2; *Why Farmers Are Poor*, by Anna Rochester, 1940, 317 pp., $2.25; *Trade Union Facts*, 1940, 128 pp., 25¢. Also numerous pamphlets issued in the International Pamphlet Series.

Staff: Full-time paid employees, 3; part-time paid employees, 2; unpaid workers, 3.

Finances: The budget for 1940 was $10,300. Receipts are from sales of the association's publications, from services rendered unions and labor organizations, and from individual contributions.

NATIONAL BUREAU OF ECONOMIC RESEARCH (1920); 1819 Broadway, New York, N.Y.; William J. Carson, Executive Director.

Membership: Directors and members, 27.

Purpose: To encourage, in the broadest and most liberal manner, investigation, research and discovery, and the application of knowledge to the well-being of mankind; in particular, to conduct, or assist in the conduct of, exact and impartial investigations in the field of economic, social, and industrial science.

Activities: The bureau is concerned with research in socially significant problems susceptible of scientific treatment and has committees and conferences to study special aspects. In order to integrate its operations with work in progress elsewhere, the bureau maintains a Universities-National Bureau Committee, composed of representatives of the bureau and ten important universities; the committee likewise sponsors conferences and committees on such problems as prices, national income, research in finance, and research in fiscal policy.

Publications: *Bulletin*, brief monographs, 5 issues annually; $1 a year, 25¢ a single copy. Studies in Consumer Instalment Financing: *Personal Finance Companies and Their Credit Practices*, 170 pp., $2; *Sales Finance Companies and Their Credit Practices*, 298 pp., $3; *Commercial Banks and Consumer Instalment Credit*, 318 pp., $3; *Pattern of Consumer Instalment Debt, 1935–1936*, 238 pp., $2.50; *Volume of Consumer Instalment Credit, 1929–1938*, 137 pp., $1.50. *Studies in Income and Wealth*, Vol. I (1937, 368 pp.), Vol. II (1938, 342 pp.), Vol. III (1939, 500 pp.), $7.50 for the set; *Report of the Committee on Prices in the Bituminous Coal Industry*, 1938, 144 pp., $1.25; *Textile Markets—Their Structure in Relation to Price Research*, 1939, 304 pp., $3; *Price Research in the Steel and Petroleum Industries*, 1939, 224 pp., $2; and numerous other monographs.

Staff: Full-time paid employees, 95; part-time paid employees, 18.

Finances: For the calendar year 1939 income totaled

$290,665.42; expenditures for the same period aggregated $272,995.25.

NATIONAL ECONOMIC AND SOCIAL PLANNING ASSOCIATION (1934); 1721 Eye St., N.W., Washington, D.C.; E. Johnston Coil, Director.

Membership: Individuals, 725, about half of whom are teachers in universities, colleges, and high schools who use the publications of the association in classwork with youth. Members are resident in 41 states and 29 other countries. Annual dues, $2.50.

Purpose: To design methods and formulate policies for the more effective organization of our society. Believing that a functioning democracy needs social engineering, the association seeks the rational direction of change, as distinct from haphazard drift.

Activities: Study of special national problems which require planning, each study being carried on by a committee of experts. In 1940 the following studies were under way: (1) the effects of the European war on this country and America's possible role after eventual peace; (2) the effects of the introduction of mechanical cotton pickers; and (3) the development and utilization of Alaska's natural resources.

Publications: *Plan Age*, monthly; free to members, $2.50 a year to others. *N.E.S.P.A. Guide*, monthly; $1.50 a year to members, $2 to others. *Report of the Committee on the Maintenance of American Neutrality*, 1937, 52 pp., 25¢; *War and Our Latin American Trade Policy*, 1939, 36 pp., 25¢; *Report of the Committee on the Textile Industry in the U. S.*, 1937, 52 pp., 25¢; *Survey of Planning Courses in American Colleges*, 1938, 24 pp., 25¢; *A Selected Bibliography of Books on Economic and Social Planning*, 1937, 11 pp., free; *Foundations of American Population Policy*, by Frank Lorimer, Ellen Winston, and Louise K. Kiser (New York: Harper, 1940), $2.50; *National Policy for Radio Broadcasting*, by C. B. Rose, Jr. (New York: Harper, 1940), 289 pp., $3.

Staff: Full-time paid employees, 6; part-time paid employees, 3; part-time unpaid worker, 1.

Finances: Value of equipment at national headquarters, $2,000. Income is derived from voluntary contributions from members and organizations, from membership fees, and from grants from foundations. For the calendar year 1939 expenditures aggregated $20,030.64.

NATIONAL RESEARCH COUNCIL (1916); 2101 Constitution Ave., Washington, D.C.; Ross G. Harrison, Chairman; Albert L. Barrows, Executive Secretary.

Membership: Individuals, 220, consisting mainly of representatives of 83 national scientific and technical societies in the United States, scientific agencies of the federal government, and other research institutions, together with a limited number of members-at-large. Government representatives are appointed by the president of the United States. All members are appointed by the president of the National Academy of Sciences upon suitable nomination.

Purpose: To promote research in the mathematical, physical, and biological sciences, and in the application of these sciences to engineering, agriculture, medicine, and other useful arts, with the object of increasing knowledge, of strengthening the national defense, and of contributing in other ways to the national welfare.

Activities: Maintains through its divisions a large number of committees for the purpose of fostering research in a wide range of scientific and technical fields representing the physical sciences, engineering and industrial research, chemistry and chemical technology, geology and geography, the medical sciences, biology and agriculture, and anthropology and psychology. Administers postdoctoral fellowships in the natural sciences and in medicine. Acts under certain conditions as fiscal agent for the administration of funds contributed from nongovernmental sources for the support of investigations conducted by government bureaus and other organizations, and cooperates in various ways with agencies of the federal government. Also maintains divisions of foreign relations and of educational relations. Has not undertaken investigations bearing directly upon the problems of youth except in so far as the results of certain basic research in fields of medicine, biology, and psychology may have applications to the study of problems of adolescence and education.

Publications: Two series, with issues of each appearing irregularly: Bulletin Series (total number of issues, 102) for the publication of directories, monographs, and reports upon special investigations or the status of research in various fields of science; Reprint and Circular Series (total number of issues, 107) for the publication of less extensive papers and the extended distribution of articles of special interest which may have appeared originally elsewhere. Also occasional miscellaneous reports and other publications.

Staff: Full-time paid employees, 35 to 40; part-time paid employees, 7.

Finances: A fund of $5,000,000 was given to the National Academy of Sciences by the Carnegie Corporation of New York to erect a building in Washington and to constitute an endowment for the National Research Council. The productive endowment is now approximately $3,500,000. The council has also received funds in varying amounts from other philanthropic foundations and numerous other sources for the support of its various activities. For the fiscal year ending June 30, 1940, total expenditures were $630,165.93.

PUBLIC ADMINISTRATION CLEARING HOUSE
(1931); 1313 East 60th St., Chicago, Ill.; Louis Brownlow, Director.

Membership: Trustees, 7, organized as a nonprofit corporation under the statutes of Illinois: Frank O. Lowden, *chairman;* Ralph Budd, *vice chairman;* and Richard S. Childs, Frederick M. Davenport, Robert M. Hutchins, George Fort Milton, and Louis Brownlow.

Purpose: To facilitate the interchange of information, points of view, ideas, and experience among organizations of public officials, organizations of citizens, and other groups which are planning for improvements in the administrative technique of governments; to bring together operating officials and research and technical experts in order to reduce the gap between theory and practice.

Activities: Functions as a center of liaison among organizations in the field of public administration; calls special conferences; maintains a personnel exchange service; disseminates information concerning significant developments in public administration; manages the building in which several organizations of public officials are housed, and conducts a joint reference library, publicity service, and other services for them. The organizations include the American Municipal Association, the American Public Welfare Association (see p. 187), the American Public Works Association, the American Society of Planning Officials (see p. 71), the Civil Service Assembly, the Council of State Governments, the Federation of Tax Administrators, the Governors' Conference, the International Association of Chiefs of Police, the International City Managers' Association, the Municipal Finance Officers' Association, the National Association of Assessing Officers, the National Association of Housing Officials, the National Association of State Auditors, Comptrollers, and Treasurers, and the Public Administration Service.

Publications: *News Bulletin,* weekly, distributed only to editors of newspapers and magazines. *Public Administration Organizations—A Directory 1941,* fifth edition, $1.50; *Thirteen-Thirteen East Sixtieth Street, Chicago,* free.

Staff: Full-time paid employees, 50.

Finances: Special grants from foundations have supported the organization's work, and no general appeal for gifts or membership fees has been made.

SOCIAL SCIENCE RESEARCH COUNCIL (1923);
230 Park Ave., New York, N.Y.; Robert T. Crane, Executive Director.

Membership: Individuals, 30: three representatives from each of seven national organizations of social scientists, namely, the American Anthropological Association, the American Historical Association, the American Economic Association, the American Political Science Association, the American Psychological Association, and the American Sociological Society (see p. 122); and nine members-at-large chosen in rotating order from other fields of scientific and scholarly inquiry.

Purpose: To plan, foster, promote, and develop research in the social field.

Activities: Brings together for research planning men from the different social sciences and from different localities; conducts special meetings and conferences of research workers in the social sciences; promotes research by awarding fellowships and grants-in-aid; organizes a considerable number of special research committees in various social science problems, and, in some cases, staffs these committees with research workers for limited periods of time.

Publications: *Annual Report 1938–39*, 54 pp. Occasional bulletins, and numerous publications growing out of the work of the several committees. In recent years the Committee on Social Security and the Committee on Public Administration have each produced notable series of books, examples of which are *Old-Age Security—Social and Financial Trends*, by Margaret Grant, 1940, 255 pp., $2.50, and *Administration of Federal Grants to the States*, by V. O. Key, Jr., 383 pp., $3.75.

Staff: Full-time paid employees at headquarters, 12. The number of employees of the several committees fluctuates.

Finances: The operations of the council have been made possible by support from various foundations and other sources. On June 30, 1939 the fund balance was $191,129.10, not including balances held by the council as fiscal agent. Total receipts for the fiscal year ending on that date were $349,345.68, and total disbursements were $344,685.64.

Table XI

STATISTICS OF ORGANIZATIONS FOR RESEARCH AND SOCIAL PLANNING

Organization	Year Founded	Approximate Aggregate Membership (individuals)	Total Employees on Headquarters Staff	Aggregate Endowment of National Headquarters	Plant and Equipment (headquarters only)	Approximate Annual Budget (headquarters only)
American Educational Research Association	1930	539	1	$ ...	$ 100	$ 7,400
American Planning and Civic Association	1935	1,800[a]	6	...	...	40,000
American Society of Planning Officials	1934	750	18	22,000	1,000	35,000
American Society for Public Administration	1939	1,000	[b]	...	...	...
American Youth Commission of the American Council on Education	1935	15	35	none[c]	4,000	117,000[d]
Commission on Teacher Education of the Am. Council on Education	1938	15	23	none[c]	...	187,000
Coordinating Councils	1938	234[e]	2	...	...	8,500
Educational Policies Commission	1935	20	9	none[c]	...	50,000
Institute of Public Administration	1906	12[f]	11	1,207,301	20,248	85,700
Labor Research Association	1927	100[g]	5	none	...	10,300
National Bureau of Economic Research	1920	27[h]	118	none	...	290,700
National Economic and Social Planning Association	1934	725	9	none	2,000	20,000
National Research Council	1916	220[i]	41	3,500,000	...	630,200
Public Administration Clearing House	1931	7[f]	50	none	...	...
Social Science Research Council	1923	30[i]	12	...	...	349,300

a Includes libraries and governmental bureaus as well as individuals.
b No paid staff.
c The work of the commission is financed by grants from the General Education Board.
d Exclusive of special projects.
e Adult membership only.
f Number of trustees.
g Includes the directors and persons in the research field closely associated with the work of the organization.
h Directors and members.
i Largely representatives of national scientific or professional societies and agencies.

XI. Patriotic, Political, Fraternal, and Labor Organizations

Four types of organizations are juxtaposed here for the purpose of disclosing the divergencies as well as the similarities among their purposes and activities. There are some sharp contrasts, and perhaps irreconcilable conflicts, among the programs for which these types of associations severally stand. Conflict of opinion is a natural and healthy characteristic of a democratic society. It is only necessary that all shades of opinion be accorded a reasonable tolerance until the conflicts are softened by wider understanding, both among the contestants themselves and among the general public, regarding the validity of their respective premises.

The presence of such great groups as organized labor and organized veterans affects profoundly the pattern of American politics. Within the limits of the present section it is possible only to describe a few of the principal organizations, with special reference to the efforts they make to render service to youth or to capture the interest and support of young persons.

Likewise only a token sample of the fraternal associations is presented here. As for the strictly partisan political groups for youth, only the minor left-wing parties maintain nationally cohesive and continuing organizations which enlist the enthusiasm of their members in season and out. Each of the two major parties makes more or less strenuous efforts to pump up a national association of young partisans during the few months preceding a national election; but the product, often "mushroomed" to astonishing proportions, is vastly deflated after the frosts of November.

An effort to organize American youth nationally, with a view toward supporting demands for national legislation providing employment and educational opportunities, has been under way for several years. In 1934 a small group of young people at New York University, some of whom were persons of extraordinary energy and possessed of a keen sense of the power of publicity, organized the Central Bureau for Young America. A schism within the ranks immediately occurred, and the surviving wing, known as the American Youth Congress, has received much attention in the press throughout the supervening years.

The American Youth Congress is a loose federation purporting to represent a great variety of national and local young people's associations. Annual meetings of delegates from the affiliated groups have been held since 1935, usually attracting nation-wide attention in the press. In 1939 a schismatic group under Socialist leadership departed to form an independent federation of youth organizations, consisting chiefly of labor, Jewish, and Socialist groups, which adopted the name, Campaign for Youth Needs.

At the 1940 meeting there arose another factional dispute which took the form of refusal to seat a small group of dissenters who allegedly lacked proper credentials as delegates. The dissenters withdrew, asserting that the American Youth Congress was dominated by Communist elements and was operated by dictatorial methods. In this instance the seceding group, backed by Gene Tunney, set up a new organization known as the National Foundation for American Youth, with Mr. Tunney as its chairman. The American Youth Congress continues despite these defections and asserts its devotion to American democracy.

In the present section, organizations whose membership consists chiefly of young persons, as distinguished from those composed wholly or largely of persons above the age of 25, are:

American Youth Congress
American Youth League
Antlers of the Benevolent and Protective Order of Elks
Campaign for Youth Needs
International Workers Order, Young Fraternalists and Junior Section
National Foundation for American Youth
Order of the Builders
Order of the Rainbow for Girls
Pioneer Youth of America
Sons of the American Legion
Steuben Society of America, Junior League of the
Young Circle League of the English-Speaking Division of the Workmen's Circle
Young Communist League of the U.S.A.
Young People's Socialist League, U.S.A.

Cross references: American Federation of Teachers, p. 117; American Legion, National Child Welfare Division, p. 196; Labor Research Association, p. 75; National Consumers League, p. 215; Order of De-Molay, p. 25.

AMERICAN FEDERATION OF LABOR (1881); 901 Massachusetts Ave., N.W., Washington, D.C.; William Green, President.

Membership: Constituent national and international unions, 105; state federations, 49, including one in Puerto Rico; city central bodies, 806; local trade and federal labor unions (local unions in trades or callings in which a national trade organization has not yet been established), 1,563; local unions of national and international unions, 33,744. Departments for the more effective cooperation of allied trades, 4: Metal Trades, Building Trades, Label Trades, Railway Employees; local department councils of the trades represented primarily in the departments, 942. The membership of all affiliated organizations aggregated 4,006,354 individuals, chiefly adult men, in August 1939.

Purpose: To better the conditions of the workers in all fields of human activity; to secure adequate wages and other essentials of good living for workers; to encourage trade and labor unions and the closer federation of such unions for mutual advantage; to promote and advance the economic and political and social rights of workers.

Activities: Makes collective bargaining its primary objective. Seeks for wage-earners proportionately higher standards of living in keeping with national progress. Represents the interests of workers in connection with federal and state legislation affecting their welfare. Seeks the expansion of educational facilities to make equal opportunities effectively available to all. Maintains that all wage-earners should have the right to organize to promote their own welfare collectively; that minimum wages and maximum hours should be fixed to prevent unfair competition in low labor standards; that every person seeking work should have an opportunity to earn a living, with social insurance legislation providing an income for unemployment and disability interfering with income earning. Seeks to assure wage-earners the protection of civil rights.

Publications: *American Federationist,* monthly, $2 a year; *A. F. of L. Weekly News Service; Monthly Survey of Business;* convention proceedings, annually, 75¢; report of the executive council, annually. Numerous free pamphlets, including: *Labor and Education; Wage Negotiations and Practices,* by Matthew Woll; *The Science of Labor Relations,* by William Green; *Labor's Charter of Rights; Consumers' Cooperation,* 1938; and others. List on request.

Finances: Balance on hand August 31, 1939, $546,-504.36. For the fiscal year ending on that date, operations were as follows:

Income

Per capita tax	$ 583,972.13
American Federationist	385,732.68
Other fees	328,127.56
Assessments	441,563.29
Other sources	60,854.04
	$1,800,249.70

Expenditures

Salaries	$ 206,578.58
American Federationist	200,864.44
Organizers' salaries and expenses	889,549.66
Other purposes	400,383.85
	$1,697,376.53

AMERICAN LEGION (1919); 777 North Meridian St., Indianapolis, Ind.; Milo J. Warner, National Commander; Frank E. Samuel, National Adjutant.

Membership: Individuals, 1,071,229 veterans of the World War (1917–18), in 11,691 local posts grouped into 58 state and territorial departments. These figures are as of October 1, 1940. See also Sons of the American Legion (p. 86).

Purpose: To uphold and defend the Constitution of the United States of America; to inculcate a sense of individual obligation to the community, the state, and the nation; to combat the autocracy of both the classes and the masses; to make right the master of might; to promote peace and good will on earth; to safeguard and transmit to posterity the principles of justice, freedom, and democracy.

Activities: Annual national and state conventions. Committees and commissions on (1) finance, (2) rehabilitation, (3) Americanism, (4) child welfare, (5) legislation, (6) national defense, (7) world peace, and (8) foreign relations. The principal channels of service to youth are the National Americanism Commission (see p. 82), the National Child Welfare Division (see p. 196), and the Sons of the American Legion.

Publications: *American Legion Magazine,* monthly; $1.30 a year, subscription price included in dues. *National Legionnaire,* monthly; 20¢ a year, subscription price included in dues. *Legion-Heir,* monthly, for the Sons of the American Legion. *Reports to the 22nd Annual National Convention,* 1940, 330 pp.; *Summary of Proceedings,* 1940, 80 pp. *Constitution and By-Laws,* 15 pp.; *Post Handbook,* 56 pp. Numerous department and post publications.

Staff: Full-time paid employees, 207, of whom 8 spend major time in field work; part-time paid employees, 18.

Finances: On July 31, 1940 the American Legion endowment fund was $5,000,560.22; the reserve fund was $1,186,649.99; and the restricted fund was $973,686.16. For the year ending on that date the general budget was $339,932.58, for which the chief source of revenue was membership fees. For the same period there was a special budget of $233,-526.80 for rehabilitation and child welfare, largely derived from income from endowment. Thus the aggregate annual budget exceeded $550,000.

AMERICAN LEGION, NATIONAL AMERICAN-ISM COMMISSION (1919); 777 North Meridian St., Indianapolis, Ind.; H. L. Chaillaux, Director.

Membership: The commission is composed of 15 men, five of whom are chosen each year for three-year terms, under such regulations as the national executive committee of the American Legion prescribes. The various state departments and posts of the American Legion (see p. 81) appoint "Americanism committees" which are responsible for carrying on the program of the commission in their respective communities.

Purpose: To plan, establish, and conduct a continuous, constructive educational system to promote understanding of the principles of democratic government; to encourage education in every way possible; to disseminate knowledge of and promote respect for the national flag and bring about a more fitting display of the flag throughout the country on national holidays; to combat revolutionary radicalism and all movements which have for their aim the downfall of democracy in America; to work for the assimilation of aliens in the United States through schools of citizenship and other agencies, and to stand for the restriction of immigration so that this assimilation may be made perfect; to strive for maintenance of the national defenses at a strength sufficient to guarantee security of the country from war until such time as war is definitely eliminated as a fact in the world; to give sound, practical service in communities, working to make them better places in which to live.

Activities: American Legion posts, through Americanism committees, sponsor and organize character-building clubs for youth, including Boy Scout troops, Girl Scouts, Camp Fire Girls, 4-H Clubs, Sons of the American Legion, junior baseball clubs, junior rifle clubs, and Boys' State organizations. Many posts observe National Boys and Girls Week and promote junior athletics on a large scale. A trophy is awarded annually by the commission to the department of the American Legion which has within its jurisdiction the junior baseball team winning the "Little World Series," and another trophy is awarded to the department having the greatest percentage of increase of junior baseball teams over the previous year.

Publications: *Americanism Manual*, revised 1940, 63 pp.; *Service to Community, State, Nation*, 16 pp.

Staff: Full-time paid employees, 4.

AMERICAN YOUTH CONGRESS (1934); 907 15th St., N.W., Washington, D.C., and 230 Fifth Ave., New York, N.Y.; Joseph Cadden, Executive Secretary.

Membership: Representatives of 63 cooperating national organizations of youth or serving youth, with an asserted aggregate individual membership of 4,697,915 young people, as of July 1939. At that time 12 state assemblies of youth and approximately 30 city youth councils were said to be affiliated with the congress.

Purpose: To be a nonprofit educational association which will serve as a cooperating center and clearing-house for all youth organizations, youth-serving agencies, and local, state, or regional youth councils or assemblies desiring to promote the welfare of young people.

Activities: Carries on continuing educational campaigns regarding legislation affecting youth welfare in the areas of jobs, health, civil liberties, international peace and social justice, and educational, recreational, and vocational opportunities. Holds annual meetings and interim conferences on current problems. Sponsors regional, state, and local conferences from time to time. Has special research commissions studying jobs, health, education, interfaith problems, rural youth, civil liberties, housing, and recreation. Prepares manuals, program guides, factual analyses, and survey reports.

Sponsors the American Youth Act, introduced in Congress in 1936 and in subsequent sessions. The 1940 draft provides for the following: public works projects for unemployed youth between the ages of 16 and 25, with a minimum weekly wage of $12.50, a maximum working week of 30 hours, and provision for part-time study at an educational institution; employment of vocational advisers and securing of apprentice training; academic work projects, with a minimum hourly wage of 50¢, for needy young persons in institutions of higher learning; federal scholarships to needy young persons to meet the costs of professional or technical education.

Publications: *Youth*, news magazine, 10 issues annually; $1 a year. *Youth Defends America* (report of the sixth American Youth Congress, July 1940), 47 pp., 5¢; *This Is Youth Speaking*, 1940, 31 pp. lithoprinted, 5¢; *Now Is the Time: The Fight for Civil Liberties*, 1940, 23 pp., 3¢; *Here's a Real Job for You!* 1940, 11 pp., 1¢; American Youth Congress commission materials (small manuals on jobs, peace, civil liberties, health, housing, rural youth), packet, 50¢. History and activities of the organization are described in *American Youth Today*, by Leslie Gould (New York: Random House).

Staff: Full-time paid employees, 4, of whom 2 spend major time in field work.

Finances: For the fiscal year ending August 31, 1939, operations were as follows:

Income

Gifts for current expenses	$ 7,458.91
Affiliation fees	158.50
Annual dinner	2,298.40
Congress of Youth	4,132.15
Other sources	1,453.04
	$15,501.00

Expenditures

Salaries	$ 4,209.50
Office expenses	2,212.85
Annual dinner	2,291.56
Congress of Youth	4,466.45
Other purposes	2,103.67
	$15,284.03

AMERICAN YOUTH LEAGUE (1936); 1744 Pryor Ave., Chicago, Ill.; President, Warren Yaap; Founder, Eston V. Tubbs, Principal, Morgan Park High School, Chicago, Ill.

Membership: Boys and girls aged 14 to 25, approximately 800. There are four local units in three states. Members are chiefly students in senior high schools.

Purpose: To bring about in the hearts and minds of young people a deep appreciation of the real meaning of American democracy; to impress upon them their duties and responsibilities in maintaining those fundamental rights which are the heritage of all Americans.

Activities: Study of the principles underlying American democracy; forums, debates, essay contests, and public declamation contests on questions of civic interest. Emphasis is on constructive implementation of democracy, not merely upon hostility toward other philosophies.

Publications: *The American Youth League*, 27-page pamphlet.

Staff: No paid employees.

ANTLERS OF THE BENEVOLENT AND PROTECTIVE ORDER OF ELKS (1922); 405 Montgomery St., San Francisco, Calif.; C. Fenton Nichols, Founder and Organizer.

Membership: Young men between the ages of 15 and 22, approximately 3,500, who are white American citizens sound in mind and body, of good moral character, and believing in the existence of a Supreme Being. Persons over 21 years of age may not be initiated. There is no sectarian or political test, and it is not necessary for applicants to be relatives of Elks. Minimum initiation fee, $2.50; minimum annual dues, $3.

Purpose: To foster the spirit of American patriotism; to instill in the members respect for parents and love of home; to inculcate the fundamentals of good citizenship; and to encourage tolerance for the convictions of other in matters of worship.

Activities: Local units hold weekly or biweekly meetings; sponsor and engage in athletics, musical groups, drill teams, dances, dramatics, debating, picnics, and hikes; assist at special functions of the local adult lodge and at civic celebrations and public holiday observations, such as Thanksgiving and Christmas charities, Mother's Day observances, and Flag Day ceremonials; conduct a patriotic program to overcome anti-American and Communist activities. Other activities include cooperation with police traffic squads on safety drives, work with crippled children, cooperation with Boy Scout troops and committees, and assistance to the American Red Cross, National Tuberculosis Association, and fresh-air funds.

Publications: *Rules and Regulations* (containing by-laws), 40 pp.; *Rituals*, 45 pp.

CAMPAIGN FOR YOUTH NEEDS (1939); 112 East 19th St., New York, N.Y.; Lewis Conn, Executive Secretary.

Membership: Consists of cooperating organizations, among which are: Avukah, the American Student Zionist Federation (see p. 56); Youth Committee Against War; Fellowship of Reconciliation, Youth Section; War Resisters' League, Youth Section; Young People's Socialist League (see p. 88); and Young Circle League (see p. 87). Affiliation fee, $10.

Purpose: To establish liaison and cooperation between organized labor and organized youth; to make a vigorous assault on unemployment and other domestic ills; to promote democratic principles, excluding cooperation with fascist or communist groups.

Activities: Sponsored a two-day Youth and Labor Conference for Democracy at Camp Goodwill, Butler, N.J., in October 1940. The organization studies the possibilities of mass job-hunts, cooperative and self-help activities, and the coordination of national and local youth programs.

Publications: *Heritage*, periodical newspaper. Occasional news releases.

Staff: Employees, 3.

Finances: Support is derived chiefly from sympathetic labor organizations and partly from individual contributors.

CONGRESS OF INDUSTRIAL ORGANIZATIONS (1935); 1106 Connecticut Ave., N.W., Washington, D.C.; Philip Murray, President.

Name changed from Committee for Industrial Organization to present form, 1938.

Membership: Constituent international unions, 43, aggregating 4,000,000 individuals. Most of the unions have some members under the age of 25.

Purpose: To organize the workers in mass production industries on an industrial basis; to bring about the effective organization of the working men and women of America regardless of race, creed, color, or nationality, and to unite them for common action into labor unions for their mutual aid and protection; to secure legislation safeguarding the economic security and social welfare of the workers of America, to protect and extend our democratic institutions and civil rights and liberties, and thus to perpetuate the cherished traditions of our democracy.

Activities: The principal undertakings are organization and legislative activity on behalf of organized labor and the unemployed. Activities in behalf of youth have included support of the NYA, the CCC, and the American Youth Act introduced in the Congress of the United States (see American Youth Congress, p. 82). Statements and resolutions on the problems of youth have been adopted at the conventions of the CIO and of its component organizations. The Unemployment Division at the national headquarters, directed by Ralph Hetzel, Jr., has been particularly active in the interests of unemployed youth.

Publications: *The C. I. O. News*, weekly; $1 a year; Len De Caux, editor. *Economic Outlook*, monthly; free; Ralph Hetzel, Jr., editor. *Union News Service*, weekly clipsheet; free to editors. Numerous pamphlets, including: *C. I. O.'s 1940 Legislative Program for Jobs, Security and Peace*, 14 pp.; *C. I. O., What It Is and How It Came to Be*, 54 pp.; *The C. I. O. Wants Jobs for Youth*, 6 pp.; *The C. I. O. and the Negro Worker*, 8 pp.; *Save the Wagner Act*, 16 pp.; *Organize the Unorganized*, 46 pp.; *Your Civil Liberties—How to Protect Them*, 32 pp.; and others, all at nominal prices.

INTERNATIONAL WORKERS ORDER, INC., YOUNG FRATERNALISTS and JUNIOR SECTION (1930); 80 Fifth Ave., New York, N.Y.; Helen Vrabel, National Secretary, Young Fraternalists; Ernest Rymer, National Junior Director.

Membership: Young people between the ages of 16 and 25, 20,000; juniors up to 16 years of age, 27,000.

Purpose: To promote the social security of American people through legislation and mutual aid; to provide low-cost insurance and other forms of mutual aid to American people in the small-income groups; to promote public welfare by cooperating with organized labor and other interested community agencies; to cultivate a social and cultural program for the appreciation and enjoyment of art and literature as well as to foster the spirit of brotherhood; to promote a program of Americanism and good citizenship based on defense of democratic institutions and principles as set forth in the Declaration of Independence and the Constitution of the United States.

Activities: Supports the labor union movement and provides social and educational enterprises for members. Annual district training schools and week-end training camps are maintained for youth and junior leadership. Full-time youth directors have been established in New York, Illinois, Pittsburgh, and Ohio; volunteer youth directors function in Michigan, New Jersey, and Los Angeles. In 1940 the youth division of the International Workers Order was reorganized as a semi-independent body called the Young Fraternalists; their first annual convention was held in November of that year. Locally the

clubs and district committees of the Young Fraternalists conduct competitive and noncompetitive sports; under the guidance of the National Athletic Commission of the International Workers Order, the organization conducts a yearly national basketball and softball tournament; through the allied membership of the International Workers Order in the Amateur Athletic Union of the United States (see p. 152), members also participate in other sports competitions on a local and national scale. The clubs organize dance groups, choruses, orchestras, and dramatic groups; many districts conduct dramatic contests with groups from all the clubs competing. The Young Fraternalists, on a national and local scale, participate in and cooperate with the American Youth Congress (see p. 82). The Junior Section sponsors exhibitions of arts and crafts, annual drum and bugle corps competition, and camps for children; the local units organize baseball teams and other sports, dance, dramatics, and music groups, and trips to places of historical interest.

Publications: Special sections of the *Fraternal Outlook*, monthly publication of the International Workers Order, are devoted to the youth divisions.

Staff: Full-time paid employees of Young Fraternalists, 6; full-time paid employees of Junior Section, 5.

Finances: Finances of the Young Fraternalists are handled as part of the general funds of the International Workers Order. Balance of the Junior Section, December 31, 1939, $82,272.35; for the preceding calendar year, its operations were as follows:

Income	
Grant from adult section	$ 2,250.00
Received from members (initiation fees, mortuary fund, etc.)	45,415.40
Interest	1,307.24
	$48,972.64

Expenditures	
Salaries	$ 7,042.00
Travel	804.15
Office supplies and equipment	1,294.12
Organizing and educating lodges	5,670.00
Rent	1,500.00
Supplement in official organ of adult section	6,000.00
Other purposes	6,082.00
	$28,392.27

LEAGUE FOR INDUSTRIAL DEMOCRACY (1905); 112 East 19th St., New York, N.Y.; Harry W. Laidler, Executive Director.

Membership: Individuals, 2,500, in local organizations in New York City, Detroit, Boston, and Washington, D.C. Prior to 1921 this organization was known as the Intercollegiate Socialist Society and had chapters in many colleges. A revival of activity in colleges was instituted in the fall of 1940. Annual dues for adult active membership, $3.

Purpose: To promote an intelligent understanding of the labor movement and of the movement for a new social order based on production for use and not for profit.

Activities: Research, lecture, and information services on economic and social problems. Sponsors conferences, forums, luncheon discussions, and radio talks in leading cities where local chapters exist. Services to youth and youth organizations include: lectures in colleges and high schools by Joel Seidman, Leroy Bowman, Harry W. Laidler, and other speakers; renewed organization of college chapters in 1940; and the annual six-week summer school conducted in New York City for about 20 students interested in the labor movement, who study labor history, cooperation, civil liberties, and socialism, make contacts with labor groups in the city, and hear addresses.

Publications: *L. I. D. News Bulletin*, 4 times annually, sent only to members. Six to eight pamphlets a year are published at a subscription price of $1. Members paying $3 annual dues receive all the foregoing publications free. Numerous pamphlets and books are available at 5¢ to $3. Authors include Stuart Chase, Norman Thomas, Abraham Epstein, Harry W. Laidler, and others.

Staff: Full-time paid employees, 4; part-time field workers, 2.

Finances: Value of equipment at headquarters, $3,928.42. For the fiscal year ending December 31, 1939, operations were as follows:

Income	
Gifts for current expenses	$19,169.32
Membership fees	3,240.19
Publications	1,557.42
Lecture fees	1,562.75
Other sources	1,050.73
	$26,580.41

Expenditures	
Salaries	$15,636.02
Travel	1,944.16
Communications	2,628.73
Office supplies	229.24
Publications	1,556.62
Rent, insurance, etc.	926.00
Other purposes	4,202.24
	$27,123.01

NATIONAL FOUNDATION FOR AMERICAN YOUTH (1940); 30 Rockefeller Plaza, New York, N.Y.; Gene Tunney, Chairman; Murray Plavner, National Director; Samuel Mines, Assistant Director.

Membership: There are no individual memberships or permanent affiliations. The organization establishes cooperative relationships on specific projects with existing youth-serving organizations and with individuals.

Purpose: To function as a nonpolicy-making, nonpartisan clearinghouse and coordinating center for independent local and state youth groups dedicated to the American system; to create projects for youth activity and to stimulate interest in youth by working with youth groups already functioning.

Activities: The first project, operated in the fall of 1940, was a national Young Voters' Exchange, carrying on a campaign to bring a larger proportion of the youth vote to the polls in the presidential election. Without favoring any particular political party, efforts were made to stimulate legitimate pre-election activities by American youth.

Publications: Occasional news releases. Pamphlets: *What about the 9,000,000?* 1940, 4 pp.; *Youth Congress and the Communistic Blight*, by Gene Tunney, 1940, 2 pp.; *American Youth Congress: Nature Will Take Its Course*, by Gene Tunney, 1940, 3 pp. A publication issued by the national director prior to the founding of the organization was *Here Are the Facts: Is the American Youth Congress a Communist Front?* 1939, 93 pp., 50¢.

Staff: Full-time paid employees, 2.

NATIONAL WOMEN'S TRADE UNION LEAGUE OF AMERICA (1903); 307–308 Machinists' Bldg., Washington, D.C.; Elisabeth Christman, Secretary-Treasurer.

Membership: Individuals in 18 local units in 9 states and in affiliated organizations, including national and international unions and women's auxiliaries to men's unions. The grand aggregate of active and affiliated individual members is more than 1,000,000, located in 38 states of the United States.

Purpose: To serve the interests of wage-earning women through organization of workers into trade unions, collective agreements between trade unions and employers, legislation for the workers' economic and social good, workers' education, and interpretation of labor problems to the public.

Activities: Promotion of workers' organization, education, and legislation. Active efforts to secure social legislation, both federal and state. Regional conferences and state units also work toward those ends. Substantial numbers of young people are in the league membership and in workers' classes conducted by the local units. Working girls and young women are invited to the national conventions and regional and state conferences. Scholarships enabling 15 young southern working women to attend the 1936 national convention were awarded. One local unit operates a summer camp.

Publications: *Life and Labor Bulletin*, 10 issues annually; free to members, $1 a year to others. Leaflets and pamphlets, industrial reprints, and mimeographed data. Authors include Margaret Bondfield, Mary Anderson, and others. List on request.

Staff: Full-time paid employees, 3; part-time unpaid workers, 3.

Finances: Value of equipment at headquarters, $1,300. For the fiscal year ending April 30, 1940, income and expenditures approximated $10,000.

ORDER OF THE BUILDERS (1921); Suite 512, 203 North Wabash Ave., Chicago, Ill.; Arthur M. Millard, President of Central Council.

Membership: Boys aged 14 to 25, approximately 80,000, in local chapters throughout the eastern and central sections of the United States. The order is sponsored by members of the Masonic fraternity. The charter membership of a chapter must consist of boys between the ages of 14 and 21 who are endorsed by a Mason or Masons. After a chapter is formed, all boys of the required standards may be admitted to membership. The initiation fees in the different chapters range from $5 to $10; the annual membership dues, from $2 to $6. These fees accrue to the chapter except for a small initiatory and annual per capita fee which accrues to the central council.

Purpose: To promote the mental, moral, physical, and spiritual development of its members; to provide a means of developing, through fraternal association and relationship, activities aiming at the mutual and constructive advancement of those coming within its range.

Activities: Local chapters promote community gatherings, athletic programs, drills, and entertainments. The spirit of fellowship and brotherhood is actively developed in connection with the ritualistic program. Mothers' organizations are fostered in connection with the chapters, and large active councils of young men termed "Legionnaires," associated with the chapters of which they have been members, are also promoted. Each chapter has an adult advisory council. All service by adults, locally and nationally, is without pecuniary compensation.

Publications: Pamphlets: *Order of the Builders*, 8 pp.; *The Welfare of the Boy of Today Means the Development of the Manhood of Tomorrow*, 11 pp. Numerous other pamphlets and folders issued at intervals.

ORDER OF THE RAINBOW FOR GIRLS (1922); McAlester, Okla.; W. P. Freeman, Supreme Worthy Advisor; W. Mark Sexson, Supreme Recorder.

Membership: Girls and women, about 400,000, of whom approximately 50,000 are active members aged 13 to 20 and the remainder are "majority members" aged 21 or over. There are 955 local assemblies in the United States, Alaska, Hawaii, the Canal Zone, Cuba, Canada, and Australia. Each is sponsored by a Masonic lodge, an Eastern Star chapter, or a club whose membership consists entirely of Eastern Stars and Masons. Membership is not restricted to girls from Masonic families.

Purpose: To train and teach girls how to divide their time and use it in a helpful and constructive way;

to teach them the power of color, how their lives are affected by it, and how it can be made useful each day; to instruct them in the principles of leadership, how to preside over an organization, and how to plan its program and direct its activities.

Activities: Local assemblies hold regular meetings presided over by a "worthy adviser" elected from their own membership. Each has an adult advisory board which selects an adult "mother adviser" to supervise the affairs of the assembly. Ritualistic work is designed to impress the girls with the beauties of life. Programs include developing a drill team, contests with nearby teams in exemplification of the ritual, entertainments, study clubs, attending church services, assistance in beautifying the community, summer camps, and other recreational activities. An international session is held biennially.

Publications: *Training for Rainbow Leadership*, revised, 64 pp. Various local Rainbow assemblies publish periodical bulletins.

Staff: Full-time paid employees, 8.

Finances: Estimated value of plant and equipment at headquarters, $30,157.43. Approximate annual budget, $32,620.

PIONEER YOUTH OF AMERICA, INC. (1924); 219 West 29th St., New York, N.Y.; Mrs. Samuel Frumes, Executive Secretary.

Membership: Children aged 8 to 16, about 1,000. There are camps at Rifton, N.Y., and Old Fort, N.C., and a branch in Philadelphia.

Purpose: To promote the welfare of children aged 8 to 16 through clubs and recreation camps and also through junior unions run in cooperation with labor organizations.

Activities: The camp at Rifton, N.Y., includes a section for children aged 6 to 14 and a work camp for youth aged 15 to 17. The camp at Old Fort, N.C., is for children aged 6 to 14. Year-round clubs and junior unions operate in New York City, Philadelphia, and North Carolina.

Publications: *Handbook for Junior Union Leaders*, 52 pp., 25¢. Occasional bulletins and educational materials and descriptive free literature, including fifteenth anniversary booklet (1939).

Staff: Full-time paid employees, 2, of whom 1 spends major time in field work; part-time unpaid workers, 2.

Finances: The organization receives support from the William C. Whitney Foundation, the Greater New York Fund, and various trade unions.

SONS OF THE AMERICAN LEGION (1932); 777 North Meridian St., Indianapolis, Ind.; C. M. Wilson, Director.

Membership: Individuals, 72,663, male descendants, adopted sons, or stepsons of members of the American Legion (see p. 81), or of male or female veterans who died in service during the World War or subsequent to honorable discharge from such service. There are 3,259 squadrons in 48 states, the District of Columbia, France, Hawaii, Alaska, Mexico, the Canal Zone, and Puerto Rico. Annual national dues, 25¢ a member.

Purpose: To adopt in letter and spirit all the great principles for which the American Legion stands and to assist in carrying on for God and country.

Activities: The national headquarters recommends eight major enterprises: (1) occupational introduction, consisting of firsthand contact with various professions and occupations under the tutelage of American Legion members; (2) boys' camps, providing a constructive program of citizenship education, recreation, and entertainment; (3) holiday observances; (4) playtime activities for younger members; (5) the five-point program of service, embracing patriotism, citizenship, discipline, leadership, and knowledge of the American Legion; (6) aviation activities, including model contests of various types; (7) assistance in the fraternal and civic activities of the Legion post; and (8) uniformed bands, trumpet and drum corps, and other marching units. A wide variety of other activities in citizenship education, recreation, and social service is also sponsored.

Publications: *The Legion-Heir*, monthly, free to paid-up members; *Bulletin Service*, 5 to 6 times annually, free to departments. *Squadron Handbook*, revised 1940, 55 pp.

Staff: All administrative work is carried on by members of the national headquarters staff of the American Legion.

STEUBEN SOCIETY OF AMERICA, JUNIOR LEAGUE OF THE (1924); 369 Lexington Ave., New York, N.Y.; Theodore H. Hoffman, Chairman, National Council.

An auxiliary branch of the National Council of the Steuben Society of America, organized 1919.

Membership: Individuals, approximately 200, in four junior units. Members are American-born, white young men and women, between the ages of 15 and 21, one of whose ancestors has been of German origin. German-born youth between the ages of 15 and 21, who have expressed willingness to become citizens of the United States, may be admitted to membership. Individual dues are $3 a year.

Purpose: To instill in the members a just pride in the race from which they sprang and, whenever possible, to cultivate a love for German literature, music, and art and to encourage debate and platform speaking and the study of parliamentary rules; to furnish such information and knowledge as will enable them, when of age, to become good and useful citizens of the United States and to fit themselves to become members of the Steuben Society of America, which they anticipate joining as soon as they become eligi-

ble; to promote the moral, social, and mater.a well-being of its members.

Activities: Each junior unit holds two meetings each month. Programs are designed with the idea of carrying out the aims and purposes above described.

Publications: *Constitution, Statutes and By-Laws; Foreword and Historical Bibliography.*

VETERANS OF FOREIGN WARS (1913); Broadway at 34th St., Kansas City, Mo.; Robert B. Handy, Jr., Adjutant-General; Victor E. Devereaux, Director, National Department of Americanism, Tower Bldg., Washington, D.C.

Membership: Men, 250,000, in 3,200 local posts. All have had campaign service in the military or naval forces of the United States on foreign soil or in foreign waters. Local dues vary from $3 upward.

Purpose: To preserve and strengthen comradeship among the veterans of foreign campaigns; to foster patriotism; to assist disabled and needy veterans and their widows and orphans.

Activities: The Department of Americanism carries on an extensive program among youth in building for future citizenship, especially among underprivileged boys. The various local units sponsor 200 Boy Scout troops, 300 musical units (bands and drum and bugle corps), 500 local corps of the Sons of the Veterans of Foreign Wars, and 600 bicycle safety clubs (bicycle safety clubs are under the direction of S. L. Buxton at the Kansas City headquarters). Approximately 75,000 boys aged 12 to 24 are engaged in these several activities, which include community service, music and dramatics, camping and hiking, hobbies, organized sports, social recreation, junior rifle clubs, model boat clubs, and model airplane-building clubs.

Publications: *Foreign Service*, monthly; Barney Yanofsky, editor, Broadway at 34th St., Kansas City, Mo. *The Acorn*, monthly for the Sons of the VFW; Victor E. Devereaux, editor, Tower Bldg., Washington, D.C. Pamphlets, printed and mimeographed, and other materials on a variety of subjects related to the Americanism program number about 150 pieces, intended primarily for use of VFW local units. Limited quantity available for free issue to individuals upon request.

Staff: Full-time paid employees, 47.

Finances: Approximate annual budget, $250,000.

YOUNG CIRCLE LEAGUE OF THE ENGLISH-SPEAKING DIVISION OF THE WORKMEN'S CIRCLE (1929); 175 East Broadway, New York, N.Y.; Dr. Israel Knox, National Director; Benjamin Levitin, Chairman, National Committee on Youth and English-Speaking Activity.

Membership: The English-Speaking Division enrolls 7,100 persons, of whom a majority are members of the Young Circle League. There are 4,500 youth of both sexes, including 450 aged 12 to 16, 1,150 aged 16 to 18, and 2,900 aged 18 to 25. Slightly more than half of the total membership is in New York City, with the remainder in the larger metropolitan areas in the United States and Canada.

Purpose: To offer youth an opportunity for physical, intellectual, social, and ethical development in an atmosphere sympathetic to the ideals of the labor movement; to provide youth with fraternal and social insurance against the hazards of modern life.

Activities: (1) Lectures, symposiums, debates, dramatics, musical and dance activities, and classes emphasizing progressive and Jewish culture; (2) aid to organized labor, opposition to anti-Semitism and all forms of racial and religious intolerance and discrimination, opposition to fascism and totalitarianism, support for the defense and extension of civil liberties, for social legislation, and for recognition by the state of its responsibility for providing youth with educational, recreational, and vocational opportunities and economic security; (3) sports, entertainments, outings, gymnastics, theater and concert attendance, camps (there are 11 Workmen's Circle camps in United States and Canada); (4) fraternal benefits, including life insurance, sickness and disability allowances, tuberculosis treatments, cemetery and funeral provision, medical care, social service, vocational guidance.

Publications: *The Workmen's Circle Call,* monthly; *National Intermediate News,* monthly; subscriptions included in membership dues. Some local groups also issue periodicals, one of which is the *Circle-Lite,* monthly, in New York City. Leaflets and pamphlets describing purposes and activities and containing educational outlines, discussion guides, songs, and games.

Staff: Full-time paid employees, 9, of whom 3 spend major time in field work; part-time paid employees, 2 at headquarters and 2 in field work.

Finances: Income is derived from membership dues.

YOUNG COMMUNIST LEAGUE OF THE U.S.A.
(1922); 35 East 12th St., New York, N.Y.; Max Weiss, National President.

Membership: Persons aged 16 to 30, about 22,000, located in 46 states.

Purpose: To promote activities of youth dedicated to character building and education in the spirit of socialism; to fight against imperialist war.

Activities: Supports the national and local candidates of the Communist party. Emphasizes keeping the United States out of imperialist war, maintenance of the Bill of Rights, academic freedom, and the right of youth to jobs, education, and vocational training. Advocates enactment of the American Youth Act (see American Youth Congress, p. 82); opposes discrimination against Negroes and oppression of the Negro people. Conducts study groups, lectures, dramatic performances, sports, and general cultural and educational activities. Cooperates with community civic and youth movements.

Publications: *The Review,* 26 issues annually; $1 a year (5¢ a copy, 6 issues for 25¢); Joseph Clark, editor-in-chief. *Clarity,* 6 issues annually; $1 a year (20¢ a copy). *Vote Against War,* an election folder; *Youth Fights for Peace, Jobs, Civil Rights,* 1940, 5¢; *Life Begins with Freedom,* by Henry Winston, 5¢; *Jim Crow in Uniform,* by Claudia Jones. All published by New Age Publishers, P.O. Box 28, Station "D," New York, N.Y.

YOUNG PEOPLE'S SOCIALIST LEAGUE, U.S.A.
(1915); 549 Randolph St., Chicago, Ill.; Judah Drob, National Secretary.

Membership: Youth of both sexes, aged 15 to 25, 3,000, in 100 local circles in 35 states. About 60 per cent are young men, and about 75 per cent are between the ages of 18 and 25.

Purpose: To organize young people into the Socialist movement; to educate them in the principles and practice of the labor movement and of Socialism; to join their efforts with those of young Socialists the world over; to join with all workers and farmers in the building of a Socialist America.

Activities: Participates in such enterprises as the Youth Committee Against War, the Campaign for Youth Needs (see p. 83), and the Youth Campaign for Thomas and Krueger (1940 Socialist nominees for president and vice president of the United States). Seeks to organize youth to secure their economic rights and to protect their civil and academic liberties.

Staff: Full-time paid employees, 2 at headquarters and 5 in field work.

Finances: Approximate annual budget, $2,000.

TABLE XII

STATISTICS OF PATRIOTIC, POLITICAL, FRATERNAL, AND LABOR ORGANIZATIONS

Organization	Year Founded	Approximate Aggregate Membership (individuals)	Number of Members under 25 Years of Age	Total Employees on Headquarters Staff	Aggregate Endowment of National Headquarters	Plant and Equipment (headquarters only)	Approximate Annual Budget (headquarters only)
American Federation of Labor	1881	4,006,354	...	...	$5,000,560a	$ ...	$1,800,000
American Legion	1919	1,071,229	none	225	none	...	573,500
American Youth Congress	1934	4,697,915b	...	4	none	...	15,500
American Youth League	1936	800	800	c	none	none	none
Antlers of the Benevolent and Protective Order of Elks	1922	3,500	3,500	...	...	...	...
Campaign for Youth Needs	1939	d	...	3	none	...	...
Congress of Industrial Organizations	1935	4,000,000	...	...	...	...	...
Int. Workers Order, Young Fraternalists and Jr. Section	1930	47,000	47,000	11	none	...	49,000e
League for Industrial Democracy	1905	2,500	...	6	...	3,928	27,100
National Foundation for American Youth	1940	...	...	2	...	...	...
National Women's Trade Union League of America	1903	1,000,000	...	3	none	1,300	10,000
Order of the Builders	1921	80,000	80,000	...	...	...	...
Order of the Rainbow for Girls	1922	400,000	50,000f	8	...	30,157	32,600
Pioneer Youth of America	1924	1,000	1,000	2	...	...	...
Sons of the American Legion	1932	72,663	72,663	g	...	...	...
Steuben Society of America, Junior League of the	1924	200	200	...	...	...	...
Veterans of Foreign Wars	1913	250,000	none	47	...	...	250,000
Young Circle League of the English-Speaking Division of the Workmen's Circle	1929	4,500	4,500	13	...	...	...
Young Communist League of the U.S.A.	1922	22,000	22,000h	...	...	...	...
Young People's Socialist League, U.S.A.	1915	3,000	3,000	7	...	...	2,000

a Also reserve and restricted funds totaling $2,160,336.
b Underlying membership of 63 cooperating national organizations.
c No paid staff.
d Federation; no provision for individual membership.
e Junior Section only.
f Number of members between the ages of 13 and 21.
g All administrative work is carried on by members of the national headquarters staff of the American Legion.
h Includes members up to 30 years of age.

XII. Agricultural and Rural Life Organizations

Farming is both an industry and a way of life. The American farm, with few exceptions, is both a business and a family home. About one-third of the population of the United States now lives on farms. Another substantial fraction has its habitation in towns and villages of less than urban magnitude, but considerably fewer than one-half of our people now live outside cities and towns having a population of 2,500 or more.

In the days of George Washington nine Americans out of ten lived on farms, and until only a few decades ago the farm dwellers were still in the majority. Now the rural population has become a minority and has tended to gravitate toward the status of an economically underprivileged class, as the great industries of manufacturing and transportation have outstripped it in organization and economic power.

The continued flow of young men and young women from country to city has altered the vigorous rural social institutions of earlier days and in many ways has promoted their decay. Despite vast improvement in facilities of transport and communication, rural youth do not yet have equal opportunity for social intercourse and educational advancement with their urban cousins. The problem of building up the rural school and other rural community agencies on new patterns to fit the new conditions, and to form the basis of a twentieth-century American rural culture, is acute.

Many farm people sense the essence of the problem and contribute toward its solution through farm organizations of long standing. In our great system of land-grant colleges and experiment stations, and in the state and federal departments of agriculture and of education, devoted scientists labor not only upon the biological and chemical problems of agricultural production but also on the improvement of rural living.

These workers have encouraged the building of national organizations of farm boys and girls to assist them in developing their vocational efficiency and their appreciation of the values in rural life. Each of the farm organizations for adults has an interest in youth, as the descriptions in the present section will make plain.

Organizations whose membership consists chiefly of young persons, as distinguished from those composed wholly or largely of persons above the age of 25, are:

American Country Life Association, Youth Section
4-H Clubs
Future Farmers of America

Cross references: Alliance for Guidance of Rural Youth, p. 143; Hechalutz Organization of America, p. 58; Jewish Agricultural Society, p. 59; Protestant Episcopal Church, Department of Christian Social Relations, p. 41.

AMERICAN COUNTRY LIFE ASSOCIATION (1919); 297 Fourth Ave., New York, N.Y.; Benson Y. Landis, Executive Secretary.

Membership: Rural sociologists and other persons interested in improving country life, 330. In addition there is a Youth Section composed of 80 local affiliated groups on college campuses and in rural communities in 22 states, with an aggregate membership of 12,000 individuals between the ages of 16 and 25. The Future Farmers of America (see p. 93), with a membership of approximately 230,000 boys, is also affiliated. Classes of membership and annual dues: individual, subscription $3, regular $5; organizational, community or county $5, collegiate $5, state $10.

Purpose: To be of service in the building of a rural civilization finer than any the world has ever known, with emphasis on social development, not merely on economic improvement. The stated aim of the Youth

Section is to promote discussion of rural life problems, to disseminate information for a better understanding and appreciation of country life, and to work for improvement in rural areas.

Activities: The annual Country Life National Forum or Conference is the major activity of the associati n. The Youth Section meets at the same time and place for a program largely of its own, but partly in conjunction with that of the senior organization. State conferences are encouraged, and extensive efforts are made to improve local programs for rural youth and the rural community through affiliated and cooperating local organizations such as rural life clubs, 4-H groups, Junior Farm Bureaus, Granges, chapters of Alpha Zeta, home economics organizations, and others. Suggestions and mimeographed materials are supplied to such organizations.

Publications: *Rural America*, monthly, September through May; $2 a year. Proceedings of the annual

County Life Conferences, $2 each, as follows: *What's Ahead for Rural America?* 1939; *Disadvantaged People in Rural Life*, 1938; *The People and the Land*, 1937; *Education for Democracy*, 1936; *Country Life Programs*, 1935; *National Planning and Rural Life*, 1934. Youth Section materials: *Handbook, Youth Section*, 1938, 43 pp.; *The Rural Community*, 1940, 31 pp.; *What's Ahead for Rural America?* 1939, 29 pp. mimeo.; *Improving Our Rural Civilization*, 1938, 29 pp. mimeo.; *Conservation and Rural Life*, 1936, 29 pp. mimeo.; *A Guide to the Literature of Rural Life*, 1939, 15 pp.

Staff: Part-time paid employees, 2; unpaid workers in the field, 2 to 6.

Finances: Value of equipment at headquarters, $1,000. Current balance December 31, 1939, $112.18. For the fiscal year ending on that date, operations were as follows:

Income

Gifts for current expenses	$ 8,225.50
Membership fees	1,401.35
Publications	1,109.95
Conference registration	536.00
	$11,272.80

Expenditures

Salaries	$ 3,111.60
Travel	550.61
Communications and supplies	1,054.77
Publications	1,474.20
Annual conference	5,179.60
Other purposes	436.83
	$11,807.61

AMERICAN FARM BUREAU FEDERATION (1919); 58 East Washington St., Chicago, Ill.; Edward A. O'Neal, President; R. W. Blackburn, Secretary.

Membership: State farm bureau federations, 39; county organizations, 1,800; community organizations, 15,000, embracing 400,000 farm families including an estimated 1,500,000 individuals, with 500,000 women members of the Associated Women of the American Farm Bureau Federation. Some of the state federations, particularly in midwestern states, have special organizations for rural youth.

Purpose: To correlate and strengthen the state farm bureaus and similar state organizations; to promote, protect, and represent the business, economic, social, and educational interests of the farmers of the nation; and to develop agriculture.

Activities: Conducts educational, social, legislative, and cooperative enterprises; holds an annual meeting. Maintains information and service bureaus for members. The legislative bureau is in the Munsey Building, Washington, D.C. The state and county organizations plan and execute their own programs of service of varied types, often including sports,

conferences, and summer camps for youth. The organization cooperates with the Agricultural Extension Service, teachers of vocational agriculture, the 4-H Clubs, the Future Farmers of America, the Boy Scouts of America, and other organizations serving youth.

Publications: *Nation's Agriculture*, 12 issues annually; J. J. Lacey, editor, Room 1116, Garland Bldg., Chicago, Ill. *Official News Letter*, bimonthly. Annual report and proceedings of annual conventions. Numerous small explanatory and promotional bulletins also appear at intervals.

Staff: Full-time paid employees at headquarters, 8.

Finances: On November 30, 1939 operating balance and reserve fund aggregated $157,257.23. For the fiscal year ending on that date, current income was $253,878.67, and expenditures were $228,204.61.

FARMERS' EDUCATIONAL AND CO-OPERATIVE UNION OF AMERICA (1902); 18 North Klein St., Oklahoma City, Okla.; J. M. Graves, Secretary-Treasurer. President, James G. Patton, 1441 Welton St., Denver, Colo.; National Director of Education, Mrs. Gladys Talbott Edwards, Jamestown, N.D.

Membership: Farmers in all parts of the United States, 85,000. There are state organizations in 21 states, chiefly in the Mississippi Valley and on the West Coast. There are 25,000 juniors 16 to 21 years of age, who are full-fledged members of the senior organization but also have their own special activities fostered by national and state junior leaders.

Purpose: To secure equity, establish justice, and apply the Golden Rule; to discourage the credit and mortgage system; to assist members in buying and selling; to educate the agricultural classes in scientific farming; to systematize methods of production and distribution; to secure and maintain profitable and uniform prices for products of the farm.

Activities: Promotes cooperative buying and selling by farmers; advocates legislation for the regulation of grain and cotton exchanges and livestock markets and for the encouragement and protection of cooperative marketing associations among farmers. The 1939–40 program advocated expansion of the program of the Farm Security Administration of the U.S. Department of Agriculture, effectual and complete transfer of the Farm Credit Administration to the Department of Agriculture, continuation of the Federal Surplus Commodities Corporation, and expansion of the "stamp plan" of distribution. Maintains friendly attitude toward organized labor; advocates the establishment of peace among nations by the substitution of cooperative business for the competitive profit-seeking order. Conducts brief summer camps for juniors in several states. Junior local units have programs of sports and entertainment and are sometimes made responsible for the recreational features of the programs of their respective senior locals. They also study and debate the literature sent out at intervals from the national office.

Publications: *The National Union Farmer*, semi-monthly newspaper; 30¢ a year to members, 50¢ to others. Occasional pamphlets, including *National Legislative Program Adopted at the Thirty-Sixth Annual Convention*, 1940, 12 pp.

Staff: Full-time paid employees, 5.

Finances: Value of equipment at national headquarters, $725. Estimated annual value of space, heat, light, and similar services received without charge, $600. Balance November 9, 1940, $2,876.58. For the fiscal year ending on that date, operations were as follows:

	Income	
Membership fees		$21,067.99
Publications		1,977.86
Other sources		1,408.07
		$24,453.92
	Expenditures	
Salaries		$ 8,289.78
Publications		2,130.00
Other purposes		15,281.38
		$25,701.16

4-H CLUBS (1907); Extension Service, U.S. Department of Agriculture, Washington, D.C.; Dr. M. L. Wilson, Director of Extension Work.

Conducted by the Extension Service of the U.S. Department of Agriculture in cooperation with the state colleges of agriculture and with the territories. National, regional, and state adult leaders and nearly 7,000 county extension agents devoting a third of their time to 4-H Club work are public employees; adult leaders of local clubs are on a volunteer basis.

Membership: Individuals, 1,528,945, including 147,-350 local adult leaders and 1,381,595 boys and girls 10 to 20 years of age inclusive in 78,599 clubs in the United States, Hawaii, Alaska, and Puerto Rico. Of these young people 599,420 are boys, and 782,175 are girls; 774,399 are between the ages of 10 and 13 inclusive, 335,692 are 14 to 15 years of age, and 271,504 are between the ages of 16 and 20 inclusive. In addition 71,701 young people between the ages of 16 and 25 in analogous organizations for rural youth are also served by the Extension Service.

Purpose: To help rural boys and girls to develop desirable ideals and standards for farming, homemaking, community life, and citizenship, and a sense of responsibility for their attainment; to afford them technical instruction in farming and homemaking; to provide them with an opportunity to "learn by doing"; to instill in their minds an intelligent understanding and an appreciation of nature and of the environment in which they live; to teach them the value of research and to develop in them a scientific attitude toward the problems of the farm and the

home; to train them in cooperative action to the end that they may increase their accomplishments and better assist in solving rural problems; to develop in them habits of healthful living, to provide them with direction in the intelligent use of leisure, and to arouse in them worthy ambitions and a desire to continue to learn; to teach and to demonstrate to them methods designed to improve practices in agriculture and homemaking to the end that farm incomes may be increased, standards of living improved, and the satisfactions of farm life enhanced.

Activities: Each local club is composed of voluntary members who elect their own officers and receive instruction from a volunteer adult leader. In accordance with democratic procedure, each club develops a self-determined program, based on the solving of immediate needs and consisting of regular meetings, demonstrations, tours, exhibits, judging events, and social and recreational activities. The price of membership is that each member shall do a substantial piece of work of his own, designed to demonstrate improved practices on the farm or in the home or community. Because of the varying types of agriculture in the United States, more than 30 different phases of homemaking and farm demonstrations may be undertaken by 4-H Club members. For example, in homemaking activities, a club member may plan, prepare, and serve attractive and healthful meals; make or select for himself and other members of the family attractive, suitable clothing in keeping with the family budget; keep personal accounts; assume a share of responsibility for daily household tasks; take over the management of the home when mother is away; render more comfortable and satisfying the home itself; add to the attractiveness of its exterior by planting native shrubs and trees; or help in the intelligent care of younger brothers and sisters.

In the agricultural club activities a club member may voluntarily, under the direction of his local leader and county extension agent, and in accordance with recognized improved practices, grow an acre or more of some crop; raise a garden, market such fresh vegetables and fruits as may be practicable to sell, and can the surplus; raise a flock of poultry; purchase, breed, and care for a sow and for her litter of pigs to maturity; care for a dairy calf to maturity and build a dairy herd; or run and repair farm machinery.

Much emphasis is placed on the development of constructive leadership and intelligent ability to follow, the improvement of the health of the individual and the community, and the services that may be rendered in the home, on the farm, and in the local community. Members are trained to help in times of emergency and to study and discuss world affairs as related to their own community interests and responsibilities. Considerable emphasis is being placed on citizenship training in a democracy through group discussions and special project work of particular economic and social importance. A 4-H citizenship ceremonial has been developed for all rural young people who are about to vote for the first time.

County extension agents, together with supervisors and specialists of the extension services of the state agricultural colleges, assist the local volunteer leaders in actual teaching and demonstrating and in conducting the various 4-H Club activities. They also conduct training conferences to enable the volunteer leaders to improve and extend their work. Nearly all states and territories have annual state camp or conventions of 4-H Club members at the state agricultural colleges and often at state fairs. The U.S. Department of Agriculture sponsors and directs annually a National 4-H Camp in Washington, D.C. Among other national events is the National 4-H Club Congress in Chicago. In 1939 there were over 2,000 county 4-H Club camps with an aggregate attendance of 229,558 young people.

Publications: No official nation-wide periodical for members, but the *Extension Service Review*, monthly publication of the Extension Service of the U.S. Department of Agriculture, carries frequent stories and reports of 4-H Clubs. Recent circulars issued by the Department of Agriculture include: *Boys and Girls 4-H Club Work*, by C. B. Smith, Miscellaneous Circular No. 77, revised 1935, 14 pp.; *Organization of 4-H Club Work*, by Gertrude L. Warren, Miscellaneous Publication No. 320, 1938, 33 pp.; *Short-Time Camps*, by Ella Gardner, Miscellaneous Publication No. 346, 1939, 90 pp.; *25 Years of 4-H Club Work, Analysis of Statistical Trends*, by Barnard D. Joy, Extension Service Circular 312, 1939, 30 pp. mimeo.

Printed or mimeographed circulars and periodical newsletters to county extension agents, leaders, and members are published by many states and counties. Bulletins descriptive of the program in each state are prepared from time to time by the several state colleges of agriculture, and copies may be obtained upon application to the director of extension at the college.

Staff: There is no national headquarters personnel apart from the staff of the Extension Service of the U.S. Department of Agriculture.

Finances: National and state organization work is an inseparable part of the Cooperative Extension Service undertaken by the U.S. Department of Agriculture and the state colleges of agriculture and financed by federal, state, and county appropriations. Local leadership and facilities for 4-H Club work are generally obtained without cost. Usually there are no annual dues or other fees, but local clubs are permitted to establish nominal dues by unanimous consent.

FUTURE FARMERS OF AMERICA (1928); U.S.
Office of Education, Federal Security Agency, Washington, D.C.; W. A. Ross, National Executive Secretary.

Membership: About 230,000 farm boys, students of agriculture in public high schools under the provisions of the National Vocational Education Act. Over 6,800 local chapters in 47 states, Hawaii, and Puerto Rico.

Purpose: To strengthen the confidence of the farm boy in himself and his work; to create more interest in the intelligent choice of farming occupations; to create and nurture a love of country life; to improve the rural home and its surroundings; to encourage cooperative effort; to promote thrift; to improve scholarship; and to encourage organized recreational activities.

Activities: Annual conventions for the discussion of the problems of farm youth and the plans and policies of the organization. Local chapters and state associations conduct livestock judging contests, cooperative projects, public speaking, and a great variety of conservation and community service projects, with the advice and supervision of local teachers of vocational agriculture and state supervisors for agricultural education.

Publications: There is no official national periodical, but most of the state associations print or mimeograph a periodical of their own. *Official F.F.A. Manual*, 15¢; *The Future Farmers of America Organization, What It Is and Does*, 11 pp., 3½¢ in lots of 100; both obtainable from the French-Bray Printing Co., Baltimore, Md. Proceedings of the national conventions; *National Constitution and By-Laws*.

Staff: Full-time paid employees, 2.

Finances: Income is derived chiefly from national dues and charter fees. For the year ending September 31, 1939, expenditures were as follows:

Travel of national officers	$ 4,254.52
Twelfth national convention	4,681.53
American Farmer keys	1,174.50
National prizes and awards	2,530.54
Printing	1,842.10
National radio program	202.46
National office expense	655.15
Clerical assistance	2,879.28
	$18,220.08

NATIONAL COMMITTEE ON BOYS AND GIRLS CLUB WORK, INC. (1921); 56 East Congress St., Chicago, Ill.; G. L. Noble, Managing Director.

Membership: A board of directors of 9 members and an additional membership of 22 nationally prominent businessmen and educators from 15 states. The organization serves the 4-H Clubs (see p. 92), thus affecting large numbers of rural youth.

Purpose: To supplement and assist the efforts of the extension departments of the state agricultural colleges and the U.S. Department of Agriculture in developing the program of 4-H Clubs for rural youth; to coordinate and assist in extending the efforts of other private agencies which sponsor some phase of 4-H Club activity; to make the benefits of 4-H Club work available to much larger numbers of rural youth; through research to discover and publish results having a bearing on the methods used in the program.

Activities: Assists the Extension Service in conducting the National 4-H Club Congress annually attended by 1,400 delegates from 44 states and Canada; assists with 4-H Division of the National Dairy Show; produces and distributes recreational and other supplemental material for the use of local 4-H Clubs; helps secure legislation providing funds for extension work; maintains mail order Supply Department providing equipment for use of clubs; solicits and supervises approximately $200,000 worth of 4-H Club prizes annually; disseminates 4-H publicity through news mediums, including radio; secures funds for scientific research and publishes results.

Publications: *National 4-H Club News*, monthly; 35¢ a year, 3 years for $1. *4-H Handy Book*, by G. L. Noble, 1937, 21 pp., 5¢; *National 4-H Club Song Book*, edited by R. A. Turner, 1938, 64 pp., 15¢; *Song Leaders' Manual*, edited by Kenneth S. Clark, 1938, 16 pp., 5¢; *When Old Songs Were New*, by Howard Southgate, 1938, 32 pp., 15¢; *4-H Supply Catalogue, 1939*, 32 pp., free. Numerous pamphlets and plays priced at 5¢ to 25¢.

Staff: Full-time paid employees, 18.

Finances: Value of plant and equipment, $20,000. Operating balance February 29, 1940, $8,235.07. During the fiscal year ending on that date, funds totaling $65,421.25, supervised wholly or in part by this organization, were turned over directly to 4-H Club leaders and organizations by donors without transfer through the banking facilities of this committee. During the same fiscal year regular budget operations were as follows:

Income

Unrestricted gifts or grants	$ 3,400.00
Designated specific contributions	21,857.14
Advertising in *Club News*	11,894.51
Operating charges	46,263.00
Registration and bus tour	10,115.25
Profit on supply sales	2,301.94
Other sources	291.51
	$96,123.35

Expenditures

Salaries (proportion)	$19,549.69
Travel	1,980.83
Communications and office supplies (proportion)	12,265.56
Publications	22,691.48
National 4-H Club Congress, including awards	35,260.52
Other purposes	4,431.21
	$96,179.29

NATIONAL GRANGE (1867); 970 College Ave., Columbus, Ohio; Louis J. Taber, Master.

Membership: Individuals, 800,000, of whom 75,000 are boys and girls between the ages of 14 and 25, in 37 states of the United States. There are about 8,000 local units, or subordinate Granges, grouped within given districts into Pomona Granges. Subordinate and Pomona Granges are grouped into State Granges, which hold annual meetings and have voting representation at the annual convention of the National Grange. Each subordinate member pays a small monthly fee, a portion of which goes to the State and National Granges. There are also approximately 1,000 Juvenile Granges with more than 50,000 members aged 6 to 15.

Purpose: To promote cooperation among the farmers of America, develop leadership among them, improve community and rural life, defend the interests of agriculture, and unselfishly promote the national welfare.

Activities: Unites farmers in cooperative undertakings, such as cooperative marketing and cooperative purchasing; works for legislation of benefit to farmers; promotes mutual insurance companies (fire, automobile, tornado, hail, and life) for its members. Services of various kinds, arising from the organization's interest in the churches, schools, roads, playgrounds, marketing facilities, and every other agency that makes for a satisfying community life, are performed for the welfare of the local communities. Grange halls, of which there are over 3,600 with a valuation of over $25,000,000, are used for rural entertainment, Farmers' Institutes, 4-H Clubs, and meetings of the Future Farmers of America. Boys and girls from 6 to 14 may join the Juvenile Grange, a character-building organization under the auspices of the National Grange. Grange degree teams are usually composed of young people under 25. The Grange supports vocational education, club work, and all similar activities. The National Grange has ever been strong in behalf of opportunities for the farm boys and girls.

Publications: *The National Grange Monthly. The Grange Blue Book; The Farmer's Best Friend; The Farm Home;* pamphlets descriptive of the Grange organization.

Staff: Full-time paid employees, 10.

Finances: The National Grange is financed entirely by the fee of 1 per cent a month for each member and by a portion of the sixth and seventh degree fees. Building fund, $75,000; active account, $90,000. Approximate annual budget, $110,000.

TABLE XIII

STATISTICS OF AGRICULTURAL AND RURAL LIFE ORGANIZATIONS

Organization	Year Founded	Approximate Aggregate Membership (individuals)	Number of Members under 25 Years of Age	Total Employees on Head-quarters Staff	Aggregate Endowment of National Headquarters	Plant and Equipment (headquarters only)	Approximate Annual Budget (headquarters only)
American Country Life Association	1919	330[a]	12,000[b]	2	none	$ 1,000	$ 11,800
American Farm Bureau Federation	1919	1,500,000[c]	....	8	none[d]	....	253,900
Farmers' Educational and Co-operative Union of Am.	1902	85,000	25,000	5	none	725	25,700
4-H Clubs	1907	1,528,945	1,381,595[e]	f	none	f	f
Future Farmers of America	1928	230,000	230,000	2	none	....	18,200
National Committee on Boys and Girls Club Work	1921	31	....	18	....	20,000	96,100
National Grange	1867	800,000[g]	75,000[g]	10	none[h]	....	110,000

a Adult membership only.
b Exclusive of the Future Farmers of America, affiliated with the Youth Section of the association.
c Estimated number of individuals in 400,000 farm families enrolled in 15,000 community organizations.
d Operating balance and reserve fund aggregated $157,257 on November 30, 1939.

e 71,701 young people between the ages of 16 and 25 in analogous organizations for rural youth are also served by the Extension Service.
f None apart from that of the Extension Service of the U.S. Department of Agriculture.
g Exclusive of approximately 50,000 members aged 6 to 15 enrolled in Juvenile Granges.
h The organization has a building fund of $75,000 and an active account of $90,000.

XIII. Negro and Interracial Organizations

Negroes in the United States constitute about one-tenth of the population. Their progenitors have been in America for the most part since the seventeenth and eighteenth centuries. They have been a factor in the nation's life since early Colonial days.

Unfortunately the great majority of American Negroes were in a state of chattel slavery until the wartime proclamation of emancipation made by President Lincoln in 1863; and their legal status was still a parlous one until after the triumph of that principle had been confirmed by the adoption of the Thirteenth Amendment to the Constitution of the United States.

To the economic privations suffered by the Negro upon suddenly finding himself a free man without property, there was added interracial embitterment and prejudice growing out of the mistakes and mismanagement of the Reconstruction period. In the face of these difficulties,

remarkable progress has been made by Negroes in their economic status, education, art, music, and in all that contributes to a useful and happy citizenship. But the road ahead is long.

While much of the leadership in Negro welfare comes from persons of the Negro race, important contributions have also been made by white persons who believe that the advancement of the common welfare depends in large degree upon the dissipation of racial prejudice and the promotion of interracial cooperation and harmony. Thus it is that some of the leading private associations for Negro welfare number among their membership both white and colored leaders and workers.

Cross references: Association of Southern Women for the Prevention of Lynching, p. 106; Federal Council of Churches of Christ in America, p. 35; Young Communist League, p. 88; Young Men's Christian Associations, p. 27; Young Women's Christian Associations, p. 28.

AMERICAN TEACHERS ASSOCIATION (1904); P.O. Box 271, Montgomery, Ala.; H. Councill Trenholm, Executive Secretary.

Formerly the National Association of Teachers in Colored Schools.

Membership: Individuals, 2,990 in 22 states, including 2,788 annual members and 202 life members.

Purpose: To promote the professional interest of teachers of Negro children on a national basis; to stimulate the more adequate realization of the American ideal of equality of educational opportunity for all children irrespective of race, place of residence, or economic circumstance; to stimulate increased effectiveness of subordinate state and local teachers' organizations; to stimulate the improvement of classroom and administrative practices among teachers of Negro children; to contribute to the removal of racial differentials in the remuneration of teachers.

Activities: Disseminates professional information and promotional appeals to the teachers of Negro children through publications and conferences, including an annual meeting. Participates in policy-forming organizations and conferences where issues relating to the improvement of education should properly include adequate consideration of aspects peculiar to the interests of the three million Negro children enrolled in segregated and nonsegregated

schools. Major emphasis is on the situation in the 18 states where Negro children constitute approximately one-fourth of the school population.

Publications: *Bulletin*, 6 issues annually; $1 a year. Numerous mimeographed releases for purposes of description and promotion.

Staff: Part-time paid employees, 3.

Finances: Value of equipment at headquarters, $500. Balance July 14, 1940, $701.85. For the fiscal year ending on that date, operations were as follows:

Income

Membership fees	$3,054.55
Affiliated associations	670.00
Publications (advertising)	13.00
Temporary loans	1,331.50
	$5,069.05

Expenditures

Salaries	$ 974.71
Travel	160.95
Communications	268.41
Office supplies	264.68
Publications	1,381.04
Temporary loans	1,470.00
Other purposes	331.07
	$4,850.86

ASSOCIATES IN NEGRO FOLK EDUCATION
(1935); Box 636, Benjamin Franklin Station, Washington, D.C.; Dr. Alain Locke, Secretary and Editor.

Membership: Individuals, 10, as follows: Eugene Kinckle Jones, adviser on Negro affairs, U.S. Department of Commerce; Dr. Alain Locke, Howard University; Dr. Garnet C. Wilkinson, assistant superintendent of public schools of the District of Columbia; Mary McLeod Bethune, president, Bethune-Cookman College; Mary Beattie Brady, director, Harmon Foundation; Professor Lyman Bryson, Columbia University; A. L. Foster, executive secretary, Chicago Urban League; Alphonse S. Henningburg, dean, North Carolina College for Negroes; Franklin F. Hopper, chief, Circulation Department, New York Public Library; and Professor Charles S. Johnson, Fisk University.

Purpose: To prepare materials on Negro history, life, and culture for the use of adult education groups.

Activities: Preparation and publication of the materials mentioned below and the projected studies: The Negro in the West Indies; The African Background; and A Portfolio of Negro Art.

Publications: The Bronze Booklet Series: *Adult Education among Negroes*, by Ira DeA. Reid; *The Negro and His Music*, by Alain Locke; *Negro Art: Past and Present*, by Alain Locke; *A World View of Race*, by Ralph J. Bunche; *The Negro and Economic Reconstruction*, by T. Arnold Hill; *The Negro in American Fiction*, by Sterling Brown; *Negro Poetry and Drama*, by Sterling Brown; *Negro History in Outline*, by Arthur A. Schomburg. Paper bound, 25¢ each; paper-board binding, 50¢ each.

Staff: Part-time paid employee, 1; part-time unpaid worker, 1.

Finances: Estimated annual value of unpaid staff services, $1,500. On July 1, 1939 the operating balance was $1,500. Operations for the fiscal year ending on that date were as follows:

Income

Gifts or grants	$1,000
Publications	539
	$1,539

Expenditures

Office supplies	$ 200
Publications	2,500
	$2,700

ASSOCIATION OF COLLEGES AND SECONDARY SCHOOLS FOR NEGROES (1934);
Barber-Scotia Junior College, Concord, N.C.; L. S. Cozart, Secretary.

Membership: Institutions, 138, including 40 colleges, 7 junior colleges, and 91 secondary schools.

Purpose: To develop the colleges and secondary schools for Negroes and to maintain helpful relations between them.

Activities: Annual educational meetings with professional programs. The association has a Commission on Higher Education, with committees on Negro life, and a Commission on Secondary Schools, at present active chiefly in the field of vocational guidance and qualitative requirements of accreditment.

Publications: Proceedings, annually; L. S. Cozart, editor-in-chief.

Staff: Part-time unpaid workers, 4, of whom 2 spend some time in the field.

Finances: Estimated annual value of unpaid staff services, $400. The association reports a total of $4,142.10 in savings account. The operating balance on November 30, 1939 was $2,352.18. For the fiscal year ending on that date, operations were as follows:

Income

Membership fees	$2,780.00
Other sources	1.00
	$2,781.00

Expenditures

Travel	$ 737.65
Publications	271.75
	$1,009.40

ASSOCIATION FOR THE STUDY OF NEGRO LIFE AND HISTORY (1915); 1538 Ninth St., N.W., Washington, D.C.; Carter G. Woodson, Director.

Membership: Approximately 1,100 individuals and institutions, including 450 active members paying annual dues of $3, about 450 subscribing members (schools and libraries) paying $4 annually, about 100 life members making a single payment of $100, and about 100 annual donors of $5 to $100. Additional sustaining members, 5,200, small donors and subscribers to the *Negro History Bulletin*.

Purpose: To collect sociological and historical data; to publish books on Negro life and history; to promote the study of the Negro through clubs and schools; to bring about harmony between the races by interpreting the one to the other.

Activities: Conducts and promotes research in Negro history; collects and preserves important manuscripts and rare books; serves libraries, schools, and colleges; stimulates and trains young Negro scholars for historical research. Holds annual meetings, the most recent of which (September 6–9, 1940, in Chicago) was a notable celebration of the twenty-fifth anniversary of the association. The magnitude of the activities during a quarter of a century, as measured in money, is shown in the statement of receipts and disbursements for the period from September 9, 1915 to July 1, 1940:

Receipts

Research and printing	$133,336.53
Subscriptions	36,229.86
Memberships	22,048.30
Contributions	101,975.61
Advertising	3,476.50
Publications	9,806.21
Negro History Bulletin	6,762.86
Sundry income	24,290.37
	$337,926.24

Disbursements

Research	$100,951.14
Printing and stationery	107,032.07
Stenographic service	20,250.49
Rent	16,217.11
Salaries	42,828.37
Traveling expenses	22,617.20
History prizes	1,125.00
Sundry expenditures	26,904.86
	$337,926.24

Publications: *Journal of Negro History*, quarterly; $4 a year (circulation, 1,300). *The Negro History Bulletin*, monthly; $1 a year, 5 subscriptions for $2.70 (circulation, 7,000). Twenty-eight books and monographs, among which are: *A Side-Light on Anglo-American Relations 1839–1858*, by Annie Heloise Abel and Frank J. Klingberg, $2; *Extracts from the Records of the African Companies*, by Ruth A. Fisher, $1; *The Negro in the Reconstruction of Virginia*, by A. A. Taylor, $2; *Slavery in Kentucky*, by Ivan E. McDougle, $1; *The Company of Royal Adventurers Trading into Africa*, by George F. Zook, $1; *The Negro Professional Man and the Community*, by Carter G. Woodson, $3; *The Rural Negro*, by Carter G. Woodson, $2.50; *The Negro Wage-Earner*, by Carter G. Woodson and Lorenzo J. Greene, $3. Complete list on request.

Staff: Full-time paid employees, 6.

Finances: Balance June 30, 1940, $508.31. For the fiscal year ending on that date, operations were as follows:

Income

Membership fees	$ 2,608.48
Gifts for current expenses	4,749.26
Publications	5,269.06
Other sources	548.85
	$13,175.65

Expenditures

Salaries	$ 5,079.18
Research and publication	6,254.14
Rent, travel, accounting	1,798.99
Other purposes	500.82
	$13,633.13

COMMISSION ON INTERRACIAL COOPERATION, INC. (1919); 710 Standard Bldg., Atlanta, Ga.; Will W. Alexander, Executive Director; Emily H. Clay, Secretary-Assistant Treasurer.

Membership: Individuals, 137. Six active state committees and numerous autonomous local and regional committees over the South. Texas has a youth group, representing 18 colleges (white and Negro), organized as a part of the state interracial committee.

Purpose: To work for the improvement of interracial attitudes, the correction of injustices, and the betterment of conditions affecting all people, without regard to race or religion.

Activities: Through its Conference on Education and Race Relations, promotes the study of race relations in the schools and colleges of the South; maintains contact with newspapers, churches, and other opinion-forming agencies in this region; works with local, regional, and state interracial committees on programs of education and action for the improvement of educational facilities, health and hospitalization, housing and sanitation, recreation, delinquency, and equity before the law; through its Association of Southern Women for the Prevention of Lynching (see p. 106), seeks to prevent mob violence and campaigns aggressively against lynching.

Publications: *The Southern Frontier*, monthly; 25¢ a year; Mrs. Jessie Daniel Ames, editor. Pamphlets and bulletins issued at intervals. Samples on request.

Staff: Full-time paid employees, 9, of whom 1 spends major time in the field; part-time paid employees in field work, 5.

Finances: Approximate budget for the calendar year 1939, $75,000.

NATIONAL ASSOCIATION FOR THE ADVANCEMENT OF COLORED PEOPLE (1909); 69 Fifth Ave., New York, N.Y.; Walter White, Secretary.

Membership: Individuals, 100,000, in 340 adult councils, 144 youth councils, and 45 college chapters. Of the members, 2,000 are young persons between the ages of 12 and 25. Classes of membership, with fees, are: minimum, $1; annual, with the *Crisis* magazine, $2.50; blue certificate, $5; gold certificate, $10; contributing, $25; donor, $100; life, $500.

Purpose: To end lynching and disenfranchisement; to end the peonage and debt slavery of southern sharecroppers and tenant farmers; to abolish injustices in legal procedure based solely upon color or race; to secure equitable distribution of funds for public education; to abolish segregation, discrimination, insult, and humiliation based on race or color; to secure equality of opportunity to work in all fields with equal pay for equal work; to abolish discrimination against Negroes in the right of collective bargaining through membership in organized labor unions; to secure equitable opportunity to participate in all of the armed forces of the nation.

Activities: Seeks enactment of antilynching legislation and other laws aimed to eliminate racial injustices; employs legal counsel for the defense of Negroes accused of crime and tried under conditions of inflammatory race prejudice, and for the arguing of cases in constitutional law involving the civil rights of the Negro; seeks to secure equality of consideration and integration of qualified Negro citizens in every branch of national defense. Campaigns for educational opportunity for Negro youth, calling attention to shortness of school terms, low salaries of teachers, inadequate school plant and equipment, inequitable distribution of state school funds, lack of transportation facilities for rural children, frequent absence of Negro administrators in Negro schools, inequality in enforcement of truancy laws, and exclusion of qualified Negroes from some state-supported universities and technical schools.

Publications: *The Crisis*, monthly; $1.50 a year.

Staff: Full-time paid employees, 18, of whom 2 spend major time in field work.

Finances: Endowment funds, $2,000; reserve funds other than endowment, $2,711.51. Value of equipment at national headquarters, $4,256.51. Balance December 31, 1939, $489.96. For the preceding calendar year, operations were as follows:

Income

Gifts and grants	$13,877.87
Membership fees	39,981.49
Crisis	13,089.41
Special funds	7,918.41
Endowment and reserve funds	1,102.89
Benefits, etc.	9,769.26
	$85,739.33

Expenditures

Salaries	$39,253.13
Travel	6,344.57
Communications	5,231.48
Office supplies	2,744.71
Publications	20,746.05
Rentals, insurance, etc.	2,551.56
Other purposes	8,512.68
	$85,384.18

NATIONAL ASSOCIATION OF TEACHERS IN COLORED SCHOOLS
See American Teachers Association (p. 96).

NATIONAL CONGRESS OF COLORED PARENTS AND TEACHERS (1926); State Teachers College, Bowie, Md.; Leonidas S. James, Executive Secretary.

Membership: Individuals, 60,000, in 3,200 units located in 22 states and the Virgin Islands. The organization has inaugurated a Junior Department with membership of 500 youth aged 12 to 20.

Purpose: To promote child and youth welfare in the home, school, church, and community; to raise the standards of home life; to secure more adequate laws for the care and protection of children and youth; to bring into closer relation the home and the school that parents and teachers may cooperate intelligently in the training of the child; to develop between educators and the general public such united efforts as will secure for every child the highest advantages in physical, mental, moral, and spiritual education.

Activities: Holds annual conventions. The work of the organization is carried on in 22 different fields with emphasis on character education, child hygiene, homemaking, juvenile protection, humane education, library service, mental hygiene, parent education, radio service, recreation, safety, social hygiene, student aid, study of use and effect of narcotics, music and art, and international relations. Serves more than 150,000 youth annually by sponsoring school bands, glee clubs, recreational clubs, nature clubs, and health clubs, and cooperates with 4-H Clubs, Boy and Girl Scout troops, and Girl Reserves.

Publications: *Our National Family*, quarterly; free to local units; Leonidas S. James, editor-in-chief. *Juvenile Protection*, by Mrs. M. B. Lewis, 9 pp. The literature of the National Congress of Parents and Teachers (see p. 130) is distributed to the local units of this organization.

Staff: Full-time paid employees, 2, of whom 1 spends major time in field work; part-time unpaid workers, 26, of whom 22 spend major time in field work.

Finances: Reserve funds, $1,181.20. Value of equipment at national headquarters, $200. Estimated annual value of unpaid staff services, $1,000; estimated annual value of space, heat, light, and similar services received without charge, $200. Balance on hand June 30, 1940, $4,918.55. For the fiscal year ending on that date, operations were as follows:

Income

Gifts and grants	$ 50.00
Membership fees	2,200.20
Other sources	455.87
	$2,706.07

Expenditures

Salaries	$1,010.00
Travel	259.69
Publications	346.47
Other purposes	637.91
	$2,254.07

NATIONAL NEGRO CONGRESS (1935); 717 Florida Ave., N.W., Washington, D.C.; John P. Davis, National Secretary.

Membership: Local councils, 72, in 31 states and the District of Columbia. Youth Councils, 30; regional organization of youth, 1, in the South.

Purpose: To gain complete citizenship rights for Negroes and to attain for them social and economic security.

Activities: Advocates legislation on such issues as antilynching, poll tax repeal, prolabor laws, health, housing, civil liberties, and the adoption of the American Youth Act (see American Youth Congress, p. 82). Develops cultural activities among Negroes by sponsoring art exhibits, forums, plays, and recitals; prepares and distributes educational material on the cultural contribution of the Negro in America. Promotion of trade union membership among Negroes is carried on in cooperation with existing trade unions. Efforts are made to open all trade unions to Negroes and to win apprenticeship opportunity for Negro youth.

Publications: *National Bulletin*, monthly, 50¢ a year; official proceedings, published after each biennial congress. Pamphlets on various aspects of Negro life.

Staff: Full-time paid employees, 3, of whom 2 spend major time in the field; part-time paid employees, 2.

Finances: Value of equipment at national headquarters, $850. Estimated annual value of unpaid staff services, $900. Balance on hand December 31, 1939, $510. For the calendar year ending on that date, operations were as follows:

Income

Gifts or grants	$ 3,000
Membership fees	2,700
Publications	1,200
Other services	900
Other sources	4,875
	$12,675

Expenditures

Salaries	$ 5,800
Travel	1,300
Communications	700
Office supplies	400
Publications	1,625
Rent, taxes, insurance	875
Other purposes	2,150
	$12,850

NATIONAL URBAN LEAGUE FOR SOCIAL SERVICE AMONG NEGROES (1910); Room 826, 1133 Broadway, New York, N.Y.; Eugene Kinckle Jones, Executive Secretary.

Membership: Individuals, 40,000, white and colored persons in 45 affiliated local branches in principal cities of the United States. Annual dues vary from $1 upward.

Purpose: To improve the lives of urban Negroes, through advocacy of better employment opportunities, adequate housing accommodations, and proportionate benefits for the Negro population in all community welfare programs; to promote more humane and enlightened interracial relations.

Activities: Maintains departments of (1) industrial relations, (2) publicity, and (3) research. Awards fellowships for social work training; cooperates with public and private social agencies through loans of staff personnel; emphasizes vocational and educational guidance; conducts field work in several states of the South. In 1940 the local units had an aggregate of 187 persons on their paid staffs, performing a great variety of social services, of which the following are examples in different localities: establishment of a house for delinquent girls; promotion of boys' clubs; placement of interns in hospitals; provision of heart disease work in public schools; campaign for reduction of infant mortality; provision of day nursery service. The local units have the endorsement and financial assistance of the community chests in 37 cities.

Publications: *Opportunity*, monthly; $1.50 a year; Elmer A. Carter, editor. *Secretariat*, a house organ, quarterly. *A Quarter Century of Progress in Race Relations*, 1935, 32 pp.; *The National Urban League's Work in 1939 for "Not Alms, but Opportunity."*

Staff: Full-time paid employees, 16.

Finances: Estimated value of equipment at national headquarters, $3,500. Expenditures for the calendar year 1939 were approximately $60,000 for the national organization alone, and approximately $526,000 for the aggregate of the local units.

Table XIV

STATISTICS OF NEGRO AND INTERRACIAL ORGANIZATIONS

Organization	Year Founded	Approximate Aggregate Membership (individuals)	Number of Members under 25 Years of Age	Total Employees on Headquarters Staff	Aggregate Endowment of National Headquarters	Plant and Equipment (headquarters only)	Approximate Annual Budget (headquarters only)
American Teachers Association	1904	2,990	...	3	$ ...	$ ...	$ 5,000
Associates in Negro Folk Education	1935	10	...	1	...	...	2,700
Assn. of Colleges and Secondary Schools for Negroes	1934	138[a]	...	[b]	...	...	2,800
Association for the Study of Negro Life and History	1915	6,300	...	6	none	...	13,600
Commission on Interracial Cooperation	1919	137	...	14	...	...	75,000
National Assn. for the Advancement of Colored People	1909	100,000	2,000	18	2,000[c]	4,257	85,700
National Congress of Colored Parents and Teachers	1926	60,000	500	2	[d]	200	2,700
National Negro Congress	1935	72[a]	30[a]	5	none	850	12,800
Natl. Urban League for Social Service among Negroes	1910	40,000	...	16	...	3,500	60,000

a Number of constituent bodies.
b No paid staff.
c Also reserve funds of $2,712.
d The organization has reserve funds of $1,181.

XIV. Commercial and "Service" Clubs

The early twentieth century has witnessed the development of a type of community organization and leadership among business and professional men which has become familiar throughout the land. The names of Rotary, Kiwanis, Lions, Civitan, and Optimist are household words. These organizations have been lampooned by a school of sardonic writers, whose criticisms are admittedly to some extent valid; but this only tends to stimulate these organizations in more effective activities as spearheads of civic betterment.

The service clubs commonly place local work in behalf of underprivileged children high among the projects to which they devote attention. Often they also sponsor various types of junior clubs and other local youth organizations for boys and girls of all classes. Always they have a kindly interest in the progress of free public education, and sometimes they provide scholarships or other aids to higher education for selected worthy student beneficiaries.

The manifold activities in behalf of young persons carried on in thousands of localities by these groups are not easily reduced to a composite statistical record. It must be admitted that sometimes these activities are somewhat sporadic, springing from generous impulses of the moment; but the national organizations foster permanent and consistent policies of child welfare and youth service and thus make effective an immense reservoir of good will and power for social improvement in thousands of communities.

Cross references: Section XV, Women's Clubs, pp. 106–11. *See also:* National Boys and Girls Week Committee for the United States, p. 198.

CIVITAN INTERNATIONAL (1920); 800 Farley Bldg., Birmingham, Ala.; Arthur Cundy, International Secretary.

Membership: Business and professional men, 6,500, in 200 clubs in the United States, and one in Toronto, Ont. There are Junior Civitan Clubs with an aggregate membership of 750 boys and men aged 12 to 21.

Purpose: To develop the building of good citizenship, curbing of crime, elimination of tuberculosis, and control of venereal diseases.

Activities: The major activity is the conduct of Citizenship Essay Contests. In the Chicago area in 1940–41, $5,000 is being set up for awards, and each of the city's high schools is participating. Approximately 100,000 boys and girls, in schools and youth organizations, participate in similar contests throughout the country. The program is worked out along lines of sound knowledge to advise and guide youth in choosing their careers.

Publications: *The Civitan*, monthly; $2 a year (circulation, 7,500); Arthur Cundy, editor. *Civitan in Brief* and other purely organizational booklets and forms for use of members.

Staff: Full-time paid employees, 6, of whom 3 spend major time in the field.

Finances: Estimated value of equipment at national headquarters, $4,000. Cash on hand June 1, 1940, $5,000. Income for the fiscal year ending May 31, 1940 was $31,000; expenditures were $23,000.

KIWANIS INTERNATIONAL (1915); 520 North Michigan Ave., Chicago, Ill.; Fred. C. W. Parker, Secretary.

Membership: Men engaged in business, agricultural, or professional pursuits, 110,000, in 2,100 clubs in every state in the United States and all provinces in Canada. It is estimated that approximately 1,000 members are below the age of 25.

Purpose: To give primacy to the human and spiritual rather than to the material values of life; to encourage the daily living of the Golden Rule in all human relationships; to promote the adoption and the application of high social, business, and professional standards; to develop, by precept and example, a more intelligent, aggressive, and serviceable citizenship; to provide through Kiwanis clubs a practical means to form enduring friendships, to render altruistic service, and to build better communities; to cooperate in creating and maintaining that sound public opinion and high idealism which make possible the increase of righteousness, justice, patriotism, and good will.

Activities: The current program of civic effort includes service to underprivileged children, vocational guidance, establishment of closer relations between rural and urban communities, support of churches in their spiritual aims, initiation and support of constructive policies of conservation, continued interest in public safety, furnishing a broader knowledge of the fundamentals of popular government and the good will existing between the Dominion of Canada and the United States of America. Kiwanis International has one special committee and six standing committees actively concerned wholly or in part with youth, each of which issues timely suggestions to the local clubs. The total of local activities being carried forward includes numerous types of service to children and youth, some executed directly and others through a wide variety of other youth-serving organizations. In March 1940, Kiwanis launched a new organization for young men aged approximately 16 to 21, known as Young Builders.

Publications: *The Kiwanis Magazine*, monthly; $1 to members, $1.50 to nonmembers; Fred. C. W. Parker, editor. Proceedings of international conventions, annually, 500 pp. *Kiwanis Counselor's Handbook: A Guide to Successful Vocational Counseling by Kiwanians*, 20 pp.; *Suggestions for Club Committees on Agriculture*, 10 pp. Numerous printed and mimeographed pamphlets and bulletins covering a wide range of subjects, including agriculture, boys' and girls' work, public affairs, underprivileged children, and vocational guidance.

Staff: Full-time paid employees, 78, of whom 6 spend major time in the field.

Finances: Reserve fund, $79,000. Value of equipment at national headquarters, approximately $25,000. Operating balance at the end of the calendar year 1939, $19,016.41. For that year operations were as follows:

Income

Convention	$ 33,705.00
Membership fees	199,292.99
Publications	112,374.67
Other services	24,415.20
Interest on bonds and bank balances	2,380.01
	$372,167.87

Expenditures

Salaries	$143,738.57
Travel	33,694.76
Communications	13,493.07
Office supplies	7,486.30
Publications	101,625.52
Rent, taxes, insurance, depreciation, and exchange	25,230.92
Addition to equipment	2,230.76
	$327,499.90

LIONS INTERNATIONAL (1917); 332 South Michigan Ave., Chicago, Ill.; Melvin Jones, Secretary General.

Membership: Individuals, 140,000, in 3,800 clubs in the United States and territories, Canada, China, Cuba, Mexico, Colombia, Panama, and Costa Rica.

Purpose: To foster "Liberty: Intelligence: Our Nation's Safety."

Activities: Distributes Juvenile Braille Magazine to blind children between the ages of 8 and 15. Boys' and girls' work includes cooperation with Boy Scouts, Sea Scouts, Girl Scouts, Camp Fire Girls, Girl Reserves, YMCA, YWCA, juvenile court authorities, 4-H Clubs, Future Farmers of America, and other organizations. Civic improvements sponsored by the clubs and of especial benefit to youth include establishment, maintenance, and aid to libraries, and parks, playgrounds, swimming pools, and other recreational projects. Educational activities include cooperation with school authorities in athletic and educational matters, Moral Code of Youth and character education textbooks, educational contests, student aid, presentation of scholarships, prizes, and gifts. The welfare of youth is promoted through all of the service activities, which in general are grouped under eight headings: sight conservation and blind work, boys' and girls' work, citizenship and patriotism, civic improvements, community betterment, education of youth, health and welfare, and safety.

Publications: *The Lion*, monthly; $1 a year. Annual report.

OPTIMIST INTERNATIONAL (1911); 1721 Railway Exchange Bldg., St. Louis, Mo.; Russell F. Meyer, Secretary-Treasurer.

Membership: Individuals, 12,500, in 250 clubs in 37 states, the District of Columbia, and 4 provinces of Canada. The Junior Optimist Clubs have a membership of between 5,000 and 10,000 boys.

Purpose: To develop optimism as a philosophy of life; to promote an active interest in good government and civic affairs and inspire a respect for law; to foster patriotism and work for international accord and friendship among all people. The Optimist slogan "Friend of the Boy" expresses the aims of the clubs in civic and community life and welfare.

Activities: The Optimist International, through its Boys' Work Council, encourages all member clubs to adopt some youth-serving program and assists them in selecting this program; prepares various publications and bulletins to guide member clubs. Each club adopts the program which seems to meet the needs of its own community. These programs include the formation of Junior Optimist Clubs; cooperation with Boy Scouts, Sea Scouts, YMCA, Boys' Clubs, institutional homes, industrial schools, and other social agencies; the Optimist Uncle Plan, under which a needy or delinquent boy is assigned to one member of the senior club who becomes a big brother to him; providing scholarship funds; furnishing equipment for existing playgrounds and camps; employment bureaus; vocational guidance; medical and dental care; and instructions in craft work. Annual oratorical contests are held, the district winners competing at the international convention.

Publications: *The Optimist International*, monthly; $1.50 a year, free to senior Optimists; Russell F. Meyer, editor. "*Friend of the Boy*," booklet. Various pamphlets and bulletins on boys' work.

Staff: Full-time paid employees, 23, of whom 15 spend major time in the field; part-time paid employee, 1.

Finances: Reserve fund, $6,500. Estimated value of plant and equipment at national headquarters, $13,500. Operating balance at the end of the latest fiscal year, $9,000. Operations for the year ending June 30, 1941 are budgeted as follows:

Income

Membership fees	$66,500
Supply sales	6,000
Other sources	2,500
	$75,000

Expenditures

Salaries	$16,000
Travel	7,500
Communications	5,300
Office supplies	650
Publications	7,500
Rent, taxes, insurance	2,800
Addition to plant and equipment	400
Other purposes	12,700
	$52,850

ROTARY INTERNATIONAL (1905); 35 East Wacker Drive, Chicago, Ill.; Chesley R. Perry, Secretary.

Membership: Business and professional men, 210,000, in nearly 5,000 clubs located in approximately 60 countries and geographical regions of the world.

Purpose: To encourage and foster the ideal of service as a basis of worthy enterprise and, in particular, to encourage and foster: (1) the development of acquaintance as an opportunity for service; (2) high ethical standards in business and professions, the recognition of the worthiness of all useful occupations, and the dignifying by each Rotarian of his occupation as an opportunity to serve society; (3) the application of the ideal of service by every Rotarian to his personal, business, and community life; (4) the advancement of international understanding, good will, and peace through a world fellowship of business and professional men united in the ideal of service.

Activities: In general, activities are indicated by the aforementioned objectives. Specifically, in the field of youth activities, clubs engage in: vocational guidance, training, placement, and counseling for youth; work for crippled and otherwise handicapped children; various character- and body-building activities such as provision of playgrounds, swimming pools, camps, boys' clubs, cooperation with Boy and Girl Scouts, and promotion of Boys and Girls Week (see National Boys and Girls Week Committee for the United States, p. 198); aid to underprivileged children through milk funds, shoe and stocking funds,

and special entertainments; promotion of recreational projects such as boys' bands and hobby fairs; measures for reduction of juvenile delinquency; aid to rural youth through 4-H Club cooperation; special aids to young people between the ages of 16 and 24 through student loan funds and scholarships; and the formation of local youth councils.

Publications: *The Rotarian*, monthly; $1.50 a year in the United States, Canada, and other countries to which minimum postal rate applies, $2 in other countries, 25¢ a single copy (circulation, 179,500); Leland D. Case, editor and manager. *Revista Rotaria*, $1.25 a year (circulation, 13,125); M. Hinojosa-Flores, managing editor. Proceedings of annual international conventions, $2. *Careers for Youth*, by Walter B. Pitkin, 25¢; *This Rotarian Age*, by Paul P. Harris, $1.50.

Staff: Full-time paid employees, 147. This figure includes the personnel of the Chicago office and also the Bombay, India, and Zurich, Switzerland, offices of the secretariat of Rotary International.

UNITED STATES JUNIOR CHAMBER OF COMMERCE (1920); Merchandise Mart Bldg., Chicago, Ill.; Thomas R. Reid, Executive Vice President.

Membership: Business and professional men aged 21 to 35, 110,000, in 850 local organizations in 38 state organizations. A very small percentage of the membership is under 24 years of age.

Purpose: To teach civic responsibility; to express the younger man's point of view; to encourage cooperative action between and among local junior chambers of commerce; to render specific service to local units through the medium of bulletins and other materials prepared by the national office.

Activities: The work is carried out by national committees dealing with the following subjects: Americanism, safety, public health, civil identification, city beautification, and public welfare. The National Youth Welfare Committee with corresponding state and local youth welfare committees cooperates with the Boy Scouts, the Boys' Clubs, and other existing social agencies in the community, especially those agencies working for the prevention of juvenile delinquency; sponsors science clubs to train youth in technology. The Americanism Committee has inaugurated a number of training programs on the duties and privileges of citizenship. Each year the clubs observe Americanism Week (February 12–22), holding rallies and citizenship training meetings to which boys and girls are invited for training.

Publications: *Future Magazine*, monthly. Numerous pamphlets and booklets on various committee activities and organization matters, including a manual on the formation of junior science clubs, a manual on cooperation with Boy Scouts, and a manual on cooperation with Boys' Clubs.

Staff: Full-time paid employees, 11.

TABLE XV

STATISTICS OF COMMERCIAL AND "SERVICE" CLUBS

Organization	Year Founded	Approximate Aggregate Membership (individuals)	Number of Members under 25 Years of Age	Total Employees on Headquarters Staff	Aggregate Endowment of National Headquarters	Plant and Equipment (headquarters only)	Approximate Annual Budget (headquarters only)
Civitan International	1920	6,500	750	6	none	$ 4,000	$ 31,000
Kiwanis International	1915	110,000	1,000	78	none[a]	25,000	372,200
Lions International	1917	140,000	…	…	…	…	…
Optimist International	1911	12,500[b]	7,500[c]	24	none[d]	13,500	75,000
Rotary International	1905	210,000[e]	…	147[f]	…	…	…
United States Junior Chamber of Commerce	1920	110,000	…	11	none	…	…

a The organization has reserve funds of $6,500.
b Adult members only.
c Membership of Junior Optimist Clubs.

d The organization has reserve funds of $79,000.
e Includes membership in all parts of the world.
f Includes staff members outside of the United States.

XV. Women's Clubs

One of the most significant developments in Western civilization during the nineteenth and twentieth centuries has been the rapidly changing status of women. One has but to reflect upon the myriad contrasts between the life of the average woman of the late Victorian era and that of her daughter or granddaughter today to set in motion a train of thought which will reveal how startlingly different the place of women in society has already become.

The recognition of women as individuals in their own right, no longer mere appendages to the male head of the household, and bearing equal responsibilities in citizenship and in the intellectual realm, is an important phase of the world-wide progress of democracy which characterizes modern times. The increasing interest of women in social problems, and their increasing entry into the professions and other occupations, has naturally led to the forming of many women's organizations both for the study of civic questions and for the advancement of the professional interests of their members.

These organizations are federated in several large national groupings, such as the General Federation of Women's Clubs, the National Federation of Business and Professional Women's Clubs, and others. They seek in many ways to attract the interest, stimulate the thought, and widen the horizons of girls and young women. They also increasingly provide such concrete services as scholarships and fellowships and guidance materials. Collectively they constitute an important influence in the lives of American girls, in ways which the descriptions will to some extent disclose.

Cross references: American Association of University Women, p. 115; Foundation for Positive Health, p. 175; Institute of Women's Professional Relations, p. 147; Junior Hadassah, p. 60; National Catholic Welfare Conference, National Council of Catholic Women, p. 50; National Committee on Cause and Cure of War, p. 215; National Council of Jewish Juniors, p. 60; National Women's Trade Union League, p. 85; Women's International League for Peace and Freedom, p. 217; Young Women's Christian Associations, p. 28.

ASSOCIATION OF THE JUNIOR LEAGUES OF AMERICA, INC. (1921); The Waldorf-Astoria, 305 Park Ave., New York, N.Y.; Mrs. DeForest Van Slyck, Executive Secretary; Virginia Howlett, Secretary of the Community Service Department.

Membership: Young women aged 18 to 40, approximately 34,000, in 150 local Junior Leagues in the United States, Canada, and Mexico. The association collects an annual per capita fee of $5.

Purpose: To unite in one body all the Junior Leagues and to promote their individual purposes, i.e., to foster interest among their members in the social, economic, educational, cultural, and civic conditions of their own communities, and to make efficient their volunteer service.

Activities: The local leagues and their individual members perform volunteer social work of many types, in the fields of health, child welfare, family welfare, community organization, recreation, education, and neighborhood activities. They also foster many enterprises in the fields of music, art, the drama, history, civic planning, and nonpartisan politics. Money-raising activities for the support of welfare work also have a prominent place. In the Community Service Department there are: five social workers whose function is to effect liaison between the local leagues and the local professional social workers and with the specialized national agencies, as well as to advise local leagues on social work and to give orientation courses in this field; a staff member who fosters and stimulates interest in cultural organizations and activities on the part of local leagues and of individual members; and two children's theater staff members who supply information on children's plays, marionettes, puppets, and movies, as well as advice on playwriting, all with the purpose of developing the inherent imaginative and creative gifts of children. There is an annual conference attended by two representatives of each constituent league.

Publications: *Junior League Magazine*, 10 issues annually; $2.50 a year to nonmembers (paid circulation, 35,000); Mrs. Bradley Saunders, editor. *Handbook*, the issue for 1940 containing 134 pages, 50¢. Occasional pamphlets, e.g., *Volunteer Placement and Education in Junior Leagues*, 50¢.

Staff: Executive staff of 15 persons, of whom 8 are field representatives.

ASSOCIATION OF SOUTHERN WOMEN FOR THE PREVENTION OF LYNCHING (1930); 710 Standard Bldg., Atlanta, Ga.; Mrs. Jessie Daniel Ames, Executive Director.

Membership: Individuals, 41,000, in local women's

organizations grouped into state councils and county organizations.

Purpose: To develop methods of procedure for the use of organizations which have committed themselves to carry on through their own constituencies the educational processes which eventually must eradicate lynching.

Activities: An educational program is carried forward emphasizing facts on current lynchings and the menace of lynching to our social order, with always a repudiation of lynching for any reason whatever. The program has been endorsed by 109 organizations. The local units work to increase the number of men and women, including sheriffs, committed in writing against lynching. Signatures to the pledge have been obtained from about 41,000 individuals, in 1,033 counties. Sponsors round-table discussions in high schools and colleges on lynching, emphasizing the effect of lynching on our social order, the high crime record of the South, the cultivation of a generally lawless spirit, and the degrading effect of lynching upon the mob. In denominational and civic summer conferences of young people from the ages of 16 to 21 or 22, conducts discussion groups of five to ten days dealing with lynching as a symptom of racial attitudes in an economic condition rather than a cause in itself.

Publications: Bulletins giving pertinent information about the work of the organization and facts about lynchings; posters; and maps.

Staff: Full-time paid employees, 2; part-time paid employees, 6.

GENERAL FEDERATION OF WOMEN'S CLUBS
(1890); 1734 N St., N.W., Washington, D.C.; Mrs. Saidie Orr Dunbar, President.

Membership: State federations of women's clubs in the United States, Alaska, and the District of Columbia, 50, composed of more than 15,000 club units, with a total individual membership, including membership of affiliated national organizations, of more than 2,000,000; foreign clubs, 70; junior clubs, approximately 2,000, with an aggregate membership of 36,000 young women and girls under 30 years of age. Annual dues: affiliated organizations, $5; foreign and territorial clubs, $1; local clubs, 25¢ a club and 10¢ a member.

Purpose: To advance "educational, industrial, philanthropic, literary, artistic, and scientific culture; and to bring into communication with one another the various women's clubs throughout the world."

Activities: Promotes studies and activities in the fields of American citizenship, the home, education, fine arts, international relations, legislation, public welfare, conservation, public safety, and urban-rural cooperation. The organization and its state federations sponsor scholarship and fellowship funds; funds available for this purpose aggregate over $1,500,000. The Junior Department is composed of organized groups of young women and girls; junior clubs are primarily engaged in social service and public welfare activities. In the Department of Education is a Youth Cooperation Division, created to promote the welfare of youth throughout the nation; the program emphasizes education, employment, and recreation of youth. The Ruth McBride Powers Award of this division offers $250 in prizes to the two states reporting the most outstanding activities in youth cooperation from September 1939 to March 1941. The program of the federation includes sponsorship of Girl and Boy Scout groups, Camp Fire Girls, Young Mothers' Clubs, and similar youth organizations.

Publications: *The Clubwoman GFWC*, monthly; free to members, $1 a year to others; Vella A. Winner, editor. Numerous leaflets and pamphlets issued by the departments.

Staff: Full-time paid employees, 24; part-time paid employee, 1.

Finances: Endowment and other trust funds, $426,134.34. Value of plant and equipment of national headquarters, $90,270.18. For the fiscal year ending March 31, 1940, cash receipts and disbursements (including transfers between funds) totaled $204,580.40 and $197,040.96 respectively.

INTERNATIONAL ASSOCIATION OF ALTRUSA
CLUBS, INC. (1917); 540 North Michigan Ave., Chicago, Ill.; Mabel F. Meek, Secretary-Treasurer.

Membership: Executive business and professional women, approximately 4,500, in 170 clubs in 42 states of the United States, 1 in Puerto Rico, and 2 in the republic of Mexico. Each member is classified under an occupational unit. No single unit may furnish more than 10 per cent of a club's total membership. Unchartered club fee is $10 a member, and each affiliated club pays annual per capita dues of $4.

Purpose: (1) To encourage, promote, extend, and supervise Altrusa throughout the United States, Dominion of Canada, Mexico, and other countries that may be approved by the International Executive Committee, and to coordinate and direct generally the activities of the member clubs; (2) to cultivate friendly relationships, promote mutual understanding, and foster the solidarity of women who are actively engaged in business and the professions; (3) to encourage high ethical standards of business and professional conduct; (4) to be of service to young women entering business and professional fields; (5) to encourage participation in community and public affairs of a nonpartisan character; (6) to do any and all things conducive to the service, betterment, and ultimate welfare of women in business and in the professions; (7) to promote educational and cultural training and improvement.

Activities: Each club is urged to sponsor a vocational guidance council, composed of representatives of all local groups concerned with vocational guidance, to coordinate guidance activities and interpret techniques to the community; its function is to develop such activities as shall seem to be best suited to the needs of the community and to act as a clearinghouse of occupational information and counseling. Each year Altrusa celebrates Vocational Guidance Week. During this period young girls are given tryout opportunities in offices of Altrusans, and other guidance projects are carried on. The program of vocational guidance was expanded at the 1939 convention to include assistance to the mature woman in making a satisfactory vocational adjustment. Among other projects which many clubs are carrying on in an effort to be of service to young women are: providing members as speakers on their respective vocations before school classes, clubs, and other groups, and in private conferences when desired; sponsoring of career conferences with schools, colleges, and universities; arranging of radio interviews and programs with members of various occupations; series of talks built on one central theme and following a definite continuity; through individual clubs, offering of scholarships and loan funds to promising girls desiring to continue their education, and providing assistance in securing a position after graduation.

Publications: *International Altrusan*, monthly, September through June; $1 a year; Ruth Lemmer, editor. *The Older Woman and Her Job*, 10¢; *A Career in Verbatim Reporting*, by Fanny S. Sweeney, 5¢. Various leaflets are available to the membership from headquarters.

Staff: Full-time paid employees, 4; part-time paid employee, 1.

NATIONAL COUNCIL OF WOMEN (1888); 501 Madison Ave., New York, N.Y.; Mrs. Harold V. Milligan, President.

Affiliated with the International Council of Women, which has national councils in 36 countries.

Membership: Twenty constituent national organizations with total individual membership of about 5,000,000 women, including: Association of Women in Public Health; National Women's Party; National Kindergarten Association (see p. 135); National Women's Christian Temperance Union; Hadassah; National Association of Colored Women; Young Women's Mutual Improvement Association. Annual dues, $100.

Purpose: To serve as an information bureau for the member organizations; to disseminate and interchange ideas on citizenship, consumer interests, fine arts, economic status of women, education, human relations, international affairs, public health, music, letters, radio, and social hygiene.

Activities: Work by committees on each of the subjects mentioned above in the statement of purpose.

Publications: *News-Letters*, occasionally.

Staff: Full-time paid employee, 1.

NATIONAL FEDERATION OF BUSINESS AND PROFESSIONAL WOMEN'S CLUBS, INC. (1919); 1819 Broadway, New York, N.Y.; Louise Franklin Bache, Executive Secretary; Frances Cummings, Director of Program Coordination.

Membership: Business and professional women, 73,044 (as of July 1, 1940), in 1,641 clubs in 48 states, the District of Columbia, Hawaii, and Alaska; 48 state federations.

Purpose: To elevate the standards for women in business and in the professions; to extend opportunities to them through education along lines of industrial, scientific, and vocational activities; "to fit itself to assume real leadership on economic problems and their social implications, with a view toward establishing, through scientific methods, conditions which assure to both women and men the fullest possible opportunity for the development of whatever capacities they may possess."

Activities: Conducts research studies on legislation affecting business and professional women and currently is concerned with the restrictions affecting married women; supports the merit system in government, federal aid to public education under state control, and ratification of the child labor amendment; sponsors a program of vocational guidance consisting chiefly of the dissemination of publications offering occupational information and guides to successful adjustment to the demands of working life. Local clubs administer educational funds for students at various levels. Many persons not members between the ages of 12 and 24 are served by the clubs; they include students in high schools and other educational institutions, as well as business and professional women who have left school. Local clubs often sponsor or assist Girl Scout troops, 4-H Clubs, and similar character-building agencies. The program of the federation stimulates its members to inform themselves as to economic, social, and political problems of the day through discussion groups, suggested reading, and participation in community activities. Under able leadership the federation offers the alert business and professional woman opportunity to keep informed and to have a part in the solution of such vital problems.

Publications: *Independent Woman*, monthly; free to members, $1.50 a year to others; Winifred Willson, editor. Numerous other pamphlets, studies, and program kits on membership organization, program coordination, legislation, education, international relations, finance, health, publicity, and other subjects, ranging in price from 3¢ to $3.50.

Staff: Full-time paid employees, 32, of whom 4 spend major time in the field; part-time paid employees, 2.

Finances: There are two special reserve funds: Lena Lake Forrest Fellowship Fund, principal $12,446.96; and Lena Madesin Phillips Building Fund, principal

$43,383.76. For the fiscal year ending July 1, 1940, income totaled $156,679.49, of which $142,420.75 was derived from dues; operating expenses for the same period aggregated $150,223.34.

NATIONAL LEAGUE OF WOMEN VOTERS
(1920); 726 Jackson Place, N.W., Washington, D.C.; Marguerite M. Wells, President.

Membership: Consists of over 550 affiliated leagues in 31 states and the District of Columbia. The league is supported by the state leagues and contributions by individuals.

Purpose: To promote political education through active participation of citizens in government. The league does not ally itself with or support any political party but does endorse measures and policies.

Activities: Directs activities of league members on national, state, and local political problems. The league limits its program to certain definite governmental problems designated by vote of delegates in biennial convention. Materials are prepared and published to provide the basis for study. Secures legislative measures through, or partly through, the efforts of Leagues of Women Voters; trains thousands of women in responsible participation in government. Some of the methods used in educating members on selected questions are: fact-finding surveys; visits to legislative bodies, administrative bodies, courts of law, and public institutions; study groups; radio programs; general membership meetings; compilation and publication of replies of candidates to questionnaires; citizenship schools and institutes of government and politics. Digests of election laws, voters' handbooks, and summaries of official reports are prepared from time to time.

Publications: *News-Letters*, giving news on national events related to the league's program, 20 to 25 issues annually; $1 a year. *Member's Magazine*, monthly except July and August; sent only to members. Various pamphlets designed to assist members to carry on their work of education in government and politics. List of publications on request.

Staff: Full-time paid employees, 20.

Finances: Endowment funds, $70,000; reserve funds, $13,380. Value of equipment at national headquarters, $2,550. The budget for 1940–41 is $82,860. Balance March 31, 1940, $5,655. For the fiscal year ending on that date, operations were as follows:

Income

Gifts and grants	$24,152
State leagues	26,078
Publications	10,275
National meeting registration	426
Endowment and reserve funds	2,832
	$63,763

Expenditures

Salaries	$39,240
Travel	4,651
Communications	1,823
Office supplies	1,182
Publications	7,280
Rentals	3,600
Equipment	600
National meeting and other purposes	5,186
	$63,562

QUOTA CLUB INTERNATIONAL, INC.
(1919); 1204 18th St., N.W., Washington, D.C.; Gwladys W. Jones, General Secretary.

Membership: Active local clubs in the United States, Canada, and Australia, 124. Each club has a minimum active membership of 15 women, one being chosen from each of the business and professional classifications in the community.

Purpose: To promote the adoption and application of high ethical standards in social, business, and professional relationships; to encourage the recognition of the worth of all useful occupations as a means of service to society and to the community; to cooperate in promoting among business and professional women an intelligent advancement of ideals of righteousness, justice, mutual understanding, and good will.

Activities: Weekly luncheons or dinner meetings with discussions on good citizenship, crime prevention, extending friendly relations, recognition of the achievements of women, international relations, and girls' service; annual conventions. Since 1925 the international organization has sponsored Girls' Service Work, for the purpose of giving girls selected by local clubs greater opportunities for moral, mental, spiritual, and physical development and to assist them to secure training for business or professional life.

Publications: *The Quotarian*, monthly except June and July; Gwladys W. Jones, editor. *Quota Club— What Is It*, leaflet. Other materials prepared for personal use of members.

Staff: Full-time paid employees, 3.

ZONTA INTERNATIONAL
(1919); 59 East Van Buren St., Chicago, Ill.; Harriet C. Richards, Executive Secretary.

Membership: Business and professional executive women, approximately 4,300, in 150 clubs located in 24 states. There are 4 clubs in the Scandinavian countries and 6 clubs in Canada.

Purpose: To encourage high ethical standards in business and the professions; to improve the legal, political, economic, and professional status of women; to encourage, promote, and supervise the organization of Zonta Clubs in all commercial centers of the world; to study the work of existing Zonta Clubs and their value to their respective members and communities, and to clear the information thus acquired for the benefit of all; to promote the broad spirit of good fellowship among Zontians and among Zonta Clubs; to work for the advancement of understanding, good will, and peace through a world fellowship of executive women in business and profession, united in the Zonta ideal of service.

Activities: Local clubs are active in sponsoring educational and constructive work for girls and women. Service projects carried on by various clubs include assistance to school girls in the way of loans or clothes, vocational guidance activities, donations to community chests, providing of footwear for needy school children, relief for unemployed business and professional women, and yearly award to the individual member who has made the most constructive contribution to the life of the community. A convention of all local clubs is held each year.

Publications: *The Zontian*, monthly except June and July; $1 a year; Amy C. Fahlgren, editor.

Staff: Full-time paid employees, 4; part-time paid employees, 2.

TABLE XVI

STATISTICS OF WOMEN'S CLUBS

Organization	Year Founded	Approximate Aggregate Membership (individuals)	Number of Members under 25 Years of Age	Total Employees on Headquarters Staff	Aggregate Endowment of National Headquarters	Plant and Equipment (headquarters only)	Approximate Annual Budget (headquarters only)
Association of the Junior Leagues of America	1921	34,000	...	15[a]	$ ...	$ ...	$ ...
Assn. of Southern Women for Prevention of Lynching	1930	41,000	...	8	...	...	...
General Federation of Women's Clubs	1890	2,000,000[b]	36,000[c]	25	426,134[d]	90,270	204,600
International Association of Altrusa Clubs	1917	4,500	...	5	...	...	...
National Council of Women	1888	5,000,000[e]	...	1	...	...	...
Natl. Fed. of Business and Professional Women's Clubs	1919	73,044	...	34	none[f]	...	156,700
National League of Women Voters	1920	550[g]	...	20	70,000[h]	2,550	63,800
Quota Club International	1919	124[g]	...	3	none	...	...
Zonta International	1919	4,300	...	6	...	...	...

a Executive staff only.
b Includes membership of affiliated national organizations.
c Includes members up to 30 years of age.
d Includes trust funds.

e Underlying membership of 20 constituent organizations.
f The organization has a fellowship fund and a building fund totaling $55,831.
g Number of constituent local bodies.
h Also reserve funds of $13,380.

XVI. Educational Associations

Education in the United States is largely a tax-supported enterprise, though privately controlled institutions still play a considerable part, especially in higher education. Control of the local public schools is within the jurisdiction of the states. For this reason there is no comprehensive national administrative system for this function. It is therefore to be expected that national voluntary associations of teachers, parents, and others interested in special phases of education should come to occupy a large place in the national educational scene.

Since 1933 the federal government has directly supported and administered a notable new type of educational agency for young men in the Civilian Conservation Corps, wherein instruction and outdoor work are conducted concurrently. Since 1935 the National Youth Administration has aided the education of needy youth of both sexes, by financing part-time employment for students in schools and colleges who would otherwise be unable to continue their attendance and by providing work projects having value as vocational training and guidance for out-of-school youth aged 18 or more. In recent years this agency has also conducted an increasing number of resident training centers where work and instruction are combined.

The principles and plans involved in the financing and administration of these innovations, as well as the evaluation of their outcomes and the defining of their future relations to the public schools, are matters of great import. The American Youth Commission recommends that part-time work combined with instruction and guidance should be provided under governmental auspices for all youth aged 16 or more who are not in school and who cannot find jobs in private employment.

Regarding the future of the American educational system, the Commission also urges that many of the 120,000 public school districts in the United States, particularly the small rural districts unable to maintain modern schools, be merged to form larger and more efficient units of school support and administration. State aid to local districts should be increased in many states, and in all states its apportionment should be improved constantly to lessen inequalities.

The Commission is convinced that the achievement and maintenance of a reasonable equality of educational opportunity throughout the nation requires that federal financial aid to the states for general educational purposes be inaugurated. It also recommends that both public and private efforts to provide earning opportunities which enable competent students to continue their schooling should be improved and extended.

The national voluntary associations collectively have an important role in shaping the future of public education in America. That their number is large may be discovered by reference to the annual *Educational Directory* published by the United States Office of Education. Only a limited number of the larger or more prominent ones are described in the present section.

With the exception of the National Congress of Parents and Teachers, which reports approximately 2,330,000 individual members, the association numerically largest in point of aggregate membership is the National Education Association of the United States with more than 203,000 persons on its rolls, many of whom are also members of one or more of its twenty-seven departments, several of which are in themselves associations of considerable size.

Organized on a different basis is the American Council on Education, composed of representatives of 81 national associations in education and related fields and of 416 institutional members, most of which are accredited colleges and universities but which also include some private secondary schools, local public school systems, and state departments of public instruction. The range of the Council's interests embraces education at all levels and through all agencies, as well as the related services affecting the public welfare.

The two organizations in this section whose membership or clientele consists chiefly of young persons, as distinguished from those composed wholly or largely of persons above the age of 25, are:

Future Teachers of America
Work Camps for America

Cross references: Section V, General Character-Building Organizations for Youth, pp. 19–30; Section IX, Student Associations, pp. 66–69; Section X, Organizations for Research and Social Planning, pp. 70–79; Section XIII, Negro and Interracial Organizations, pp. 96–101; Section XVII, Organizations in the Fields of Guidance, Personnel, and Employment, pp. 142–50; Section XVIII, Leisure and Recreational Associations, pp. 151–69; Section XIX, Health and Safety Organizations, pp. 170–83; Section XXII, Organizations Serving Handicapped Youth, pp. 202–8. *See also:* Allied Youth, p. 212; Committee on Militarism in Education, p. 214; Council of Church Boards of Education, p. 34; League of Nations Association, p. 215; National League of Women Voters, p. 109.

AMERICAN ASSOCIATION FOR ADULT EDUCATION (1926); 60 East 42nd St., New York, N.Y.; Morse A. Cartwright, Director.

Membership: Individuals, 1,080; organizations (nonprofit educational), 275. Annual dues: individuals, $3; organizations, $5.

Purpose: To serve as a clearinghouse for information in the field of adult education; to assist adult education enterprises already in operation; to help groups initiate activities in adult education; to aid and advise individuals who, although occupied with some primary vocation or interest, desire to continue their education.

Activities: Maintains a library for the use of its members and the public. Stimulates, sponsors, and in some cases conducts experiments and research. Since 1936 has been issuing a series of studies in the social significance of adult education. Conducts research and practical experimentation through the Readability Laboratory at Teachers College, Columbia University, in the simplification of material for students at many educational levels. Encourages the formation of community, state, and regional associations for adult education. Holds annual meetings and sponsors regional meetings.

Publications: *Journal of Adult Education,* quarterly; $3 a year; Mary L. Ely and Morse A. Cartwright, editors. *Adult Education in Action,* edited by Mary L. Ely, 1936, 480 pp., $2.75; *Handbook of Adult Education in the United States,* edited by Dorothy Rowden, 1936, 425 pp., $2.25. Recent titles include: *The Museum and Popular Culture,* by T. R. Adam, 1939, 177 pp., $1; *The Worker's Road to Learning,* by T. R. Adam, 1940, $1.25; *Education for Social Understanding,* by Gaynell Hawkins, 1940, $1.25; *Educating for Health,* by Frank Ernest Hill, 1939, 224 pp., $1.25; *Training for the Job,* by Frank Ernest Hill, 1940, 168 pp., $1.25; *Adult Education Councils,* by Ruth Kotinsky, 1940, $1.25; *The Agrarian Revival: A Study of Agricultural Extension,* by Russell Lord, 1939, 236 pp., $1.50; *The Church and Adult Education,* by Bernard E. Meland, 1939, 114 pp., $1; and numerous other titles. List on request.

Staff: Full-time paid employees, 15, of whom 2 spend major time in field work; part-time paid employees, 3, of whom 2 are engaged in field work.

Finances: The principal source of income for all divisions is grants from the Carnegie Corporation of New York. In 1938–39, $214,345.84 was expended in special project funds and $30,125 in grants for other organizations. Balances of various special projects, study, and conference funds on September 30, 1939 aggregated $40,037.84; balances of funds for account of other organizations aggregated $5,000.

Current balance for the central organization September 30, 1939 was $14,960.29. For the fiscal year ending on that date, operations were as follows:

Income

Gifts	$50,000.00
Membership fees	4,319.44
Journal	1,225.27
Other sources	14,046.41
	$69,591.12

Expenditures

Salaries	$44,560.00
Travel	1,105.07
Publications	7,725.42
Other purposes	15,020.65
	$68,412.14

AMERICAN ASSOCIATION FOR HEALTH, PHYSICAL EDUCATION, AND RECREATION (1885); 1201 16th St., N.W., Washington, D.C.; N. P. Neilson, Executive Secretary.

Name changed from American Physical Education Association, 1938. The former Women's Division of the National Amateur Athletic Federation is now merged with this organization, and the whole is a department of the National Education Association (see p. 131).

Membership: Individuals, 10,231, teachers and administrators of health and physical education, including research, athletic, and recreational activities, in schools and other institutions. There are 49 constituent state and territorial associations. About 1,200 of the members are students, graduate and undergraduate, in physical education major courses.

Purpose: In relation to health, physical education, and recreation: to awaken and promote a wide and intelligent interest; to acquire and disseminate accurate information; and to provide such means of promotion as will secure an adequate program.

Activities: Holds an annual national convention and five district conventions. Has numerous sections and committees working on problems in all phases of the field, such as physical education in public schools, recreation, research, teacher training, therapeutics, women's athletics, men's athletics, dancing, camping, and swimming. Cooperates with other educational, recreational, and health organizations. A special meeting for students is generally featured on each convention program.

Publications: *Journal of Health and Physical Education*, 10 issues annually; $2 a year, $1.50 to students; E. D. Mitchell, editor, 311 Maynard St., Ann Arbor, Mich. *Research Quarterly*, $3 a year, $1.50 to students; same address.

Staff: Full-time paid employees, 8, of whom 1 spends major time in field work.

Finances: Endowment fund, $1,917.79. Current balance June 30, 1939, $7,482.05. For the fiscal year ending on that date, operations were as follows:

Income

Gifts for current expenses	$ 1,057.99
Membership fees	20,567.83
Publications	10,582.81
Convention	1,241.01
Interest on investments	28.28
Other sources	820.64
	$34,298.56

Expenditures

Salaries	$15,229.07
Travel	960.57
Communications	1,253.49
Office supplies	790.03
Publications	14,943.69
Other purposes	3,584.37
	$36,761.22

AMERICAN ASSOCIATION OF JUNIOR COLLEGES (1920); 730 Jackson Place, Washington, D.C.; Walter Crosby Eells, Executive Secretary.

Membership: Active members (accredited junior colleges or separately organized lower divisions of four-year colleges or universities), 345; associate members (newly organized junior colleges and those not yet having received accreditation), 39; sustaining members (interested individuals, or organizations other than junior colleges), 30; honorary members (individuals who have performed outstanding service to the junior college movement), 2. Also 6 closely affiliated regional associations and 19 loosely affiliated state associations.

Purpose: To stimulate the professional development of its members; to promote the growth of junior colleges under appropriate conditions; to emphasize the significant place of the junior college in American education; and to interpret the junior college movement to the country.

Activities: Sponsors the following special service and research studies relating to junior colleges: terminal education; consumer education; adult education;

financial accounting manual and service; and speech education. Provides a general informational and advisory service and an interpretative and publicity service. During 1940 has conducted a series of special conferences of the Commission on Junior College Terminal Education in 19 states and the District of Columbia in order to interpret the need for terminal education at the junior college level and to secure the judgment of junior college leaders regarding the problems in this field; at each center, conferences have also been held with student representatives, including editors of student papers, other student leaders, and students from terminal courses. The association indirectly serves the needs and interests of approximately 200,000 young people enrolled in some 600 junior colleges in the 48 states, the District of Columbia, and the Canal Zone.

Publications: *Junior College Journal*, monthly, September to June; $3 a year. *Junior College Directory, 1940*, annually; 32 pp., 35¢; Walter C. Eells, editor. *Twentieth Annual Meeting* (addresses and proceedings), 204 pp., 75¢. *American Junior Colleges*, edited by Walter C. Eells, 1940 (first edition), 585 pp., $3.50; *The Next Twenty Years of the Junior College Movement*, by George F. Zook, 16 pp., 10¢; *Athletic Practices in Junior Colleges* (committee report), 12 pp., 10¢; *Honor Societies in Junior Colleges* (committee report), 8 pp., 10¢; various other pamphlets.

Staff (including staff of terminal study): Full-time paid employees, 7; part-time paid employees, 3.

Finances: Value of equipment at headquarters, $1,000. Balance December 31, 1939, $2,158. For the preceding calendar year, operations were as follows:

Income

Gifts and grants	$ 1,500
Membership fees	6,570
Publications	4,122
Annual meeting exhibits	290
	$12,482

Expenditures

Salaries	$ 5,309
Travel	140
Communications	531
Office supplies and equipment	300
Publications	4,063
Rent, etc.	480
Policy Commission meeting	1,500
Miscellaneous	161
	$12,484

AMERICAN ASSOCIATION OF SCHOOL ADMINISTRATORS, A DEPARTMENT OF THE NATIONAL EDUCATION ASSOCIATION (1870); 1201 16th St., N.W., Washington, D.C.; Sherwood D. Shankland, Executive Secretary.

Name changed from Department of Superintendence, 1937.

Membership: Individuals, 4,361, superintendents and administrators in state, county, and city school systems, and heads of colleges, universities, and institutions for the education of teachers. Types of membership and annual dues: active, $5; associate (open to members of the National Education Association engaged in any phase of school work; includes all department privileges except the right to vote and hold office), $5. Life members pay $100 or secure a contribution of $250 for the Permanent Educational Research Fund; honorary members are recommended by the executive committee. Members receive the yearbook, the convention reports, subscription to the *Research Bulletin* of the NEA, advance notices of convention plans. Membership in the NEA is a prerequisite to all department privileges.

Purpose: To promote the general educational welfare in the field of administration and supervision; to make constructive studies; to further the effort and increase the efficiency of persons engaged in education; to foster professional zeal; to advance educational aims and standards; to protect and advance the interests of school administration.

Activities: Carries on important studies in education; maintains the Educational Research Service cooperatively with the National Education Association (see p. 131); appoints a special commission annually to prepare a yearbook on some topic of special interest to school superintendents; holds an annual convention the fourth Sunday in February and on the four succeeding days. Maintains committees on safety education, certification of superintendents of schools, education for family life, health education. Initiated the Educational Policies Commission (see p. 74) as a joint enterprise with the NEA. Is concerned primarily with the educational welfare of children and youth of all ages.

Publications: Official report of convention proceedings, annually; free to members, $1 to others. Yearbook, annually; free to members, $2 to others. Titles of recent yearbooks: *Educational Leadership—Progress and Possibilities*, 1933; *Critical Problems in School Administration*, 1934; *Social Change and Education*, 1935; *The Social Studies Curriculum*, 1936; *The Improvement of Education—Its Interpretation for Democracy*, 1937; *Youth Education Today*, 1938; *Schools in Small Communities*, 1939; *Safety Education*, 1940; *Education for Family Life*, 1941. Report of the Committee on Certification of Superintendents of Schools, *The Superintendent of Schools and His Work*, 48 pp., free to members, 25¢ to others.

Staff: Full-time paid employees, 12.

Finances: Assets of the Permanent Educational Research Fund as of December 31, 1939 were $24,975.07. Operating balance was $13,334.45. For the fiscal year ending on that date, operations were as follows:

Income

Membership fees	$20,785.00
Interest on Permanent Research Fund	902.04
Publications	5,663.76
Convention exhibit	20,293.10
Educational Research Service	10,460.42
	$58,104.32

Expenditures

Salaries	$21,573.00
Communications	6,264.35
Office supplies	1,516.61
Books purchased	3,479.40
Convention	9,719.40
Travel	7,598.71
Printing	13,768.16
	$63,919.63

AMERICAN ASSOCIATION OF UNIVERSITY WOMEN (1882); 1634 Eye St., N.W., Washington, D.C.; Dr. Kathryn McHale, General Director.

Membership: Women, graduates of accredited colleges or universities, 68,003; corporate members (institutions), 175; affiliated alumnae associations, 26. There are 888 local branches in 48 states, the District of Columbia, Alaska (2), Hawaii (1), Puerto Rico (1), the Philippine Islands (1), China (3), and Japan (1).

Purpose: To advance practical educational work, the collection and publication of statistical and other information concerning education, and in general the maintenance of high standards of education.

Activities: Works for high educational standards from the nursery school through the university; carries on a national program of study in the fields of education, international relations, social studies, the economic and legal status of women, and the arts, with varied community activities growing out of study; supports legislation and other public action to futher its objectives; supports graduate fellowships for gifted women scholars; maintains a Research Information Service in Secondary and Higher Education and a traveling library; cooperates with university women's groups in other countries to promote international understanding; maintains a national headquarters and club in Washington, D.C.

During the year 1939–40, special activities in educational guidance for girls of secondary school age were carried on in 128 branches, well distributed over the country. There is also widespread cooperation with other agencies in surveys of youth and in providing facilities for out-of-school unemployed youth.

Publications: *Journal of the American Association of University Women*, quarterly; $1 a year to those not eligible to membership; Mrs. Ruth Wilson Tryon, editor. Pamphlets include: *A.A.U.W.: What It Is and What It Does*, 20 pp.; *The Handbook, A*

Guide for Branch Leaders, 54 pp.; *The Lending Library,* 28 pp.; *A.A.U.W. Research Service,* 5 pp.; *A.A.U.W. Publications,* 29 pp. The last named is a catalog of publications issued by the association, study guides, bibliographies, reference materials, and suggestions for branch leaders, on child development and education for family life, standards and trends in education, international relations, the social studies, the economic and legal status of women, the arts, legislation, and AAUW fellowships. It lists a large number of pamphlets and books priced at 5¢ to $2.50.

Staff: Full-time paid employees, 27; part-time paid employee, 1.

Finances: On May 31, 1940, securities in the general fund were valued at $59,717.83; endowment for fellowship funds aggregated $650,937. Plant and equipment at headquarters were valued at $215,292 (original cost). Cash balance was $144,011.13. For the fiscal year ending on that date, operations were as follows:

Income

Membership and other dues	$123,890.25
Journal subscriptions	5,106.53
Fellowship accounts	92,592.64
Other sources	39,555.36
	$261,144.78

Expenditures

General budget	$119,215.47
Headquarters building	13,418.09
Fellowships	16,266.42
Other purposes	82,959.00
	$231,858.98

AMERICAN ASSOCIATION OF VISITING TEACHERS (1916); Green Avenue School, Madison, N.J.; Marion N. Echols, President.

Membership: Individuals, 300.

Purpose: To foster the work of the visiting teacher or school social worker in the adjustment of personality and behavior difficulties of school children; to provide a professional organization to advance the standards of the work of the visiting teacher.

Activities: Holds national meetings twice annually, in conjunction with the National Conference of Social Work (see p. 189) and with the American Association of School Administrators (see p. 114). Members conduct consultations with parents and teachers to encourage closer relations and better understanding between home, school, and community, and endeavor to correlate the work of community social agencies with that of the school and the home in solving the problems of children.

Publications: *Visiting Teacher Bulletin,* 3 issues annually.

Staff: Administrative work is done by unpaid officers.

Finances: Approximate annual budget, $500.

AMERICAN COLLEGE PERSONNEL ASSOCIATION (1923); Mount Holyoke College, South Hadley, Mass.; Helen M. Voorhees, President.

Membership: Individuals, approximately 175, engaged in personnel work in colleges and universities. Annual dues, $4.

Purpose: To join college personnel administrators for the exchange of professional ideas; to further the personnel point of view in higher education; to stimulate best practices in the various types of personnel services represented by the members; to disseminate research findings in the general area of personnel work; to foster research in areas of personnel work where needed.

Activities: Annual meetings at the same time and place as the American Association of School Administrators (see p. 114). The services studied in behalf of college youth include the administration of admission to college, educational, vocational, and personal counseling of students, extracurricular life, placement for students seeking part-time employment and for alumni seeking full-time positions, health service and mental hygiene, housing and discipline of students, development and maintenance of complete personnel records for all students. The committee on relationships with the National Youth Administration, one of several current committees, is engaged in studying the ways in which work programs under the NYA can be made of the greatest educational significance to the students who participate in them.

Publications: Proceedings and reports of annual meetings. The 1939 report is a book of 203 pages, free to members, $1.50 to others.

Staff: No full-time paid employees. Secretarial service is furnished by the institutions with which the officers are connected.

Finances: Balance February 15, 1940, $667.37. For the fiscal year ending on that date, operations were as follows:

Income

Membership fees	$ 824.00
Publications	122.85
Charter sales	4.05
Other sources	667.37
	$1,618.27

Expenditures

Clerical assistance	$ 186.93
Convention expense	140.97
Communications	158.64
Printing	925.93
Other purposes	60.00
	$1,472.47

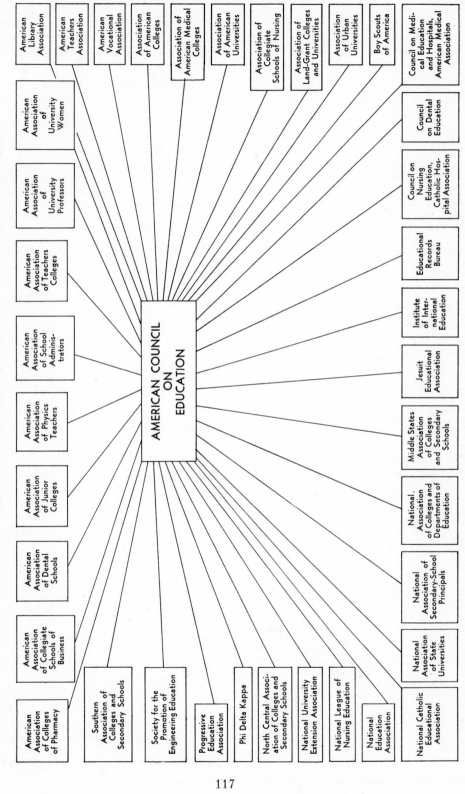

Chart II

THE AMERICAN COUNCIL ON EDUCATION—CONSTITUENT MEMBERS*

AMERICAN COUNCIL ON EDUCATION

American Library Association

American Teachers Association

American Vocational Association

Association of American Colleges

Association of American Medical Colleges

Association of American Universities

Association of Collegiate Schools of Nursing

Association of Land-Grant Colleges and Universities

Association of Urban Universities

Boy Scouts of America

Council on Medical Education and Hospitals, American Medical Association

American Association of University Women

American Association of University Professors

American Association of Teachers Colleges

American Association of School Administrators

American Association of Physics Teachers

American Association of Junior Colleges

American Association of Dental Schools

American Association of Collegiate Schools of Business

American Association of Colleges of Pharmacy

Southern Association of Colleges and Secondary Schools

Society for the Promotion of Engineering Education

Progressive Education Association

Phi Delta Kappa

North Central Association of Colleges and Secondary Schools

National University Extension Association

National League of Nursing Education

National Education Association

National Catholic Educational Association

National Association of State Universities

National Association of Secondary-School Principals

National Association of Colleges and Departments of Education

Middle States Association of Colleges and Secondary Schools

Jesuit Educational Association

Institute of International Education

Educational Records Bureau

Council on Nursing Education, Catholic Hospital Association

Council on Dental Education

* For associate members, see Chart III. There are also 497 institutional members, not listed in either chart.

117

AMERICAN COUNCIL ON EDUCATION (1918); 744 Jackson Place, Washington, D.C.; George F. Zook, President.

Membership: Constituent organizations and institutions, 497, including 38 educational associations classified as constituent members, 43 associations in related fields classified as associate members, and 416 institutional members, embracing 391 institutions of higher education, 6 private secondary schools, 3 miscellaneous educational institutions, 6 state departments of public instruction, and 10 local school systems. Annual dues: constituent members, $100; associate members, $10; institutional members, $50.

Purpose: To advance American education in any or all of its phases through comprehensive voluntary cooperative action on the part of educational associations, organizations, and institutions; and in the fulfillment of that purpose to initiate, promote, and execute such systematic studies, cooperative experiments, conferences, and other similar enterprises as may be required for the public welfare.

Activities: Functions largely through committees and commissions, chief among which are the Executive Committee and the Committee on Problems and Plans in Education. The latter has active subcommittees on the following subjects: general education, the master's degree, study of business education, professional education, educational research, rural social studies, place of religion in education, teaching materials in international relations.

Standing committees of the council are concerned with: Motion Pictures in Education, Measurement and Guidance, including the Cooperative Test Service (see p. 144), Student Personnel Work, Cooperative Study in General Education, Implementation of Studies in Secondary Education, Modern Languages, Government and Educational Finance, School Plant Research, Educational Surveys, Coordination of Accrediting, and Financial Advisory Service. There is also a standing Advisory Committee to the National Resources Planning Board.

Two of the largest current research undertakings under the auspices of the council are conducted by the American Youth Commission (see p. 72) and the Commission on Teacher Education (see p. 73). The council also sponsors occasional conferences on timely educational topics and participates in international scholarly and scientific movements. Recently created, with the National Education Association (see p. 131), a National Committee on Education and Defense to cooperate with the federal government and to coordinate the facilities of education in the defense program.

Publications: *The Educational Record*, quarterly journal; $2 a year; C. S. Marsh, editor. *History and Activities of the American Council on Education*, annually, free. *American Universities and Colleges*, edited by C. S. Marsh, 1940 (fourth quadrennial edition), 1120 pp., $4; *American Junior Colleges*, edited by Walter C. Eells, 1940 (first edition), 585 pp., $3.50. *American Council on Education Studies*, pamphlets in six series, priced from 10¢ to $1. The council also publishes other books, psychological and achievement examinations, guidance materials; acts as publisher for its projects and committees, including the American Youth Commission, Motion Picture Project, Financial Advisory Service, Commission on Teacher Education, and Cooperative Test Service.

Staff: Full-time paid employees, 24.

Finances: Value of plant and equipment at headquarters, $13,000. In 1939–40 projects and committees of the council, including the American Youth Commission, Commission on Teacher Education, Cooperative Test Service, and others, expended special grants totaling $861,109.40. Balance for the central organization June 30, 1940, $25,399.13. For the fiscal year ending on that date, its operations were as follows:

Income

Gifts for current expenses	$ 55,553.01
Membership dues	24,110.00
Publications	57,024.07
Reimbursements for special services	19,420.81
Other sources	3,500.81
	$159,608.70

Expenditures

Salaries	$ 70,824.01
Traveling expenses	5,501.50
Communications	2,154.41
Office supplies	1,620.48
Publications	57,972.06
Rentals	6,822.75
Equipment and furniture	2,997.66
Special projects	4,116.98
Committees of the council	4,525.86
General expenses	3,154.92
	$159,690.63

AMERICAN FEDERATION OF TEACHERS (1916); 506 South Wabash Ave., Chicago, Ill.; George S. Counts, President; Irvin R. Kuenzli, Secretary-Treasurer.

Membership: Individuals in the teaching profession, approximately 35,000. There are about 250 local units in good standing, in 37 states. Affiliated with the American Federation of Labor (see p. 81).

Purpose: To establish teaching on a sound basis of adequate compensation and security of tenure in order that only the ablest and most self-respecting may be the teachers of our children; to organize the teachers in such strength that they will determine the standards of their calling and raise those standards to a high level of excellence; to protect the freedom of teachers by group solidarity and intelligent militancy; to work together with other

Chart III

THE AMERICAN COUNCIL ON EDUCATION—ASSOCIATE MEMBERS*

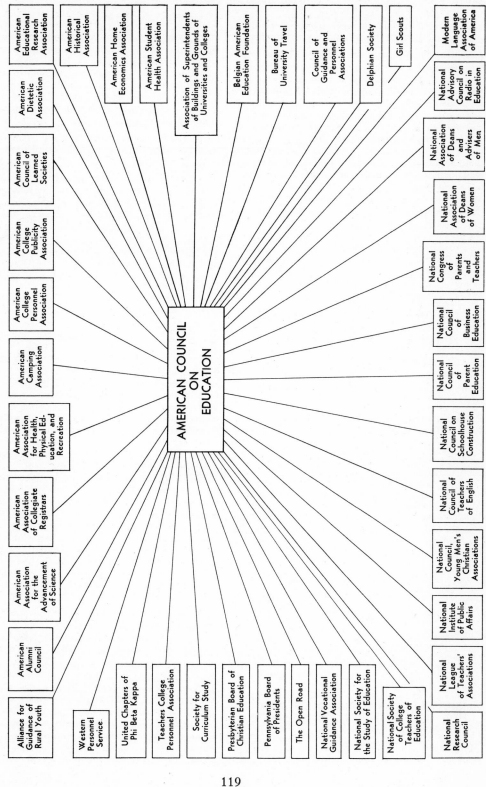

American Educational Research Association

American Historical Association

American Home Economics Association

American Student Health Association

Association of Superintendents of Buildings and Grounds of Universities and Colleges

Belgian American Education Foundation

Bureau of University Travel

Council of Guidance and Personnel Associations

Delphian Society

Girl Scouts

Modern Language Association of America

American Dietetic Association

National Advisory Council on Radio in Education

American Council of Learned Societies

National Association of Deans and Advisers of Men

American College Publicity Association

National Association of Deans of Women

American College Personnel Association

National Congress of Parents and Teachers

American Camping Association

National Council of Business Education

American Association for Health, Physical Education, and Recreation

National Council of Parent Education

American Association of Collegiate Registrars

National Council on Schoolhouse Construction

American Association for the Advancement of Science

National Council of Teachers of English

American Alumni Council

National Council, Young Men's Christian Associations

Alliance for Guidance of Rural Youth

National Institute of Public Affairs

Western Personnel Service.

National League of Teachers' Associations

United Chapters of Phi Beta Kappa

National Research Council

Teachers College Personnel Association

National Society of College Teachers of Education

Society for Curriculum Study

National Society for the Study of Education

Presbyterian Board of Christian Education

National Vocational Guidance Association

Pennsylvania Board of Presidents

The Open Road

AMERICAN COUNCIL ON EDUCATION

* For constituent members, see Chart II. There are also 497 institutional members, not listed in either chart.

119

social agencies to build a saner economic world in which social justice will prevail.

Activities: Opposes, through organized labor, pressure groups which are attempting to curtail the public school facilities by radical reduction in school revenues; vigorously opposes unjust dismissal of teachers without hearing or statement of charges. Advocates federal aid to equalize educational opportunity for all children, without discrimination on account of race, religion, social status, or political views; wide extension of programs of adult education; increased revenues to maintain and develop public education; no discrimination in the employment and standing of educated teachers because of sex, race, religion, or social status, including marriage of women; tenure laws, retirement systems, single salary schedules, and sabbatical leaves for teachers; other measures designed to elevate the profession of teaching and increase the worth of the public schools. Cooperates with the labor movement in eliminating child labor and sweatshops, in providing better educational facilities and full terms of school, in assisting with youth programs such as the NYA, the CCC, and the WPA, and in providing better health facilities and playgrounds for children.

Publications: *The American Teacher*, 9 issues annually; $2.50 a year; George T. Guernsey, editor-in-chief. *Constitution*, 16 pp. Numerous descriptive leaflets.

Staff: Full-time paid employees, 9; part-time paid employee, 1.

Finances: Value of equipment at headquarters, $500. Reserve fund, $500; defense fund, approximately $5,000. Current balance on June 1, 1939, $6,017.22. For the fiscal year ending on that date, operations were as follows:

Income

Gifts for current expenses	$ 1,326.00
Membership fees	79,155.83
Publications	1,279.63
Charter fees	770.00
Assessments	1,110.62
Other sources	697.78
	$84,339.86

Expenditures

Salaries	$23,125.17
Travel	14,469.14
Office supplies	1,304.79
Publications	22,597.04
Rent, insurance, etc.	1,465.00
Other purposes	27,260.54
	$90,221.68

AMERICAN HOME ECONOMICS ASSOCIATION (1908); Mills Bldg., Washington, D.C.; Gladys Wyckoff, Field Secretary.

Membership: Individuals, 15,000; affiliated clubs of students, 2,300, with an aggregate individual membership of about 70,000 girls. Affiliated associations, which exist in all states, collect from each member annual dues of $1 for junior membership and $3 for active membership, and from student clubs (above junior high school level) $2 annual dues for the national organization in addition to state dues. Where no affiliated association exists, memberships-at-large are accepted at $3 for active and $1 for junior membership.

Purpose: To develop and promote standards of home and family life that will best further individual and social welfare.

Activities: There are five subject-matter divisions and ten professional departments, as follows: The Family and Its Relationships, Family Economics, Housing, Food and Nutrition, Textiles and Clothing; and Child Development and Parent Education, Colleges and Universities, Elementary and Secondary Schools, Extension Service, Home Economics in Business, Home Economics in Institution Administration, Social Welfare and Public Health, Homemaking, Research, and Student Clubs.

The current program of work embraces the furthering of better socio-economic situations by such means as spreading information of assistance in restoring or maintaining adequate standards of living; emphasizing the value of education for the consumption of goods and services, improvement of quality and performance specifications for consumers' goods, and promotion of increased use of informative labels on the retail market; advancing home economics education; cooperation with other organizations having allied interests, especially those concerned with social reconstruction; and development of closer relations with organizations and institutions in other countries interested in work similar to that of the association.

The Department of Home Economics Student Clubs meets annually as part of the national convention. State affiliated clubs meet annually in all-state convention or by district or parish arrangement. The department has an active program of work consisting of professional, social, economic, and service activities adapted from the national program of work. Individual clubs are active in services to libraries, schools, and communities and in raising funds for fellowships awarded by the association to foreign students. Students in senior high schools and colleges are active participants.

Publications: *Journal of Home Economics*, monthly except July and August; included in active membership, $2.50 a year to nonmembers; Helen W. Atwater, editor. *Bulletin*, 4 times annually, free to members, $1 a year to libraries; *National Magazine of Home Economics Student Clubs*, 4 times annually, sent free to each affiliated student club; *Consumer Education Service*, $1 a year; *Family Life Education Service*, $1 a year. *Living Together in the Family*, by Lemo Rockwood, 1934, 187 pp., $1.10; *Pictures of Family Life*, by Lemo Rockwood, 1935, 303 pp., $1.40; pamphlets, at 10¢ to 25¢ each, touching many subjects under the headings of family economics and consumer problems, family relationships and child development, student clubs, entertainments and plays, the history and organization of the association, and miscellaneous topics. List on request.

Staff: Full-time paid employees, 16, of whom 1 spends major time in field work; part-time paid employees, 2.

Finances: Reserve fund, $10,000. Value of plant and equipment of national headquarters, $8,500. For the fiscal year August 1, 1938 to July 31, 1939, current operations were as follows:

Income

Membership fees	$18,774.00
Publications	21,898.31
Other sources	24,672.59
	$65,344.90

Expenditures

Salaries	$29,141.20
Travel	3,563.44
Communications	1,707.66
Office supplies	1,425.54
Publications	19,138.22
Rentals, etc.	2,205.00
Other purposes	8,163.84
	$65,344.90

AMERICAN INSTITUTE OF THE CITY OF NEW YORK (1828); 60 East 42nd St., New York, N.Y.; Dr. H. H. Sheldon, Managing Trustee.

Membership: Adult members, 595. Junior members between the ages of 12 and 18, 20,040 (75 per cent boys, 25 per cent girls), in 698 junior Science and Engineering Clubs located in 46 states, Puerto Rico, Hawaii, and the British West Indies.

Purpose: To interpret the latest developments in science to adult members; to help train and develop the youth of the country in scientific thinking through the Science and Engineering Clubs.

Activities: Activities for adults include dinners, lectures, demonstrations, and short courses in science. Activities for the junior clubs include science fairs, science congresses, photographic salons, workshop courses, radio programs, and supplying books, book lists, film lists, science plays, and science programs. Each year the institute has the privilege of awarding to a club member, chosen by competitive examination, a two-year scholarship at RCA Institutes.

Publications: *Science Observer*, official organ of the Science and Engineering Clubs, 10 issues annually; 50¢ a year, 5 free copies of each issue to all clubs; Joseph H. Kraus, editor. *The Science Leaflet*, devoted to the interests of the club sponsors, 30 issues during school year; $2 a year; Mrs. Pauline B. Mack, editor. *The World Looks to Science and Youth*, and

various other booklets on the organization of Science and Engineering Club activities.

Staff: Full-time paid employees, 19, of whom 1 spends part of time in field work; part-time paid employees, 22.

Finances: Reserve funds, $48,161.63. Value of equipment at national headquarters, $1,443. Balance December 31, 1939, $3,287.19. For the preceding calendar year, operations were as follows:

Income

.Gifts and grants	$ 75,409.29
Membership fees	3,275.90
Publications	6,454.30
Investments	3,057.98
Other sources	1,575.32
	$ 89,772.79

Expenditures

Salaries	$ 35,231.97
Travel	1,257.76
Communications	1,248.24
Office supplies	3,969.79
Publications	27,389.64
Rentals, insurance, etc.	4,466.68
Furniture	2,105.00
Exhibits, postage, etc.	27,094.98
	$102,764.06

AMERICAN LIBRARY ASSOCIATION (1876); 520 North Michigan Ave., Chicago, Ill.; Carl H. Milam, Executive Secretary.

Membership: Individuals, 13,971; institutions, 1,817. State and regional constituent associations, 45, in 42 states, Hawaii, and 2 regions; local chapters, 7. Annual dues: individual, $2 to $10; institutional, $5 to $25; contributing, $25; sustaining, $100; life membership, $200. Any person or institution interested in library work may become a member.

Purpose: To promote complete and adequate library coverage of the United States and Canada; to raise standards and promulgate ideals of library service; to assist libraries to operate with the utmost economy and efficiency; to promote studies which will tend to improve and advance library service; to make libraries more useful in the educational, social, and governmental structure of the country; to build for the future of library service by drawing into the profession some of the best qualified young men and women and by improving professional training facilities.

Activities: Promotes the diffusion of ideas through libraries accessible to all the people; gives through its headquarters and committees advisory assistance to all who are interested in library establishment, extension, and development; maintains an employment bureau serving librarians seeking positions and libraries needing librarians and assistants; stimulates effective library service through its publications and through education for librarianship. Arms of the organization directly concerned with the welfare of youth include an Adult Education Board and specialist; a Subcommittee on Readable Books; a School and Children's Library Division which, working with the appointed Board on Library Service to Children and Young People, is responsible for advisory service to public and school libraries working with young people; a Young People's Reading Round Table which brings together librarians working with public library borrowers of secondary school and out-of-school age; a joint committee of ALA and the National Education Association (see p. 131); a Committee on Parent Education, and a joint committee with the National Council of Parent Education (see p. 131).

Publications: *A. L. A. Bulletin*, 10 issues annually, free to members paying annual dues of less than $5; the *A.L.A. Bulletin*, the proceedings, and *Handbook*, free to members paying annual dues of $5 or more. *The Booklist*, 22 issues annually; $3 a year; Zaidee B. Vosper, editor. *College and Research Libraries*, quarterly; $3 a year, $2 to members of the Association of College and Reference Libraries, a section of the ALA; A. F. Kuhlman, editor. *Journal of Documentary Reproduction*, quarterly; $3 a year. *Subscription Books Bulletin*, quarterly; $2 a year. Recent books include: *By Way of Introduction—A Book List for Young People*, NEA and ALA Joint Committee, 1938, 65¢; *Books for Self-Education*, by Sigrid Edge, 1938, 75¢; *Education for the Asking*, ALA Adult Education Board, 1940, 100 copies $1.35; *Vitalizing a College Library*, by B. Lamar Johnson, 1939, $2; *Helping Adults to Learn—The Library in Action*, edited by John Chancellor, 1939, $3; *Helping the Reader Toward Self-Education*, by Chancellor, Tompkins, and Medway, 1938, $1.25; *Books for Adult Beginners*, 1939, 65¢.

Staff: Full-time paid employees, 84, of whom 14 are outside the office; part-time paid employees, 5, of whom 4 are outside the office.

Finances: There are six endowment funds aggregating $2,179,346.15, largely derived from grants by Carnegie Corporation of New York. On August 31, 1940 there was an operating deficit of $12,797.35. For the fiscal year ending on that date, operations were as follows:

Income

Membership and conference	$ 78,504.47
Booklist	32,772.67
Publishing	104,752.42
Special projects	78,923.04
Endowment income	75,884.21
Other income	1,249.64
	$372,086.45

Expenditures

Membership and conference	$ 69,474.00
Booklist	37,104.35
Publishing	100,995.77
Special projects	78,378.49
Other general activities	87,240.72
	$373,193.33

AMERICAN PHYSICAL EDUCATION ASSOCIATION

See American Association for Health, Physical Education, and Recreation (p. 113).

AMERICAN SOCIOLOGICAL SOCIETY (1905); University of Pittsburgh, Pittsburgh, Pa.; Harold A. Phelps, Secretary-Treasurer and Managing Editor.

Membership: Individuals, 1,012, in 48 states and 19 foreign countries. There are eight local chapters in places where there are concentrations of members. A special membership for students, carrying full privileges at a reduced fee, enrolls 250 individuals between the ages of 18 and 25. The regular annual fee is $6; the student fee, $4.

Purpose: To stimulate and develop the science of sociology and to maintain such committees as will advance these purposes.

Activities: Has representatives on the Social Science Research Council (see p. 77), the American Council of Learned Societies, the American Association for the Advancement of Science, the American Documentation Institute, the International Federation of Sociological Societies and Institutes, and the American Library Association (see p. 121). Maintains numerous committees, among which are those bearing the following titles: public school relations; social research; the social studies; research planning; social biology; human ecology; social statistics; sociology and psychiatry; the family; sociology and social work; social theory; sociology of religion; educational sociology; rural sociology; political sociology; criminology; the teaching of sociology; the community; and social psychology. Operates an informal placement service for trained sociologists. Encourages and cooperates with local and regional sociological societies, at least one of which has fathered a junior organization—the Ohio Sociological Students' Association. Also sponsors a National Students' Conference.

Publications: *American Sociological Review*, bimonthly; free to members, $4 a year to others (library subscription, $3; student subscription, $2.50); Read Bain, editor, Miami University, Oxford, Ohio. Volumes of the proceedings of the annual meetings for most of the years since 1905 are available to members at $1.65 each and to nonmembers at $3.15 each.

Staff: Part-time paid employees, 2; part-time unpaid workers, 3.

Finances: There are five separate endowment funds aggregating $2,113.59. Value of equipment at headquarters, $227.49. Cash balance December 14, 1939, $3,524.26. For the fiscal year ending on that date, operations were as follows:

Income

Membership fees	$5,566.00
Publications	2,736.26
Investments	138.50
Other sources	217.20
	$8,657.96

Expenditures

Salaries	$1,168.60
Travel	171.80
Communications	692.30
Publications	4,807.10
Office expense	593.43
Other purposes	460.06
	$7,893.29

AMERICAN TURNERS (1850); 8735 East Jefferson Ave., Detroit, Mich.; Carl M. Weideman, National President.

Membership: Adult men, 19,327, organized in 123 local societies in 19 districts. There are also 92 women's auxiliaries with aggregate membership of 5,643, and 74 local junior societies in 22 states with aggregate membership of 2,209 young persons aged 12 to 21, of whom 54 per cent are girls and 46 per cent boys.

Purpose: To promote physical and cultural education and disseminate rational ideas in order to advance the health, happiness, prosperity, and progress of mankind.

Activities: Courses for youth and adults in physical training, dramatics, choral singing; lectures and debates; social gatherings; special schools. Operates a normal college affiliated with Indiana University, Bloomington, Ind., which showed assets and liabilities of $84,735.22 on its balance sheet of June 30, 1939. Established in 1933 the American Boy Turners, an organization for boys aged 10 to 18, with a program of physical, social, and educational activities, sometimes referred to as the Turner Youth Organization. Summer camps are operated in Illinois, Missouri, New York, and Wisconsin, and there is a summer school at Elkhart Lake, Wis.

Publications: *American Turner Topics*, 12 issues annually; 50¢ a year; Karl Schaltenbrand, editor. Thirty-six local societies publish monthly bulletins. Annual report of the national executive committee, 63 pp.; *A Brief History of the American Turnerbund*, by Henry Metzner, translated by Theodore Stempfel, Jr., 1924; *Work of the American Turner Societies*, by Ernest A. Weir, 18 pp.; *Who These Turners Are*, 4 pp.; *Turnerism is Americanism*, edited by Arthur Kuecken, 18 pp.

Staff: Part-time paid employees, 4, of whom 1 spends major time in field work; part-time unpaid workers, 22, of whom 8 are in field work.

Finances: There are three permanent endowment funds, aggregating $85,968.43, as follows: Jafn Educational Fund, $65,694.52; Instructors' Fund, $12,544.35; Building and Endowment Fund of the Normal College, $7,729.56. Value of equipment at national headquarters, $400. For the fiscal year ending March 31, 1940, operations were as follows:

Income

Membership fees	$ 9,844.36
Promotional activities	734.03
	$10,578.39

Expenditures

Salaries	$ 1,553.00
Travel	662.27
Communications	328.58
Office supplies	837.37
Rent, insurance, etc.	240.00
Normal College	6,000.00
Other purposes	1,265.84
	$10,887.06

ASSOCIATION OF AMERICAN COLLEGES (1915); 19 West 44th St., New York, N.Y.; Guy E. Snavely, Executive Director.

Membership: Colleges and universities, 560. In universities the undergraduate college is the unit of membership. Annual dues, $50.

Purpose: To preserve and promote liberal education in all its forms among the (undergraduate) member colleges, and to prosecute such plans as may make them more efficient.

Activities: Annual meetings and regional conferences for the discussion of problems of liberal education in undergraduate colleges. Maintains several commissions: the *Commission on Academic Freedom and Academic Tenure* has cooperated constructively for some years with Committee A of the American Association of University Professors for better understanding in this field and improved quality of the teaching profession; the *Commission on College Architecture and College Instruction in Fine Arts*, in cooperation with a Special Committee on Music, conducted a careful and systematic survey of music instruction in the colleges, the findings of which were published in 1935; the *Commission on the Arts* has several projects in its field in operation and in process of development. The association's *Arts Program*, with the aid of a subvention from Carnegie Corporation of New York covering a period of six years, cooperates with the colleges in securing for them musical talent and concert programs of a high order, by acting as a buying and distributing agency. The Committees on *Public Relations* and *Insurance and Annuities* are emphasizing the obligation of the colleges in the development of intelligent public sentiment and active service in affairs national and international. The *Commission on Teacher Education* has been studying for several years ways and means of improving college teaching; it maintains liaison with the Commission on Teacher Education of the American Council on Education (see p. 73).

Publications: *Bulletin*, published in March, May, November, and December; $3 a year, with special rates to employees or officers of member colleges; $1 for individuals, or 50¢ each for ten or more subscriptions to be mailed to one address. *Comprehensive Examinations in American Colleges*, by Edward S. Jones, 435 pp., $2.50; *College Music*, by Randall Thompson, 266 pp., $2.50; *College Architecture in America*, by Charles Z. Klauder and Herbert C. Wise, 301 pp. illus., $5; *Architectural Planning of the American College*, by J. Fredrick Larson and Archie M. Palmer, 179 pp., $2; *College Instruction in Art*, by Archie M. Palmer and Grace Holton, 62 pp., $1; *Teaching with Books—A Study of College Libraries*, by Harvie Branscomb, 258 pp., $2.50; *The American Colleges and the Social Order*, by Robert L. Kelly, $2.50. Numerous reprints from the *Bulletin*, 10¢ each.

Staff: Full-time paid employees, 9.

Finances: Value of equipment at headquarters, $1,733.53. Cash balance December 31, 1939, $11,461.74. There is no endowment, but in the past, special grants for the production of books have been received from Carnegie Corporation of New York and the General Education Board. For the calendar year 1939, current operations were as follows:

Income

Membership fees	$27,275.00
Publications (*Bulletin*)	2,663.24
Publications (books)	190.38
Other sources	497.39
	$30,626.01

Expenditures

Salaries	$18,944.21
Publications (*Bulletin*)	3,144.09
Conferences, committees, and commissions	2,101.97
Office expenses	3,537.59
Other purposes	1,091.04
	$28,818.90

ASSOCIATION FOR CHILDHOOD EDUCATION

(1892); 1201 16th St., N.W., Washington, D.C.; Mary E. Leeper, Executive Secretary.

Membership: Individuals, about 36,000, of whom 4,381 are contributing members paying $2 annually direct to headquarters and 32,000 are members of 451 local branches. Annual fee for a branch is $5 until its membership exceeds 50, and 10¢ for each additional member, to a maximum of $50.

Purpose: To gather and disseminate knowledge of the movement for the education of young children; to bring into active cooperation all childhood education interests, including parent education; to promote the progressive type of education in nursery school, kindergarten, and primary grades, and to raise the standard of the professional training for teachers and leaders in this field.

Activities: Conducts national conferences, featuring study classes and group discussions; maintains committees to study current educational problems; cooperates with national and international organizations working for the welfare of children; provides advisory service for local study groups and individual information service; furnishes avenues through which teachers may give and receive professional help.

Publications: *Childhood Education*, 9 issues annually; $2.50 a year. *A Study of Reading Workbooks*, 40 pp., 35¢; *School Housing Needs of Young Children*, 40 pp., 35¢; *Uses for Waste Materials*, 12 pp., 20¢; *Bibliography of Books for Young Children*, 64 pp., 50¢; *Exploring Your Community*, 32 pp., 35¢; *Growth Through School Living*, 40 pp., 35¢; *Equipment and Supplies*, 40 pp., 50¢; *Reading—A Tool for Learning*, 32 pp., 35¢; *Science and the Young Child*, 40 pp., 35¢; *Music and the Young Child*, 32 pp., 35¢; *Practice Teaching*, 59 pp., 50¢; *Foundations in Arithmetic*, 32 pp., 35¢; *The Modern Kindergarten*, 36 pp., 35¢; *Sharing Experiences Through School Assemblies*, 40 pp., 35¢; *Studies of Environment*, 54 pp., 50¢; *Toys—What—When*, 6 pp., 15¢; *Selected List of Ten-Cent Books*, 12 pp., 15¢. Reductions on quantity orders. List of other publications on request.

Staff: Full-time paid employees, 7; part-time paid employee, 1.

Finances: Endowment fund, $20,274.40; reserve fund, $2,860.44. Value of equipment at headquarters, $837.27. Cash balance May 31, 1939, $734.93. For the fiscal year ending on that date, operations were as follows:

Income

Membership fees	$ 5,878.84
Publications	18,696.56
Other services	10,761.61
Endowment and reserve funds	356.37
Other sources	676.59
	$36,369.97

Expenditures

Salaries	$ 8,980.15
Travel	234.06
Office supplies	814.54
Publications	8,127.80
Rent, insurance, etc.	722.07
Other purposes	16,354.09
	$35,232.71

BUREAU OF UNIVERSITY TRAVEL (1891); 11 Boyd St., Newton, Mass.; Dr. Henry M. Willard, President.

Membership: A nonprofit corporation governed by a board of nine trustees.

Purpose: To interpret foreign cultures; to provide in travel a peculiar educational opportunity, supplementary to that provided in colleges and similar institutions of learning; to promote education by means of lectures, study courses, instruction, publications, and by other suitable means, whether in the United States or abroad.

Activities: Conducts travel tours, extending throughout the world, by qualified leaders; functions at home by means of a lecture service sustained by its tour leaders and designed for those who wish to prepare themselves for more intelligent appreciation of foreign travel and for those who cannot avail themselves of facilities abroad; cooperates with schools and colleges in the arrangement and conduct of vacation study tours. Sponsors the National Capital School Visitors Council (see p. 129). Travel activities at present are limited to Latin America and the United States.

Publications: Annual bulletin, published in February. Descriptive folders concerning tours.

Staff: Full-time paid employees, 3.

Finances: Estimated value of plant and equipment at national headquarters, $5,000. The annual budget varies from year to year according to change in travel conditions; for headquarters in 1939–40 it was approximately $9,000.

FEDERAL RADIO EDUCATION COMMITTEE (1935); U.S. Office of Education, Room 3355, South Interior Bldg., Washington, D.C.; J. W. Studebaker, Chairman; Leonard Power, Director of Research.

Membership: Approximately 40 committee members appointed by the Federal Communications Commission.

Purpose: To eliminate controversy and misunderstanding between groups of educators and between the industry and educators; to promote actual cooperative arrangements between educators and broadcasters on national, regional, and local bases.

Activities: Makes comprehensive surveys of the educational use of radio. Through a Script Exchange Circulating Library scripts are made available to local educational and civic groups that broadcast.

Publications: *FREC Service Bulletin*, monthly; free upon request. *Forums on the Air*, by Dr. Paul H. Sheats, 65 pp., 25¢; *Local Station Policies*, by Dr. Leonard Power, 38 pp., 15¢; *College Radio Workshops*, by Dr. Leonard Power, 52 pp., 25¢; *Listeners Appraise a College Station*, by Dr. Alberta Curtis, 70 pp., 25¢; *The Groups Tune In*, by Dr. Frank E.

Hill, 35 pp., 25¢; *Script Exchange Catalog*, listing 500 scripts, 10¢; *Americans All—Immigrants All*, handbook for listeners, by J. Morris Jones, 128 pp., 25¢.

Staff: Full-time paid employees, 6; part-time paid employees, 2.

Finances: The organization is financed wholly from private sources, principally the National Association of Broadcasters and certain educational foundations. The annual budget is approximately $25,000, exclusive of special projects carried on in the field.

FOREIGN POLICY ASSOCIATION, INC. (1918); 22 East 38th St., New York, N.Y.; Frank Ross McCoy, President; Dorothy F. Leet, Secretary.

Membership: Individuals, 19,297, including 2,732 young people and the membership of 17 local branches.

Purpose: To carry on research and educational activities in order to aid in the understanding and constructive development of American foreign policy.

Activities: Conducts nonpartisan discussion meetings at which authoritative speakers present different points of view on international problems; holds study groups, leadership institutes, and student forums.

Publications: *Foreign Policy Bulletin*, 4-page weekly, free to members, $2 a year to nonmembers; *Headline Books*, free to members, 25¢ each to nonmembers; *Foreign Policy Reports*, semimonthly, $3 a year to members, $5 to nonmembers; *Pan-American News*, biweekly, $3 a year.

Staff: Full-time paid employees, 40; part-time paid employee, 1.

Finances: Reserve funds total $10,000. For the calendar year 1939, current income totaled $171,-796.13, derived from contributions, membership fees, publications, and reserve funds; for the same period expenditures on an accrual basis were $175,234.79.

FUTURE TEACHERS OF AMERICA (1937); 1201 16th St., N.W., Washington, D.C.; Joy Elmer Morgan, Chairman, National Committee.

A project of the National Education Association (see p. 131).

Membership: Men and women students, 3,653, including 2,088 members in 116 high school clubs in 27 states and 1,565 members in 64 college and university chapters in 33 states. Annual fees: high school clubs, $1 to the national organization (for 100 Personal Growth Leaflets); individuals in college chapters, $2 ($1 for junior membership in the state education association, $1 to the national organization for the *Journal of the National Education Association* and 20 Personal Growth Leaflets).

Purpose: To develop among young people interested in teaching as a profession an organization which shall be an integral part of state and national education associations; to acquaint them with the history, ethics, and program of the organized teaching profession; to give them practical experience in working together in a democratic way on the problems of the profession and of the nation; to encourage careful selection of persons admitted to schools which prepare teachers; to seek through the dissemination of information and through higher standards of preparation to bring teacher supply and demand into a reasonable balance.

Activities: Provides a definite system of training in planning, cooperation, and leadership in professional and civic relationships; through projects and merit points, emphasis is placed on a program of local social and civic action which will prepare students for community life as well as for the classroom. Projects include beautification of school campuses, sponsoring of courses in the practice of parliamentary law, improving assembly programs, preparing newspaper publicity for the school, teaching in Sunday school, helping with Boy or Girl Scouts and 4-H Clubs, and development of recreation programs for younger children in the community. Each member is expected to take part in the projects and to earn 50 merit points a year (one point is awarded for each hour of work on a project approved by the sponsor, a faculty member); each member who has earned 200 merit points during his college course is issued a National Certificate of Merit by the national committee. The committee, working at the headquarters of the National Education Association, serves as a planning agency and clearinghouse, establishes a library of books and materials in each college chapter, and furnishes special services in planning programs and projects; each year the chairman and members of the committee spend weeks in the field in conference with FTA groups.

Publications: The following Personal Growth Leaflets of the National Education Association pertain to the Future Teachers of America: *Future Teachers of America* (No. 11); *Suggestions for FTA Sponsors* (No. 161); *Programs and Projects for FTA Clubs* (No. 162); *What It Means to Be a Future Teacher* (No. 165); *FTA at Work in Colleges and Universities* (No. 166); *Future Teacher—Ideals and Purposes* (No. 170); *Shall I Become a Teacher?* (No. 12).

Staff: Headquarters activities are handled by the staff of the *Journal of the National Education Association.*

Finances: Income from membership fees is used exclusively for the distribution of publications to members. All other activities at headquarters are financed as part of the general activities of the National Education Association.

GARDEN EDUCATION DEPARTMENT OF THE NATIONAL EDUCATION ASSOCIATION (1910); Children's Garden, Brooklyn Botanic Garden, 1000 Washington Ave., Brooklyn, N.Y.; Frances M. Miner, President.

This organization was the School Garden Association of America until 1939, when it became affiliated with the National Education Association (see p. 131).

Membership: Individuals, about 250, who are serving or working with many thousands of children in school or nonschool garden clubs.

Purpose: To arouse public interest in the great value of school gardens as a means of educating children; to provide for the public discussion phases of the gardening movement; to promote the establishment of school gardens in America; to help in the direction of garden education.

Activities: Annual meeting at same time and place as the National Education Association.

Publications: *Garden Digest*, 10 issues annually; free to members, $1.50 a year to others; Paul Jones, editor, Fordson Horticultural Gardens, Ford Public Schools, Dearborn, Mich.

Staff: Staff work is done by unpaid officers.

Finances: During the calendar year 1939 income was about $435, derived from membership fees and contributions. Expenditures were for publications.

JESUIT EDUCATIONAL ASSOCIATION (1921); 55 East 84th St., New York, N.Y.; Edward B. Rooney, S.J., Executive Director.

Membership: Constituent high schools, colleges, and universities, 77, including 17 colleges exclusively for students preparing to be Jesuits. The student constituency consists of about 65,000 young men, of whom about 16,000 are in high schools and about 49,000 in colleges and universities; there are about 2,500 students in colleges for Jesuits exclusively. The constituency is comprised chiefly of men but includes some women, especially in graduate and professional schools.

Purpose: To promote and make more efficient all Jesuit educational activities in the United States; to promote scholarship, research, and publication; to preserve essential features of Jesuit educational tradition; to cooperate with other educational associations; to collaborate with Jesuit educators in other countries on common problems; to present effectively the Catholic philosophy of life.

Activities: Has regional directors in close touch with all the constituent schools. Each school, in addition to its regular curriculum, maintains a rich program of extracurricular activities intended to develop the individual traits and capabilities of the students.

Publications: *Jesuit Educational Quarterly;* Edward B. Rooney, S.J., editor; Allan P. Farrell, S.J., managing editor, Milford Novitiate, Milford, Ohio. Occasional pamphlets are published through the individual institutions.

Staff: Part-time paid employee, 1.

Finances: Estimated annual value of space, heat,

light, and similar services received without charge, approximately $1,500. Total expenditures for the fiscal year ending June 30, 1940, approximately $2,000.

MUSIC EDUCATORS NATIONAL CONFERENCE
(1907); 64 East Jackson Blvd., Chicago, Ill.; C. V. Buttelman, Executive Secretary.

Became a department of the National Education Association (see p. 131) in June 1940.

Membership: About 15,000 persons constitute the total active membership in the conference and its associated organizations. The conference itself is a merger of six sectional music educators' conferences: California-Western, Eastern, North Central, Northwest, Southern, and Southwestern. It has four auxiliary national organizations: the National School Band Association, the National School Orchestra Association, the National School Vocal Association, and the Music Education Exhibitors Association. There are also many affiliated state organizations. Classes of membership and annual dues: active, $3; associate, $2; contributing, $10; sustaining, $50; life, $100; patron, $1,000.

Purpose: To provide a medium of mutual helpfulness for the members of the music education profession and to promote the advancement of music education through the instrumentality of schools and other educational institutions.

Activities: Maintains a continuous program of educational activities, research projects, and promotional work through the medium of its associated units and through the Music Education Research Council and appointed committees, some 33 in number. Of the auxiliary organizations, the school band, orchestra, and vocal associations are concerned largely with the annual School Music Competition-Festivals, which serve as finals for the competition-festivals conducted in all states for school orchestras, bands, and choruses, and for instrumental and vocal soloists and small ensembles; the national finals are held in 10 regions of the United States. Entries in 1940, involving a total of 57,373 high school students, aggregated 857 bands, orchestras, choruses, and glee clubs, 1,617 instrumental and vocal small ensembles, and 5,437 instrumental and vocal soloists. The conference holds biennial national conventions; in the alternate years, six division conventions are held under the auspices of the sectional conferences referred to above. At the 1940 national convention held in Los Angeles, more than 10,000 children and youth participated in the competition-festival activities. The principal service to the youth of the country is through improved professional work and community activities of members of the music education profession.

Publications: *Music Educators Journal*, 6 issues annually; $1 a year; Edward B. Birge, chairman of the editorial board, Bloomington, Ind. *Music Educators Yearbook*, recent and current annual volumes $2.50 each. Several Music Education Research Council Bulletins, including such titles as *Newer Practices and Tendencies in Music Education*, *Music Rooms and Equipment*, and *A Course of Study in Music for Rural Schools*, 15¢ each. "Outline of a Program for Music Education," outline of forthcoming report of the Music Education Research Council, containing a complete course of study for preschool through high school. Other bulletins and committee reports. List on request.

Staff: Full-time paid employees, 11.

NATIONAL ADVISORY COUNCIL ON RADIO IN EDUCATION, INC. (1930); 60 East 42nd St., New York, N.Y.; Levering Tyson, Secretary.

Membership: Approximately 75 individuals.

Purpose: To promote the business and art of radio communication with particular reference to radio broadcasting as a means and medium of education; to collect and disseminate information relating to radio communication; to assemble and interpret information concerning the practices and experience of broadcasting stations here and abroad in conducting or developing educational features; to present to the educational world the opportunities for education in the utilization of broadcasting; to seek the cooperation of the broadcasting industry in making facilities available for educational purposes as a public obligation.

Activities: Committees on various subjects have had the function of suggesting and devising radio programs in their specialties, and demonstration programs, national in scope, have been produced under council auspices in art, civic education, consumers' problems, economics, government, labor, law, international relations, psychology, public health, science, vocational guidance, and special individual broadcasts of a timely nature. The council cooperates with the U.S. Office of Education and with numerous national educational organizations. In 1936 and 1937 it joined with a score of national organizations in sponsoring the first and second National Conferences on Educational Broadcasting.

Publications: Nineteen pamphlets in an Information Series dealing with various phases of educational broadcasting, including: *Four Years of Network Broadcasting*, 1937, 25¢; *School Broadcasting in Great Britain*, 1937, $1; *The Library and the Radio*, 1938, 75¢; *Use of the Radio in Parent Education*, 1939, 75¢. Also books and pamphlets published by the University of Chicago Press, including: proceedings of the annual assemblies from 1931 to 1937, $3 each; *Education's Own Stations*, by S. E. Frost, Jr., 1937, $4; and *Is American Radio Democratic?* 1937, $2.50.

Staff: Full-time paid employee, 1.

Finances: Funds for basic administration and maintenance for a minimum period of three years were provided originally by John D. Rockefeller, Jr., and by Carnegie Corporation of New York. At present a grant from the latter maintains the council. Broadcasters have frequently made their facilities available to the council without charge for purposes of program experimentation.

NATIONAL ASSOCIATION OF DEANS OF WOMEN, A DEPARTMENT OF THE NATIONAL EDUCATION ASSOCIATION (1916); 1201 16th St., N.W., Washington, D.C.; Kathryn G. Heath, Executive Secretary.

Membership: Women, 1,011, serving as deans, counselors, and advisers in secondary schools and institutions of higher learning. Cooperating associations, not directly affiliated, include 4 regional, 36 state, and 3 city organizations. Annual membership fee, $5.

Purpose: To increase the effectiveness of women engaged in educational guidance; to strengthen their professional status; to formulate criteria for their professional training; and to direct specific research and study in problems pertinent to the work of deans, counselors, and advisers.

Activities: Annual winter convention in February with attendance of about 400 members; annual summer meeting in July with attendance of about 150 members. Maintains a center of information on the following topics in the student personnel field: functions and qualifications of deans, counselors, and advisers; counseling techniques; professional courses available; activities of regional, state, and city deans' groups; human relations course work, student government, student leadership, and vocational conferences; housing; orientation; girls' leagues; fraternities and sororities; student aid; salaries; radio programs; personnel record forms; bibliographies on pertinent subjects; student and other youth groups. Participates in the Rural Youth Committee constituted jointly with the National Vocational Guidance Association (see p. 148), the National Federation of Business and Professional Women's Clubs (see p. 108), and the Alliance for Guidance of Rural Youth (see p. 143). Maintains membership in the Council of Guidance and Personnel Associations (see p. 145).

Publications: *Journal of the National Association of Deans of Women*, quarterly; free to members, $2.50 to others; Ruth M. Strang, editor. Numerous reprints, pamphlets, and mimeographed documents relating to various aspects of student personnel work, available at 5¢ to 50¢. List on request.

Staff: Full-time paid employees, 2.

Finances: Reserve fund, $1,547.25. Current balance May 31, 1939, $1,230.34. For the fiscal year ending on that date, operations were as follows:

Income

Membership fees	$5,221.00
Publications	396.26
Convention registration	834.00
Other sources	140.38
	$6,591.64

Expenditures

Salaries	$3,423.00
Travel	119.31
Office expense	590.41
Publications	851.96
Winter convention	863.15
Other purposes	393.75
	$6,241.58

See also National Education Association (p. 131).

NATIONAL ASSOCIATION OF SECONDARY-SCHOOL PRINCIPALS, A DEPARTMENT OF THE NATIONAL EDUCATION ASSOCIATION (1916); 1201 16th St., N.W., Washington, D.C.; Paul E. Elicker, Executive Secretary.

Membership: Individuals, approximately 8,000, chiefly principals of junior high schools, senior high schools, and junior colleges. Active members are engaged in administration, supervision, or teaching of secondary education in professional schools or departments, and pay an annual fee of $1 if enrolled in a state organization of secondary school principals, or $2 if not. Associate members are persons interested in secondary education but not eligible for active membership, and pay an annual fee of $2. Institutional membership with annual fee of $5 provides enrollment of the school; the principal is a participating member, and the school receives copies of all bulletins, special reports, special studies, and *Student Life*.

Purpose: To work for the improvement and advancement of secondary education; to serve as a clearinghouse of information and of the best practices in secondary school administration; to cooperate with all other organizations of an educational character; to give a national leadership in secondary education; to originate and foster activities and projects in secondary schools; to publish and disseminate material in the interest of secondary schools.

Activities: Two meetings annually, one in connection with the winter meeting of the American Association of School Administrators (see p. 114), the other in connection with the summer convention of the National Education Association (see p. 131). Makes studies in secondary education; encourages the forming of local and state organizations and discussion groups among secondary school principals; carries on a program of long-range planning in secondary education. Sponsors the National Honor Society of Secondary Schools and the National Junior Honor Society (see p. 67), which provide services to high school youth and whose periodical to promote pupil activities is sent to 3,500 schools enrolling 700,000 pupils. Has a Youth Committee and is conducting an Occupational Adjustment Study to explore the role of the secondary school in the general welfare of youth.

Publications: *Bulletin*, 8 issues annually; free to members, $2 a year to others. *Student Life*, organ of the National Honor Society, 8 issues annually; $1 a year.

Staff: Full-time paid employees, 8; part-time paid employee, 1.

Finances: Operating balance December 31, 1939, $5,668.12. For the fiscal year ending on that date, operations were as follows:

Income

Gifts for current expenses	$ 21,050.00
Membership fees	7,621.00
Publications	5,810.46
Other services	63,088.45
Other sources	2,915.48
	$100,485.39

Expenditures

Salaries	$ 15,000.43
Travel	2,179.47
Office supplies	263.40
Publications	4,924.08
Other purposes	72,446.89
	$ 94,814.27

NATIONAL CAPITAL SCHOOL VISITORS COUNCIL (1940); Evans Bldg., 1420 New York Ave., Washington, D.C.; Dr. Henry M. Willard, Director.

A nonprofit organization subsidiary to the Bureau of University Travel (see p. 125).

Membership: Advisory board of 18 members.

Purpose: To serve the educational needs of students and teachers visiting the national capital from all parts of the United States; to promote the intrinsic value of the Washington visit in terms of training for citizenship; to give special opportunity to outstanding students with a view to developing youth leadership for intelligent civic action under the principles of American democracy.

Activities: Conducts annual Institutes of National Government, in the spring of the year, in Washington, D.C. The first Students Institute is scheduled for March 1941, followed by a separate institute for teachers of the social studies; in each case there is a carefully prearranged program of conferences and discussions with representatives of the federal government and others in Washington. The council also acts as an educational advisory body to school groups visiting Washington, in particular suggesting various classroom materials of value to use in advance of travel.

Staff: Part-time employees, 4.

Finances: Approximate annual budget of headquarters, $4,000.

NATIONAL CATHOLIC EDUCATIONAL ASSOCIATION (1904); 1312 Massachusetts Ave., N.W., Washington, D.C.; Rev. George Johnson, Ph.D., Secretary General.

Membership: Catholic educators, 3,425.

Purpose: To unite the Catholic educators of the country; to bring understanding among them; and to encourage the spirit of helpfulness in order that the Catholic educational interests of the country may be safeguarded and promoted.

Activities: Annual national meetings attended by members and nonmembers. The College and University Department and the Secondary-School Department hold regional meetings during the year.

Publications: *National Catholic Educational Association Bulletin*, quarterly (February, May, August, November); August number is the report of proceedings and addresses of the annual national meeting; free to members, $1 a year to nonmembers.

NATIONAL COMMITTEE ON EDUCATION BY RADIO (1930); Room 308, 1 Madison Ave., New York, N.Y.; S. Howard Evans, Secretary.

Membership: Constituent organizations, 9: American Council on Education (see p. 117), Association of Land-Grant Colleges and Universities, Jesuit Educational Association (see p. 126), National Association of State Universities, National Catholic Educational Association (see p. 129), National Council of State Superintendents and Commissioners of Education, National Association of Educational Broadcasters, National University Extension Association (see p. 136), National Education Association (see p. 131).

Purpose: To secure to the people of the United States the use of radio for educational purposes by protecting the rights of educational broadcasting, by promoting experiments in the use of radio in school and adult education, and by serving as a clearinghouse for the encouragement of research in education by radio.

Activities: Serves as a spokesman for organized education in all matters pertaining to the use of radio and performs the functions indicated in the foregoing statement of purpose. Serves youth indirectly through the constituent members and directly through publications which go to school libraries and to classrooms for student use.

Publications: *Education by Radio*, 4 issues annually; free on request. *An Appraisal of Radio Broadcasting*

in the Land-Grant Colleges and State Universities,
by Tracy F. Tyler, 1933, 150 pp., free; *Some Inter-
pretations and Conclusions of the Land-Grant College
Radio Survey*, by Tracy F. Tyler, 1933, 25 pp., free.

Staff: Full-time paid employee, 1; part-time unpaid
worker, 1, who spends some time in field work.

Finances: Value of equipment at headquarters,
$3,500. Current balance December 31, 1939, $100.
For the fiscal year ending on that date, income from
all sources totaled $7,500. Expenditures for the same
period were as follows:

Salaries	$1,500
Travel	2,108
Communications	150
Office supplies	224
Publications	2,293
Rent, insurance, etc.	500
Other purposes	625
	$7,400

NATIONAL CONFERENCE ON FAMILY RELA-
TIONS (1938); 1126 East 59th St., Chicago, Ill.;
Mary K. White, Executive Director.

Membership: Individuals, 1,050, including specialists and interested citizens; student members, 40;
regional conferences, 4; state conferences, 32. Annual
dues, $2.

Purpose: To advance the cultural values that are
now principally secured through family relations for
the advantage of the individual and the strength of
the nation; to unite in this common objective persons
now working in the different fields of family research
and welfare.

Activities: Holds annual conferences and encourages
the holding of regional, state, and local conferences
to present important research findings, to discuss
points of view and experience, and to consider
proposals for family welfare. Maintains national
committees on the economic basis of family life, education for marriage and family living, eugenics and
the family, marriage and family counseling, marriage
and family law and its administration, research on
marriage and the family, and youth and its problems.
The Midwest and Pacific Northwest Regional Conferences likewise have committees on youth and its
problems. Meetings of the conference are open to
students without charge.

Publications: *Living*, quarterly publication, including reports of conferences and committees; $1.50 a
year, included in annual dues; E. W. Burgess, acting
editor.

Staff: Full-time part-paid employees at headquarters, 2; part-time employee, 1.

Finances: Estimated annual value of unpaid staff
services, $2,000; estimated annual value of space,
heat, light, and similar services received without
charge, $600. Balance December 23, 1939, $400.03.

For the period September 1, 1938 through December
23, 1939, operations were as follows:

Income

Gifts and grants	$1,399.91
Membership fees	1,462.00
Publications	143.55
Conference registration fees	72.00
	$3,077.46

Expenditures

Salaries	$ 749.06
Office supplies	1,260.41
Publications	630.02
Other purposes	37.94
	$2,677.43

NATIONAL CONGRESS OF PARENTS AND
TEACHERS (1897); 600 South Michigan Blvd.,
Chicago, Ill.; Mrs. William Kletzer, President;
Ruth A. Bottomly, Office Director.

Membership: Individuals, approximately 2,330,000,
in 28,000 local parent-teacher associations in every
state, the District of Columbia, Hawaii, Alaska,
and Puerto Rico. A small percentage of the membership is under the age of 25.

Purpose: To promote the welfare of children and
youth in home, school, church, and community; to
raise the standards of home life; to secure adequate
laws for the care and protection of children and
youth; to bring into closer relation the home and the
school that parents and teachers may cooperate intelligently in the training of the child; to develop
between educators and the general public such united
efforts as will secure for every child the highest advantages in physical, mental, social, and spiritual
education.

Activities: Holds national and state conventions and
district, county, and local conferences. Renders
service to youth through its standing committees on
art, character and spiritual education, health and
summer roundup of the children, citizenship, education for home and family life, the exceptional child,
high school service, international relations, juvenile
protection, legislation, mental hygiene, motion pictures and visual education, music, parent education,
radio, reading and library service, recreation, rural
service, safety, school education, social hygiene, and
study of the effects of alcohol and narcotics.

Publications: *National Parent-Teacher*, 10 issues annually; $1 a year; Eva H. Grant, editor. Convention
proceedings, annually, $1.50. *Schools for Democracy*,
25¢; *The Child in His Community*.

Staff: Full-time paid employees, 19, of whom 1
spends major time in field work; part-time paid employees, 5, of whom 2 spend major time in field
work.

Finances: Approximate annual budget, exclusive of
state and local branches, $160,000.

NATIONAL COUNCIL OF PARENT EDUCATION, INC. (1926); Vassar College, Poughkeepsie, N.Y.; Joseph K. Folsom, Chairman and Agent of the Governing Board.

An association for the advancement of family life.

Membership: Individuals and organizations, 506, including 475 persons and 31 associations and institutions. Classes of membership and annual dues are as follows:

	Regular	Contributing	Sustaining
Institutions	$20	$50	$100
Organizations	5	10	25 or more
Individuals	2	5	10 or more

Purpose: To aid the development of education for home and family living, at all levels and through all kinds of agencies, by providing a clearinghouse of information, by stimulating professional workers through conferences and otherwise, and by stimulating and guiding public interest.

Activities: Holds national and other conferences, with the cooperation of other organizations. Participates in joint committees with other national organizations.

Publications: *Bulletin of Family Research and Education* (mimeo.), 6 issues annually; free to members, $1.50 a year to nonmembers; Ruth Mallay, editor. An extensive list of monographs, brochures, and reprints, as well as available back numbers of *Parent Education*, now suspended, may be ordered from the Child Study Association of America, 221 West 57th St., New York, N.Y. Prices range from 5¢ to 60¢. List on request. Recent titles include *Can Parents Educate One Another? A Study of Lay Leadership in New York State*, by Mary L. Shirley, 1938, 60¢, and *1938 Summer School Opportunities for Family and Parent Education Teaching and Leadership*, 15¢.

Staff: Part-time paid employee, 1; part-time unpaid workers, 2.

Finances: Value of equipment at headquarters, $200. Cash balance January 31, 1940, $223.43. For the fiscal year ending on that date, operations were as follows:

Income

Gifts for current expenses	$ 42.44
Membership fees	278.00
Publications	111.22
Other sources	136.80
	$568.46

Expenditures

Salaries	$129.00
Travel and communications	89.29
Office supplies	87.39
Other purposes	71.43
	$377.11

NATIONAL EDUCATION ASSOCIATION OF THE UNITED STATES (1857); 1201 16th St., N.W., Washington, D.C.; Willard E. Givens, Executive Secretary.

Membership: Individuals, 203,429 persons engaged in educational work or interested in the promotion of education; affiliated state associations, 52, including one in the District of Columbia, one in Alaska, one in Hawaii, and one in Puerto Rico; local affiliates about 1,000; departments, 27. Membership in the NEA is a prerequisite to department privileges. Types of membership and annual dues: members, $2 (includes the *Journal*); members, $5 (includes the *Journal*, annual *Volume of Addresses and Proceedings*, and the *Research Bulletin*); life members, $100 (includes same publications as $5 membership); state affiliates, $10; local affiliates, $5. Affiliation entitles an organization to send delegates to the Representative Assembly (the number depending on its NEA membership) and to receive all regular publications of the NEA.

Purpose: To promote the interests of the teaching profession and to advance the cause of education.

Activities: Contributes to the professional growth and economic welfare of teachers; urges higher salaries, tenure regulations, and adequate retirement allowances for teachers; interprets education to the public through radio, press, and periodicals and creates a public opinion favorable to the schools; maintains friendly relations with numerous national organizations and encourages its members to cooperate with all influential agencies; sponsors American Education Week in cooperation with the federal Office of Education, the American Legion, and the National Congress of Parents and Teachers; promotes constructive school legislation; stimulates and conducts research on educational problems; holds an annual convention in the summer. The following departments hold separate annual conventions: American Association of School Administrators, during the last week in February; American Association for Health, Physical Education, and Recreation, in April of each year; National Council for Social Studies, during November; National Association of Teachers of Speech, in December; and the Music Educators National Conference meets biennially.

Divisions at national headquarters include: Accounts and Records; Administrative Service; Affiliated Associations; Business; Field Service; Membership; Publications; Research; Rural Service; Teacher Welfare. Some of the committees and commissions dealing with special problems follow: Educational Policies Commission (see p. 74); Legislative Commission; National Committee on Education and National Defense, jointly with the American Council on Education (see p. 117); Joint Commission on Education and Resources; Committee on Academic Freedom; Committee on Bylaws and Rules; Appraisal Committee; Committee on Cooperatives; Committee on Credit Unions; Committee on Code of Ethics; Committee on Equal Opportunity; Joint

Chart IV

THE NATIONAL EDUCATION ASSOCIATION OF THE UNITED STATES*

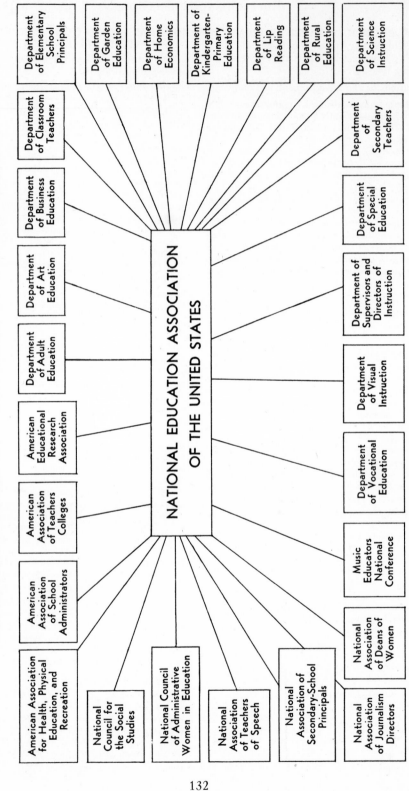

* The 27 departments. The several service divisions of the national headquarters are not exhibited in this chart.

Committee of the NEA and the American Teachers Association (see p. 96); Joint Committee of the NEA and the American Medical Association; Committee on Individual Guidance; Committee on Induction into Citizenship; Committee on International Relations; Joint Committee of the NEA and the American Legion (see p. 81); Joint Committee of the NEA and the American Library Association (see p. 121); Joint Committee of the NEA and National Congress of Parents and Teachers (see p. 130); National Council on Teacher Retirement of the NEA; Committee on Supply, Preparation, and Certification of Teachers; Committee on Tax Education; and Committee on Tenure.

The association has 27 departments: Adult Education; American Association for Health, Physical Education, and Recreation (see p. 113); American Association of School Administrators (see p. 114); American Association of Teachers Colleges; American Educational Research Association (see p. 70); Art Education (see p. 133); Business Education; Classroom Teachers; Elementary School Principals (see p. 134); Garden Education (see p. 126); Home Economics; Kindergarten-Primary Education; Lip Reading; Music Educators National Conference (see p. 127); National Association of Deans of Women (see p. 128); National Association of Journalism Directors; National Association of Secondary-School Principals (see p. 128); National Association of Teachers of Speech; National Council for the Social Studies; National Council of Administrative Women in Education; Rural Education; Science Instruction; Secondary Teachers; Special Education; Supervisors and Directors of Instruction; Visual Instruction; and Vocational Education. A number of the departments have separate membership fees and issue yearbooks, journals, or other publications.

Projects of the *Journal* include the Vitalized Commencement Movement and the Future Teachers of America (see p. 125). The Future Teachers of America is an organization with a program of activities through which college and high school students who are preparing to teach can develop leadership in professional and civic enterprises and become acquainted with the history, ethics, and services of the teaching profession. FTA seeks to interest the best young men and women in education as a life career. In 1940 there were 64 college FTA chapters with a membership of 1,565 and 116 high school FTA clubs with 2,088 members.

Publications: *Journal of the National Education Association*, monthly except June, July, and August; included in life, $2, and $5 memberships, $2 a year to others; Joy Elmer Morgan, editor. Convention addresses and proceedings, annually; included in life and $5 memberships, $3 to others. *Research Bulletin*, 5 issues annually; included in life and $5 memberships, or by annual subscription of $1. Yearbooks and periodicals published by School Administrators, Deans of Women, Elementary School Principals, Rural Education, Science Instruction, Secondary-School Principals, Social Studies, Supervisors and

Directors of Instruction, Teachers Colleges. Numerous pamphlets, reprints, and reports. List on request.

Staff: Full-time paid employees (central organization and departments), 190.

Finances: Endowment funds, $7,974.99; invested reserve funds other than endowment, $362,162.32, of which $320,280.63 is for the central organization. Value of plant and equipment of national headquarters, $570,313. Income and expenditures for the year 1939–40 for the entire association, including the American Association of School Administrators, Department of Elementary School Principals, American Association for Health, Physical Education, and Recreation, Educational Policies Commission, and other departments, totaled approximately $800,000. For the fiscal year ending May 31, 1940, income and expenditures for the central organization and its projects were as follows:

Income

Gifts and grants	$ 13,000.00
Membership fees	399,880.98
Publications	80,224.31
Endowment and reserve funds	47,725.62
Other services	38,527.99
	$579,358.90

Expenditures

Salaries	$254,761.62
Travel	52,056.13
Communications	19,340.08
Office supplies	9,278.76
Publications	146,668.02
Rentals, insurance, etc.	49,599.02
Convention and other purposes	32,687.15
	$564,390.78

NATIONAL EDUCATION ASSOCIATION, DEPARTMENT OF ART EDUCATION (1933); 1201 16th St., N.W., Washington, D.C.; President, Clara MacGowan, 1554 Howard St., Chicago, Ill.

Membership: Individuals, 546 present and prospective teachers of art, in 41 states and Canada. Annual dues, $1 (plus $2 to National Education Association).

Purpose: To strengthen the friendly and professional relations of art educators; to maintain high professional standards among art teachers and artists in educational work; to promote growth of art education; to sponsor, encourage, and publish studies; and to foster a national outlook in this field.

Activities: Semiannual conventions, in February in connection with the American Association of School Administrators (see p. 114) and in July as part of the National Education Association (see p. 131). Has three committees at work, whose reports will eventually be published: the Committee on Research for Determining Teacher Qualifications in Art; the National Committee on Research in Art Education;

and the Committee of the Department of Art Education for the National Commission on Cooperative Curriculum Planning.

Publications: Annual bulletin (1939, 188 pp.); available to nonmembers at $1 a copy, plus 10¢ postage. Earlier bulletins available at varying prices.

Staff: Officers serve without pay. No paid employees apart from the staff of the National Education Association.

Finances: Cash balance August 1, 1939, $100.41. For the fiscal year ending on that date, expenditures for all purposes totaled $858.31. For the same period, income was as follows:

Appropriation from NEA	$300.00
Membership fees	546.00
Publications	2.15
	$848.15

NATIONAL EDUCATION ASSOCIATION, DEPARTMENT OF ELEMENTARY SCHOOL PRINCIPALS (1921); 1201 16th St., N.W., Washington, D.C.; Eva G. Pinkston, Executive Secretary.

Membership: Individuals, over 6,500 principals in elementary schools, chiefly in large cities. Types of membership and annual dues: active members (principals holding administrative, supervisory, and teaching positions), $3; associate members (those not eligible for active membership), $3; life (active) members, $50.

Purpose: To educate the boys and girls in elementary school and direct them in the right type of living.

Activities: Answers questions regarding problems, furnishes suggestions on activities, supplies bibliographies on certain subjects on request, and provides other services to elementary schools. Holds two annual meetings, one in connection with the American Association of School Administrators (see p. 114), meeting in the winter, and one with the National Education Association (see p. 131), meeting in the summer. Four annual Conferences on Elementary Education have been held: (1) at the University of Michigan (199 in attendance), (2) at New York University (178 in attendance), (3) at the University of California (375 in attendance), and (4) at the University of Wisconsin (675 in attendance). Plans are being made for a Fifth Annual Conference on Elementary Education to be held at Harvard University, July 7–18, 1941.

Publications: *The National Elementary Principal*, 5 issues annually (October, December, February, April, and June), included in the membership fee of $3; December, February, and June issues, 25¢ a copy; October and April issues (official reports of meetings), 50¢ a copy. Yearbook, annually; included in the membership fee of $3, sold separately for $2. Yearbook topics include: *Personality Adjustment of the*

Elementary School Child, 1936; *Appraising the Elementary School Program*, 1937; *Newer Practises in Reading in the Elementary School*, 1938; *Enriching the Curriculum for the Elementary School Child*, 1939; *Meeting Special Needs of the Individual Child*, 1940.

Staff: Full-time paid employees, 5.

Finances: There is a permanent fund of $10,841.62, of which $985.14 is in cash and $9,856.48 is in securities. Current balance May 31, 1940 was $6,613.84. For the fiscal year ending on that date, operations were as follows:

Income	
Membership fees	$18,377.50
Sale of yearbooks	7,782.73
Sale of study outlines	144.50
Interest on bonds	367.40
	$26,672.13

Expenditures	
Salaries	$ 7,727.53
Travel	681.98
Publications	12,003.76
Office supplies	6,589.88
Conventions	341.68
Conference	97.91
Editorial committee	571.64
Other purposes	110.95
	$28,125.33

NATIONAL EDUCATION ASSOCIATION, DEPARTMENT OF SUPERINTENDENCE

See American Association of School Administrators (p. 114).

NATIONAL HOME STUDY COUNCIL (1926); 839 17th St., N.W., Washington, D.C.; J. S. Noffsinger, Director.

Membership: Private correspondence schools, 47. Membership is restricted to such schools as submit to inspection of their advertising methods, course materials, lesson papers, and financial statements, personnel, and equipment, and are approved as operating under satisfactory ethical and technical standards. Each member pays a fee of $25 for the initial inspection, and annual dues at the rate of approximately $140 for each $100,000 of tuition fees collected from its students.

Purpose: To promote sound educational standards and ethical business practices within the home study field; to cooperate with other interested agencies in making effective a constructive program designed to curb and eliminate unfair exploitation of ambitious people by unworthy correspondence schools which are unethical in their conduct and low in educational standards; to advance the standards of home study instruction.

Activities: Cooperates with the Federal Trade Commission, the Post Office Department, the Department of Justice, and Better Business Bureaus in the establishing of sound ethical trade practices among correspondence schools. Maintains a complete cross-reference index of some 25,000 courses available in all institutions offering home study instruction, publicity service for reputable correspondence instruction, legislative service to guard the interests of legitimate home study agencies, a clearing bureau regarding technical and professional developments in the field, annual conventions and conferences for discussion of home study problems, and an information service, available without charge to any person, corporation, school, or government executive upon request, regarding home study courses and schools. Approved schools annually enroll approximately 600,000 youth and young adults in their various courses.

Publications: *News Letter*, monthly; free to members. *Directory of Approved Home Study Schools*, 3 to 4 issues a year (400,000 copies), 4 pp.; *Home Study Blue Book*, annually (70,000 copies), 32 pp.

Staff: Full-time paid employees, 3; part-time paid employee, 1.

Finances: Value of equipment at headquarters, $1,000. For the fiscal year ending March 31, 1940, operations were approximately as follows:

Income

Membership fees	$20,000
Publications	800
Other sources	1,200
	$22,000

Expenditures

Salaries	$ 9,500
Travel	2,000
Telephone and telegraph	75
Office supplies and postage	1,500
Publications	1,500
Rent, insurance, etc.	1,200
Public relations	5,000
Other purposes	1,225
	$22,000

NATIONAL INSTITUTE OF PUBLIC AFFAIRS (1934); 400 Investment Bldg., Washington, D.C.; Frederick M. Davenport, President and Advisory Counsel; Henry Reining, Jr., Educational Director.

Membership: Trustees, 7, forming a nonprofit educational corporation. Each year 50 college graduates are competitively selected from the country at large for one year of "internship" under the auspices of the institute. To be eligible for appointment an applicant must (a) hold a bachelor's degree from a recognized college (seniors are eligible for appointment subject to receipt of degree); (b) have achieved a high scholastic standing; (c) possess exceptional qualities of character, ability, and aptitude for leadership; (d) have a definite interest in public af-

fairs; (e) be in good health; (f) have the endorsement of his college; (g) be a citizen of the United States.

Purpose: To increase the interest of American youth in public affairs; to help in the development of career opportunities in government administration and to add to academic preparation for the public service the experience of working with government officials; to make collegiate instruction in the social sciences more realistic and to aid in the development of a science of public administration.

Activities: Operates as a liaison unit in Washington between the colleges and universities of the country and the federal departments. Specifically, the institute engages in three main activities: (1) It supervises a carefully selected group of college graduates who are accepted by the federal government agencies for a period of intensive training, partly in research and partly in administrative and governmental leadership; it helps to coordinate public service training between the government departments and academic institutions. (2) The institute, with the cooperation of the U.S. Office of Education, conducts annually an Institute of Government for college upperclassmen, in an attempt to make the field of citizenship training more realistic. (3) It serves both government departments and collegiate institutions as a source of information, establishing contacts for the colleges with the government and vice versa, acting as consultant to college faculties and students as well as to government officials in the field of training and in the wider field of public administration and political leadership.

Publications: *National Institute of Public Affairs*, descriptive pamphlet, 20 pp.; *Announcement of the Internship Training Program*, 4 pp.

Staff: Full-time paid employees, 6; part-time paid employees, 2.

Finances: Grants from the Rockefeller Foundation are the sources of support. Value of equipment at headquarters, $5,000. Current balance September 30, 1939, $1,438.03. For the fiscal year ending on that date, operations were as follows:

Total Income

Grant for current expenses	$35,000.00

Expenditures

Salaries	$23,098.52
Travel	2,106.16
Communications	1,166.25
Office supplies	883.45
Publications	252.28
Rent, insurance, etc.	2,640.81
Other purposes	3,414.50
	$33,561.97

NATIONAL KINDERGARTEN ASSOCIATION (1909); 8 West 40th St., New York, N.Y.; Bessie Locke, Founder and Executive Secretary.

Membership: Individuals, varying from 2,245 to

8,000. Types of membership: membership, $10; sustaining membership, $25; life membership, $100.

Purpose: To assist individuals and groups in arousing interest in the establishment of kindergartens, preferably in the public schools and always under the direction of graduate kindergarteners.

Activities: Promotes kindergarten extension directly and by means of improved legislation; the promotional work, carried on by the national staff and by field secretaries, is accomplished through correspondence, speeches, conferences, resolutions endorsing kindergarten extension submitted to conventions of state and national groups, use of the press, and distribution of leaflets and lending of posters and prepared programs for meetings. Attempts to secure improved state kindergarten laws and federal funds to be apportioned to the states for kindergarten education. More than 2,300 kindergartens, enrolling over 920,000 children since their establishment, have been opened as a result of the association's activities, and 17 state laws have been passed at its incitation. Issues weekly home education articles designed to help parents solve the behavior problems commonly encountered in child development from infancy to adolescence; in June 1940 these articles were printed in 1,009 periodicals in the United States and were used by 678 home demonstration and extension agents. The activities of the association extend to all of the states.

Publications: *Home Education* articles intended for weekly use in newspapers and magazines; prepared in sheet form, 5 to a sheet, and issued every 5 weeks; sent free upon request to periodicals that agree to print them more or less regularly and to home demonstration agents and other interested social workers; Florence Jane Ovens, editor-in-chief. *The Kindergarten in the United States*, a report submitted by invitation to President Roosevelt's Advisory Committee on Education by the National Kindergarten Association, edited by Florence J. Ovens, 1937, 52 pp. planographed. Also numerous leaflets.

Staff: Full-time paid employees at home office, 7; part-time field secretaries, 48; part-time unpaid workers, 8.

Finances: Value of plant and equipment at national headquarters, $1,880.08. Balance December 31, 1939, $6,840.38. For the preceding calendar year, income totaled $34,348.20, and expenditures were $32,788.77.

NATIONAL SOCIETY FOR THE STUDY OF EDUCATION (1895); Box 22, Clifton, Mass.; Guy M. Whipple, Secretary-Treasurer.

Membership: Individual educators, approximately 1,250. Entrance fee of $1 and annual dues of $2.50.

Purpose: To promote the investigation and discussion of educational questions.

Activities: Annual meeting at the same time and place as the American Association of School Administrators (see p. 114). Special committees appointed two or three years in advance conduct studies that form the basis of the yearbooks; each yearbook in turn is the chief subject of discussion at the annual meeting.

Publications: Yearbooks annually since 1902, each dealing with one or two major current educational problems, issued usually in February and comprising about 600 to 800 pages annually; free to members, sold to others by the Public School Publishing Company, Bloomington, Ill. Some recent issues are as follows: *Thirty-Seventh Yearbook, 1938*, Part I—*Guidance in Educational Institutions*, G. N. Kefauver, chairman, $2.50 cloth, $1.75 paper; Part II—*The Scientific Movement in Education*, F. N. Freeman, chairman, $4 cloth, $3 paper. *Thirty-Eighth Yearbook, 1939*, Part I—*Child Development and the Curriculum*, Carleton Washburne, chairman, $3.25 cloth, $2.50 paper; Part II—*General Education in the American College*, Alvin Eurich, chairman, $2.75 cloth, $2 paper. *Thirty-Ninth Yearbook, 1940*, Part I—*Intelligence: Its Nature and Nurture—Comparative and Critical Exposition*, G. D. Stoddard, chairman, $3 cloth, $2.25 paper; Part II—*Intelligence: Its Nature and Nurture—Original Studies and Experiments*, G. D. Stoddard, chairman, $3 cloth, $2.25 paper. Earlier yearbooks priced according to size. Complete list on request.

Finances: Current balance June 30, 1939, $21,647.20. For the fiscal year ending on that date, operations were as follows:

	Income	
Sale of yearbooks		$12,328.05
Membership fees		3,072.50
Other sources		945.92
		$16,346.47
	Expenditures	
Salaries		$ 2,860.95
Yearbooks		7,213.31
Committees		3,614.20
Meetings		288.23
Other purposes		1,428.73
		$15,405.42

NATIONAL UNIVERSITY EXTENSION ASSOCIATION (1915); Indiana University, Bloomington, Ind.; W. S. Bittner, Secretary-Treasurer.

Membership: Institutions, 53. Annual dues, $50 an institution.

Purpose: To maintain an organization through which colleges and universities engaged in educational extension work may confer for the development and promotion of the best ideals, methods, and standards.

Activities: Acts as a clearinghouse and bureau of general information for all types of extension services and maintains a directory service concerning correspondence study. A considerable proportion of the enrollment in extension education served by the member institutions consists of persons under 25 years of age; especially is this true of supervised correspondence courses, one of the functions of which is to enrich the educational opportunities of secondary school students.

Publications: *National University Extension Association Bulletin,* monthly, September through June. Proceedings of the annual conventions (Vol. 22, covering the 1939 convention, is a document of 144 pages).

Staff: Unpaid national officers, 6.

Finances: Current balance in May 1940, $5,768.48. For the fiscal year ending in that month, operations were as follows:

Income

Membership fees	$2,635.00
Publications	114.00
Other services	38.95
Grant through American Association for Adult Education for research activities	3,750.00
	$6,537.95

Expenditures

Salaries	$1,749.98
Travel	587.56
Communications	76.13
Office supplies	172.70
Publications	746.80
Other purposes	334.80
	$3,667.97

THE OPEN ROAD, INC. (1925); 8 West 40th St., New York, N.Y.; John Rothschild, Executive Director.

Membership: Individuals, 509. Annual dues range from $2 to several thousand dollars.

Purpose: To help Americans acquaint themselves with their own country and foreign countries in order to educate the individual and to broaden public tolerance.

Activities: Prior to the outbreak of the European war in 1939 the organization was principally engaged in organizing and executing educational tours in Europe in the following categories: field courses for which academic credit was given by colleges and universities, membership principally adult; special interest tours for professional groups, membership principally adult; general cultural tours, membership principally youth. The 1940 program of the organization comprised a student tour to Mexico, a teachers' tour to Guatemala, and the following field courses in American problems: *Workshop in Social and Economic Factors Influencing Education in New England,* in conjunction with the Graduate School of Education

of Harvard University in cooperation with the Progressive Education Association (see p. 137); *Sociological Field Course in Southern Conditions,* in conjunction with Teachers College of Columbia University; *Field Seminar in the Sociology of the Tennessee Valley,* in conjunction with the Department of Educational Sociology of the School of Education of New York University; *Field Course in Life Problems on the Great Plains and in the Rocky Mountain Area,* in conjunction with the Colorado State College of Education; *Field Course in the Sociology of the Textile Industry in New England and the South,* in conjunction with Antioch College. Most of the youth served by the organization are persons of college age who come from all parts of the United States; a majority of them are young women.

Publications: *Report on the Sociological Field Course in Southern Conditions,* 1939, and similar reports on other field courses, free. Also prospectuses of tours and courses.

Staff: Full-time paid employees at headquarters, 4; part-time paid employee, 1.

Finances: Value of equipment at national headquarters, $3,754.62. Cash balances September 30, 1940, $119.98. For the fiscal year ending on that date, operations were as follows:

Income

Gifts and foundation grants	$ 3,681.00
Membership dues and contributions	15,737.44
Service fees and commissions	933.59
	$20,352.03

Expenditures

Salaries	$15,298.30
Travel	2,209.93
Communications	1,822.96
Office supplies	430.64
Publications	1,035.28
Rentals, insurance, etc.	4,192.98
Miscellaneous	1,336.82
	$26,326.91

PROGRESSIVE EDUCATION ASSOCIATION (1918); 221 West 57th St., New York, N.Y.; Frederick L. Redefer, Executive Secretary.

The United States section of the New Education Fellowship, an international organization.

Membership: Individuals, 10,000. Annual dues, $3, $4, or $10.

Purpose: To deepen the understanding of education in home, school, and community for the purpose of making these agencies serve society more constructively; to further educational progress through research and experimentation and to improve such by means of exchanging reports and information.

Activities: Regional conferences, research, and publications. Maintains the following commissions and committees: (1) *Commission on the Relation of School and College*, which has negotiated arrangements whereby 30 selected high schools have been freed from rigid college entrance requirements and enabled to do experimental work. The commission embraces the Committee on Evaluation, the Committee on College Success of Students, and the Committee on Records and Reports. (2) *Commission on Secondary School Curriculum*, producing publications indicating how the curriculum might be based on the needs of youth in American democracy. The commission includes the Committee on the Study of Adolescents. (3) *Commission on Human Relations*, which has prepared publications for high school and junior college adolescents, developed radio programs for this age group, and the Human Relations Series of films. (4) *Commission on Resources and Education*, integrating the findings of experts on national resources into curriculum materials for children of all ages. (5) *Committee on Workshops and Field Services*, which has developed, in cooperation with existing institutions for the education of teachers, a program of teacher education through summer workshops, consultation services, and study conferences.

Publications: *Progressive Education*, 8 issues annually; $3 a year; James L. Hymes, editor. *Frontiers of Democracy*, 8 issues annually; $2.50 a year; William H. Kilpatrick, editor. Numerous books, including: *The Family—Past and Present*, by Bernhard J. Stern, $2.75; *Life and Growth*, by Alice Keliher, $1.20; *Language in General Education*, $2; *Science in General Education*, $3; *The Visual Arts in General Education*, $1.50; *Mathematics in General Education*, $2.75; *The Social Studies in General Education*, $2.75; *Emotion and Conduct in Adolescence*, by Caroline B. Zachry, $3; *Physical Education in the Secondary School*, by Laurentine B. Collins and others, $1; *Youth Serves the Community*, by Paul H. Hanna, $2. Substantial reductions in all prices are made to members.

Staff: Full-time paid employees at headquarters, 13, of whom 2 spend major time in field work.

Finances: Income is derived primarily from membership fees, sale of publications, conferences, and other services. Approximate annual budget, $43,000. Research activities are supported exclusively by grants from the General Education Board.

SCHOOL GARDEN ASSOCIATION OF AMERICA

See Garden Education Department of the National Education Association (p. 126).

SOCIETY FOR CURRICULUM STUDY (1931); Stanford University, Calif.; J. Paul Leonard, Executive Secretary.

Membership: Individuals, 750, chiefly public school curriculum directors, administrative officers in charge of curriculum-making, instructors and experimenters in curriculum-making. Annual dues, $2.

Purpose: To enable curriculum workers to be mutually helpful; to promote thorough and progressive curriculum revision; to promote curriculum investigation, experimentation, and research.

Activities: Maintains eight committees working on the following problems of curriculum: home and family life; curriculum laboratories; secondary education; regional conferences and meetings; foreign cultures; rural education; visual education; and consumer education.

Publications: *Curriculum Journal*, 8 issues annually; free to members, $2 a year to others; Henry Harap, editor, George Peabody College for Teachers, Nashville, Tenn. *Building America*, 8 issues annually; $2 a year ($1.50 in groups of 10); Frances Foster, editor, 546 West 114th St., New York, N.Y.; publisher and distributor, Americana Corporation, 2 West 45th St., New York, N.Y. Each issue of *Building America* is devoted wholly to some one outstanding modern problem and is extensively illustrated with photographic reproductions.

Staff: Part-time paid employees, 2 (exclusive of the staff of *Building America*, which is independently administered). Services of the 12 members of the executive board of the society and the *Journal* are contributed.

Finances: Estimated annual value of unpaid staff services, $8,500; estimated annual value of space, heat, light, and similar services received without charge, $2,000. Balance February 28, 1940, $863.76. For the fiscal year ending on that date, operations were as follows:

	Income	
Membership fees		$1,452.50
Publications		1,837.02
		$3,289.52
	Expenditures	
Salaries		$1,260.00
Travel		90.32
Communications		211.03
Office supplies		184.32
Publications		1,359.25
Other purposes		44.21
		$3,149.13

SOCIETY OF STATE DIRECTORS OF HEALTH AND PHYSICAL EDUCATION (1926); 315 Fourth Ave., New York, N.Y.; James Edward Rogers, Secretary.

Membership: Active membership is limited to state directors of health and physical education and members of their staffs. Former active members and their staffs continue as associate members. At present there are 24 states having the office of state director. The officer is in all cases a member of the staff of the chief state school officer and is in charge of the school health, physical education, and safety programs. Annual dues, $2.

Purpose: To help establish, maintain, improve, and enrich state-wide programs of health and physical education through the chief state school office in each state; to develop a professional growth and integrity among the state directors and their staffs; to improve standards in school health, physical education, and safety.

Activities: The members are largely responsible for the development of physical education programs for all school youth between the ages of 5 and 20 in their respective states. It is roughly estimated that approximately 18,000,000 persons of these ages are affected directly or indirectly by the work of the active members of the society.

Publications: *News Bulletin*, quarterly; free to members. Occasional committee reports and mimeographed and multigraphed materials. Yearbooks: *The Public School Program in Health, Physical Education, and Recreation*, 1939; *Policies and Standards in the Organization and Administration of a State Program of Health, Physical Education, and Safety*, 1940; *Teacher Preparation in Health and Physical Education*, 1941.

TEACHERS COLLEGE PERSONNEL ASSOCIATION (1931); President, Dr. C. F. Malmberg, Illinois State Normal University, Normal, Ill.; Secretary, Dr. Nora A. Congdon, Colorado State College of Education, Greeley, Colo.

Membership: Institutions for the education of teachers, 81, of which 35 (located in 21 states) are active members, and 46 (located in 24 states) are associate members.

Purpose: To provide for (1) cooperative association and research by persons interested in personnel service and its administration, (2) national and regional meetings for the discussion of personnel problems, (3) promotion of the development, knowledge, and use of the most approved and efficient methods of personnel work.

Activities: Conducts a cooperative testing program among teachers colleges; constructs and publishes a psychological examination, an English test, an elementary subjects test, and a personal data scale; constructed a cumulative record form. Holds annual meetings at the same time and place as the American Association of Teachers Colleges. Conducts research studies looking toward more effective counseling of college students. During nine years approximately 362,000 tests have been administered to freshman entrants in 135 colleges for teachers. These were

about one-third boys and two-thirds girls, and 95 per cent were between the ages of 16 and 21 inclusive.

Publications: *Reports of the Cooperative Testing Program*, by J. D. Heilman, issued annually 1932–39, are mimeographed documents of 44 to 102 pages, 50¢ each, obtainable from the Colorado State College of Education. The 1940 report, by Nora A. Congdon, is a printed document of 32 pages, 25¢, obtainable from the president of the association.

Staff: No paid employees. The time of the officers and their part-time clerical assistants is donated by their respective institutions.

Finances: Income and expenditures are handled through various educational institutions. Tests are published and sold by these institutions in the name of the organization; sales of such tests during the year ending February 1940 totaled approximately $3,000.

WORK CAMPS FOR AMERICA, INC. (1939); 2 West 64th St., New York, N.Y.; Robert E. Lane, Executive Secretary.

Membership: Persons aged 18 to 24, 160, who have attended one or more of the four work camps operated in 1939 and 1940.

Purpose: To promote summer work camps serving some community or nonprofit association and providing opportunity for the study of current social issues as reflected in the neighboring community; to create in youth an awareness of the privileges and responsibilities of citizenship in a democracy.

Activities: In the summer of 1940 work camps were held at Green Farms, Conn., Hudson, Ohio, and Monteagle, Tenn. The activities include *work* such as constructing buildings, improving roads, painting and repairing, roofing, building a dam, and the like, for settlement camps, workers' schools, or other organizations; *study* of problems of democracy such as health, unions, housing, race and religious discrimination, conservation, and civil liberties; and *recreation* such as folk dancing, singing, living newspapers, and athletics. In all these enterprises the active cooperation of local committees is sought.

Publications: *The Work Camper*, 12 issues annually; $1 a year.

Staff: Full-time paid employees, 2.

Finances: For the fiscal year ending October 1, 1940 total income was $6,804.01, and expenditures were $6,776.16.

Table XVII

STATISTICS OF EDUCATIONAL ASSOCIATIONS

Organization	Year Founded	Approximate Aggregate Membership (individuals)	Number of Members under 25 Years of Age	Total Employees on Headquarters Staff	Aggregate Endowment of National Headquarters	Plant and Equipment (headquarters only)	Approximate Annual Budget (headquarters only)
American Association for Adult Education	1926	1,080	...	18	$ ...	$ ...	$ 69,600[a]
American Association of Junior Colleges	1920	416[b]	...	10	none	1,000	12,500
American Association of University Women	1882	68,003	...	28	650,937[c]	215,292	260,000
American Association of Visiting Teachers	1916	300	...	[d]	...	...	500
American College Personnel Association	1923	175	...		none	...	1,600
American Council on Education	1918	497[e]	...	24	none	13,000	159,600[f]
American Federation of Teachers	1916	35,000	...	10	none[g]	500	90,200
American Home Economics Association	1908	15,000[h]	70,000	18	none[i]	8,500	65,300
American Institute of the City of New York	1828	595[h]	20,040	41	none[j]	1,443	102,800
American Library Association	1876	13,971	...	89	2,179,346	...	373,200
American Sociological Society	1905	1,012[h]	250	2	2,114	227	8,700
American Turners	1850	27,179	2,209	4	85,968	400	10,900
Association of American Colleges	1915	560[e]	...	9	none	1,734	30,600
Association for Childhood Education	1892	36,000	...	8	20,274[k]	837	36,400
Bureau of University Travel	1891	9[m]	...	3	...	5,000	9,000
Federal Radio Education Committee	1935	40	...	8	...	...	25,000[a]
Foreign Policy Association	1918	19,297	2,732	41	none[n]	...	175,200
Future Teachers of America	1937	3,653	3,653	[p]	...	[p]	[p]
Jesuit Educational Association	1921	77[e]	...	1	none	...	2,000
Music Educators National Conference	1907	15,000	...	11	...	...	...
National Advisory Council on Radio in Education	1930	75	...	1	...	...	...
National Capital School Visitors Council	1940	18[q]	...	4	...	...	4,000
National Catholic Educational Association	1904	3,425	...	...	...	...	...
National Committee on Education by Radio	1930	9[e]	...	1	none	3,500	7,500
National Conference on Family Relations	1938	1,050	40	3	none	...	3,100[r]

Table XVII—Continued

Organization	Year Founded	Approximate Aggregate Membership (individuals)	Number of Members under 25 Years of Age	Total Employees on Head-quarters Staff	Aggregate Endowment of National Headquarters	Plant and Equipment (headquarters only)	Approximate Annual Budget (headquarters only)
National Congress of Parents and Teachers	1897	2,330,000	...	24	$ ...	$ ...	$160,000
National Council of Parent Education	1926	475	...	1	none	200	600
National Education Association of the United States	1857	203,429h	...	190s	7,975t	570,313	800,000s
National Home Study Council	1926	47e	...	4	none	1,000	22,000
National Institute of Public Affairs	1934	7m	50u	8	...	5,000	35,000
National Kindergarten Association	1909	...	...	55	...	1,880	34,300
National Society for the Study of Education	1895	1,250	...	..d	...	...	18,600
National University Extension Association	1915	53e	...	5	...	...	6,500
Open Road	1925	509	...	5	none	3,755	26,300
Progressive Education Association	1918	10,000	...	13	...	...	43,000
Society for Curriculum Study	1931	750	...	2	none	none	3,300
Soc. of State Directors of Health and Physical Educ.	1926	...	...	..d	...	...	...
Teachers College Personnel Association	1931	81e	...	..d	none	...	...
Work Camps for America	1939	160	160	2	...	...	6,800

a Exclusive of special projects.
b 384 junior colleges and 32 individuals.
c Endowment for fellowships; there is also a general reserve fund of $59,718.
d No full-time paid workers.
e Number of constituent bodies.
f Exclusive of American Youth Commission, Commission on Teacher Education, Cooperative Test Service, and other special projects.
g The organization has a reserve fund of $500 and a defense fund of $5,000.
h Adult membership only.
i The organization has a reserve fund of $10,000.

j The organization has reserve funds of $48,162.
k Also a reserve fund of $2,860.
m Number of trustees.
n The organization has a reserve fund of $10,000.
p None apart from that of the National Education Association.
q Number of members on advisory board.
r Budget for the organization's first 16 months.
s Total for central organization and the various departments.
t Also reserve funds of $362,162, including those of the various departments.
u Number of "interns" each year.

141

XVII. Organizations in the Fields of Guidance, Personnel, and Employment

The fields of guidance and personnel work, including placement and vocational adjustment, are relatively new. The voluntary organizations interested in various sectors of this area are among the youngest groups described in this volume. One-half of them have been founded since 1925, and the oldest ones date from 1913, thus having a life of less than thirty years.

In this field, as in the field of education, it is expected that such great public agencies as the public schools and the federal-state employment services, in cooperation with such federal agencies as the Vocational Education Division in the United States Office of Education, the Employment Service Division in the Bureau of Employment Security of the Social Security Board, and the Occupational Outlook Service in the Bureau of Labor Statistics of the Department of Labor, will carry on a large part of the vast volume of record keeping and statistical interpretation which are necessary as a basis for a satisfactory continuing system for the vocational adjustment of youth.

There is nevertheless ample room for the activities of private associations. Very great service in demonstrating the possibilities in this field and in disseminating the results of experience gained in small-scale experimental projects, as well as in publicizing the best current theories of guidance and personnel work, has already been rendered by such associations.

Occupational adjustment for youth has seemed especially needed during the decade of the nineteen-thirties because widespread unemployment made it extraordinarily difficult for youth to find places in the work of the world upon reaching maturity. It seems acutely needed in the early nineteen-forties because the international situation requires efficient use of America's human and material resources for the building of national strength for defense and for the enhancement of the values already attained in our democratic society.

The fact is that the problem of occupational adjustment is a continuing one, no less important in boom times than in depressions, and equally as acute in times of calm as in times of crisis. Nor is it limited to youth alone. It extends throughout the productive life of the individual. If he finds himself increasing in competency beyond the demands of his current job and beyond the limits of its related opportunities, adjustment should be found in another place more nearly commensurate with his present capacities. If he finds himself unable to discharge the duties of a position which is beyond his ability, whether because of a decline in ability or not, a change to a different situation is also indicated.

The American Youth Commission, as a result of an eighteen-month demonstration project in eight urban and rural localities in cooperation with the public employment services, finds that an element of basic importance is a continuing coordination of the several agencies, public and private, which have a hand in vocational education, guidance, and placement in each community. It recommends the building of coordinated community-wide programs of occupational adjustment.

Guidance in its broad sense comprehends more than vocational adjustment. It may include counseling regarding other phases of life as well as the vocational phase. It is already extensively recognized as an indispensable function of educational institutions of every type and grade.

In the present section, the one organization whose membership consists chiefly of young persons, as distinguished from those composed wholly or largely of persons above the age of 25, is Youth Service.

Cross references: Section XX, Organizations in the Field of Social Work, pp. 184–95, especially American Association of Social Workers, p. 185, and Association of Church Social Workers, p. 187; Section XXII, Organizations Serving Handicapped Youth, pp. 202–8, especially National Rehabilitation Association, p. 206. *See also:* Air Youth of America, p. 152; American Association of Medical Social Workers, p. 170; American College Personnel Association, p. 116; B'nai B'rith Vocational Service Bureau, p. 57; Future Farmers of America, p. 93; Future Teachers of America, p. 125; Hechalutz Organization of America, p. 58; International Association of Altrusa Clubs, p. 107; Jewish Agricultural Society, p. 59; Jewish Occupational Council, p. 59; National Association of Deans of Women, p. 128; National Federation of Business and Professional Women's Clubs, p. 108; National Organization for Public Health Nursing, p. 179; Society of Recreation Workers of America, p. 167; Teachers College Personnel Association, p. 139.

ALLIANCE FOR GUIDANCE OF RURAL YOUTH
(1914); Grace-American Bldg., Richmond, Va.; O. Latham Hatcher, President.

Name changed from Southern Woman's Educational Alliance to present form, 1937.

Membership: Individuals, approximately 350, in four branches located in Chicago, New York City, Richmond, and Washington. The Chicago branch consists of two chapters: North Shore and University of Chicago. These branches function to interpret and assist in supporting the alliance program. Annual dues: active, $5; subscribing, $10; contributing, $25; sustaining, $100. Founder (life), $1,000.

Purpose: To further the provision of individual and group guidance, especially educational and vocational guidance, for in-school and out-of-school rural youth; to help other agencies render such service; to spread public consciousness of the need for such service; and to strengthen the public sense of obligation to provide it.

Activities: Assembles, and encourages others to assemble, facts needed as a basis for sound guidance of rural youth; uses such facts in direct counseling of rural youth and makes these facts available for the use of others; interprets and supplies information on guidance in rural areas; cooperates with rural educators and other rural community leaders in launching county guidance programs; develops local demonstrations of rural guidance institutes or workshops in which rural teachers have opportunity to learn the principles and practices of guidance in terms of their own school problems and to apply them there directly; develops as demonstrations a few intensive county programs in especially representative counties such as Breathitt County, Ky., and Craven County, N.C.; cooperates with other national agencies or groups of agencies by providing rural guidance features or sections of programs at conventions or conferences; brings together rural and urban leaders, including local, state, and national technicians, to work on such guidance problems as the migration of youth to cities for work; coordinates the services of other agencies in special guidance undertakings. The beneficiaries of the organization's services are rural youth ranging in age from 6 to 27, about half of whom are between the ages of 12 and 20. Approximately 15,000 have been helped individually, and far larger numbers less directly and intensively through alliance cooperation with adults supervising rural school or community programs.

Publications: *Twenty-five Years of Work*, 1940, $1; *Guiding Rural Boys and Girls*, by O. Latham Hatcher (New York: McGraw-Hill Book Company, 1930), 344 pp., $2.50; *Rural Girls in the City for Work*, 1930, 173 pp., $1 plus postage; *A Mountain School* (Richmond: Garrett & Massey, 1930), 274 pp., $1; *Programs for Which Out-of-School Young People in Breathitt County, Ky., Are Asking*, 1935, 18 pp. mimeo., 20¢. Many other books and pamphlets. Lists on request.

Staff: Full-time paid employees at Richmond office, usually 3, with additional temporary workers for special undertakings; also paid clerical and some professional assistance as needed for conferences and executive work in New York and Washington. The bulk of the paid staff for intensive rural field work, except for those under alliance supervision, is usually provided by local authorities. Much professional service at headquarters and in urban field work is contributed.

Finances: Various financial resources amounting to income in the alliance program development cannot be incorporated into its audit because funds involved do not actually pass through its bank account. This applies to various expenses in intensive guidance programs worked out with rural educators on a county-wide basis, to rural guidance institutes, to urban professional services contributed to the alliance, and to the material resources provided in cities. Value of equipment at headquarters, $1,159.84. Balance September 30, 1938, $3,987.39. For the fiscal year ending on that date, operations were as follows:

Income

Gifts, benefits, etc.	$ 9,269.73
Memberships	1,893.30
Publications	49.50
Interest on investments and bank balances	87.76
Refunds from branches	99.18
Miscellaneous service	168.05
	$11,567.52

Expenditures

Salaries	$ 4,185.33
Travel	1,019.08
Communications	558.23
Office supplies	338.26
Rent	790.04
Branch expenses and refunds	298.76
Other purposes	595.89
	$ 7,785.59

AMERICAN COUNCIL OF GUIDANCE AND PERSONNEL ASSOCIATIONS

See Council of Guidance and Personnel Associations (p. 145).

AMERICAN OCCUPATIONAL THERAPY ASSOCIATION (1917); 175 Fifth Ave., New York, N.Y.; Mrs. Meta R. Cobb, Executive Secretary.

Membership: Professional workers, 1,200.

Purpose: To promote the use of occupational therapy; to advance the standards of education and training in this field; to promote research; and to engage in any other activities that in the future may be considered advantageous to the profession and its members.

Activities: Functions as a center of information regarding occupational therapy in all its phases from training to placement. Holds an annual meeting in conjunction with the American Hospital Association. Distributes literature on occupational therapy training to vocational guidance departments of high schools and colleges regularly.

Publications: *Occupational Therapy and Rehabilitation*, bimonthly. *Directory of Qualified Occupational Therapists.*

Staff: Full-time paid employees at headquarters, 2; part-time paid employee, 1.

Finances: For the fiscal year ending August 31, 1939, income totaled $8,954.24; expenditures for the same period totaled $9,463.10.

AMERICAN VOCATIONAL ASSOCIATION, INC.
(1925); Denrike Bldg., 1010 Vermont Ave., Washington, D.C.; L. H. Dennis, Executive Secretary.

Membership: Individuals, 23,804, including 429 life members. The membership is comprised of teachers, supervisors, and directors of vocational education in industrial and rural communities.

Purpose: To stimulate and improve public education in agriculture, industry, commerce, and home economics; to promote the development of industrial education, part-time schools, vocational guidance, and vocational rehabilitation; to provide a clearinghouse and information center for workers in these enterprises.

Activities: Conducts surveys of need for vocational education and studies of effectiveness of vocational education. Fosters, promotes, and advises Future Farmers of America (see p. 93), a national organization with a membership of 230,000 farm boys. Also serves many other country, village, and city groups of youth enrolled in industrial arts, vocational, industrial, and home economics education classes.

Publications: *A. V. A. Journal and News Bulletin*, dealing with vocational guidance, vocational training, practical arts education, and employment opportunities for youth; 4 issues annually; free to members, $1 a year to school, college, university, and organization libraries; L. H. Dennis, editor-in-chief. *Standards of Attainment in Industrial Arts Bulletin*, 25¢; *Report of Occupational Graduates in Williamsport, Pennsylvania, Area*, 50¢.

Staff: Full-time paid employees at headquarters, 4.

Finances: Endowment funds, $28,613; reserve funds other than endowment, $6,387. Value of equipment at national headquarters, $3,100. Balance November 30, 1939, $2,915.74. For the fiscal year ending on that date, operations were as follows:

Income

Affiliated memberships	$22,575.25
Life memberships	1,922.50
Publications	240.66
Interest on bonds	1,067.50
Convention exhibits	4,580.00
Miscellaneous	410.21
	$30,796.12

Expenditures

Salaries	$12,845.15
Travel	5,060.86
Communications and printing	1,111.32
Supplies and equipment	1,062.01
A.V.A. Journal	6,233.99
Rent	1,200.00
Convention	700.23
Other purposes	3,278.75
	$31,492.31

AMERICAN YOUTH COUNCIL
See Youth Service (p. 148).

COOPERATIVE TEST SERVICE OF THE AMERICAN COUNCIL ON EDUCATION
(1930); 15 Amsterdam Ave., New York, N.Y.; Ben D. Wood, Director; John C. Flanagan, Associate Director; David G. Ryans, Executive Secretary.

Membership: None. Service is under direction of Committee on Measurement and Guidance of the American Council on Education (see p. 117).

Purpose: To prepare and distribute comparable achievement tests in fundamental subject-matter fields of high school and college and to advise with educational institutions and organizations regarding the use of these tools in guidance.

Activities: In 1939–40 issued 38 tests in various subjects, of which more than 1,120,000 copies were sold. Prepared, administered, and scored a series of tests for candidates for teaching positions for use by the American Council on Education's National Committee on Teacher Examinations.

Publications: Annual catalog, reports of testing experiments, guidance handbooks, and reports of other researches in measurement.

Staff: Full-time paid employees, 27.

Finances: The service was financed from 1930 to 1940 by a grant of $500,000 from the General Education Board. In 1939 Carnegie Corporation of New York contributed a special 3-year appropriation of $85,000 for teacher examination work. For the fiscal year ending June 30, 1940, income and expenditures of the distributing office and the test producing division totaled approximately $100,000. Total budget for 1940–41 is $155,176.

Value of equipment of the distributing office, $1,078.67. Estimated annual value of space, heat, light, and similar services received without charge, $3,600. Cash reserves of the distributing office June 30, 1940, $62,399.31. For the fiscal year ending on that date, operations of the distributing office were as follows:

Income

Publications	$69,258.22
Sale test items	263.20
Reserve funds	213.90
	$69,735.32

Expenditures

Salaries	$17,296.40
Communications	3,063.46
Office supplies	1,232.28
Publications	32,666.84
Equipment	1,132.56
Advisory service and miscellaneous	9,425.65
	$64,817.19

COUNCIL OF GUIDANCE AND PERSONNEL ASSOCIATIONS (1934); Chairman, Dr. Warren K. Layton, Director of Division of Guidance and Placement, Board of Education, Detroit, Mich.; Secretary-Treasurer, F. B. Shannon, Public Relations Manager, Western Electric Company, 100 Central Ave., Kearny, N.J.

Membership: Organizations whose interests are primarily or indirectly in the guidance and personnel field, 12: Alliance for Guidance of Rural Youth (see p. 143), American Association of Collegiate Registrars, American College Personnel Association (see p. 116), Eastern College Personnel Officers, Institute of Women's Professional Relations (see p. 147), International Association of Altrusa Clubs (see p. 107), National Association of Deans of Women (see p. 128), Personnel Research Federation, National Federation of Business and Professional Women's Clubs (see p. 108), National Vocational Guidance Association (see p. 148), Teachers College Personnel Association (see p. 139), Western Personnel Service.

Purpose: To effect cooperation among the member organizations to the end that mutual acquaintance may be cultivated and principles, practices, and professional standards in the guidance and personnel field may be advanced; to foster the aims that these organizations have in common without in any way minimizing their activities in carrying on the special aims of each association in its own field.

Activities: The member organizations are working toward the solution of the problems of youth. The council coordinates the efforts of these organizations through yearly joint sessions devoted to topics of common interest and is studying other areas of cooperation such as the promotion of research in the guidance and personnel field.

Publications: Proceedings of the annual meeting are printed in *Occupations*, official organ of the National Vocational Guidance Association.

Staff: No paid employees.

Finances: Balance February 29, 1940, $968.29. For the fiscal year ending on that date, operations were as follows:

Income

Carnegie Corporation grant	$ 500.00
Membership contributions	825.00
Registration	24.00
	$1,349.00

Expenditures

Travel	$ 32.00
Publicity	136.93
Office supplies	62.12
Convention expenses	305.63
	$536.68

ENGINEERS' COUNCIL FOR PROFESSIONAL DEVELOPMENT (1932); 29 West 39th St., New York, N.Y.; C. E. Davies, Secretary.

Membership: A conference of seven engineering bodies: American Society of Civil Engineers, American Institute of Mining and Metallurgical Engineers, American Society of Mechanical Engineers, American Institute of Electrical Engineers, American Institute of Chemical Engineers, Society for the Promotion of Engineering Education, and National Council of State Boards of Engineering Examiners.

Purpose: To enhance the professional status of the engineer through the cooperative support of those national organizations directly representing the professional, technical, educational, and legislative phases of an engineer's life; to promote higher professional standards of education and practice, greater solidarity of the profession, and greater effectiveness in dealing with technical, social, and economic problems.

Activities: Annual meetings, with the following interim program of research and action: study of guidance by which promising aspirants may be directed into the engineering profession and those not having desirable qualifications may be discouraged from entering it; cooperation between the practicing profession and the formal educational agencies; establishment of a program of post-collegiate training for engineers; and correlation of the various current methods of formal recognition of the development of an engineer.

Through its program of counseling for high school students 100 members of national engineering societies will participate in 1940 in counseling 2,000 New York City high school seniors interested in engineering. The council has also encouraged the formation of groups of engineers to conduct guidance activities in various cities and states; in 1940 these groups will give counsel to several thousand students. Peoria (Ill.), Beloit (Wis.), Buffalo, Rochester, Syracuse, St. Louis, Baltimore, Birmingham, Detroit, Denver, Omaha, and Toronto have all had committees of the national engineering societies doing constructive guidance work in their field in conjunction with the guidance activities of the high school authorities. Among the subjects discussed are the kinds of work which young engineers engage in, promotion to work of designers, personal qualities, and production, operation, and management.

Publications: *List of Accredited Engineering Curricula* (available December 15), preprint of annual report, 25¢; annual report, 25¢. *Present Status and Trends of Engineering Education in the United*

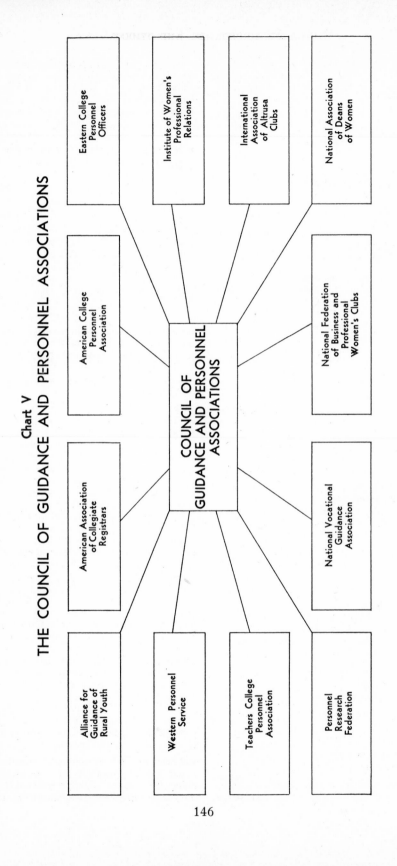

Chart V

THE COUNCIL OF GUIDANCE AND PERSONNEL ASSOCIATIONS

COUNCIL OF GUIDANCE AND PERSONNEL ASSOCIATIONS

Eastern College Personnel Officers

Institute of Women's Professional Relations

International Association of Altrusa Clubs

National Association of Deans of Women

American College Personnel Association

National Federation of Business and Professional Women's Clubs

American Association of Collegiate Registrars

National Vocational Guidance Association

Alliance for Guidance of Rural Youth

Western Personnel Service

Teachers College Personnel Association

Personnel Research Federation

States, written by D. C. Jackson and published by the council's Committee on Engineering Schools with the cooperation of the Carnegie Foundation, 1939, $1. *Engineering: A Career—A Culture*, offering guidance to high school students (New York: Engineering Foundation, 1932), 60 pp., 10¢; *Guidance Manual*, prepared for the use of counselors, revised 1940, 16 pp. mimeo., 5¢; *Suggestions to Junior Engineers*, including personal appraisal blanks and list of general readings, 1934, 10 pp., 10¢; *University Extension Facilities*, description of nontechnical courses in class or by correspondence, 1937, 9 pp., 10¢. *Selected Bibliography of Engineering Subjects*, 5 sections (Mathematics and Physics, Mechanics; Aeronautical and Civil Engineering; Chemical and Industrial Engineering; Electrical and Mechanical Engineering; Metallurgical and Mining Engineering), 1937, 55 pp., 10¢ each section. Discounts on quantities. Various other pamphlets.

Staff: Full-time paid employee at home office, 1; part-time paid employees in field work, 2.

Finances: Balance September 30, 1939, $10,443.61. For the fiscal year ending on that date, operations were as follows:

Income

Contributions from Engineering Foundation and other professional societies	$ 7,260.00
Publications	600.40
Accrediting fees	1,403.60
	$ 9,264.00

Expenditures

Administrative salaries	$ 4,060.00
General office expenses	2,056.18
Publications	1,140.54
Rent	1,237.68
Accrediting committee	5,350.37
Research	2,680.33
	$16,525.10

INSTITUTE OF WOMEN'S PROFESSIONAL RELATIONS (1928); research headquarters, Connecticut College for Women, New London, Conn.; general office, 1066 National Press Bldg., Washington, D. C.; Mrs. Chase Going Woodhouse, Managing Director.

Membership: The institute depends for its support on private funds. Believing that the work is of interest and value to employers, educators, and parents as well as to students and to business and professional women, it is asking individuals in all these groups to become members. Memberships and annual subscriptions are as follows: subscribing, $5; sustaining, $25; founder, $100; organization group, $25.

Purpose: To maintain a panorama of women's work for the college and business and professional woman;

to indicate the relation of college, professional, and other courses to particular occupations; to serve as a clearinghouse for information on women's work and education; to reduce the cost to business and industry of "training on the job" by providing information to help in the choice of career and in the training for it; to advise with groups and individuals in planning conferences, research, curricula, etc.; to carry on research so that these objectives may be realized.

Activities: Most of the organization's activities are directed toward helping young women. Guidance conferences are held annually. In 1939 the following conferences were held: opportunities in the public service (Washington); photography—profession, adjunct, recreation (New York); desirable preparation for civil service positions (Connecticut College for Women, New London).

Publications: *Women's Work and Education*, quarterly; $1.50 a year, free to members; edited at research headquarters in New London.

Staff: Full-time paid employees at headquarters, 4; part-time paid employees, 24.

Finances: Estimated annual value of space, heat, light, and similar services received without charge, $1,200; estimated annual value of unpaid staff services, $5,000.

INTERNATIONAL ASSOCIATION OF PUBLIC EMPLOYMENT SERVICES (1913); President, V. C. Phelan, Employment Service of Canada, Ottawa, Ontario, Canada; Secretary-Treasurer, B. C. Seiple, Ohio State Employment Service, 1242 West Third St., Cleveland, Ohio; General Secretary, Charles L. Hodge, Railroad Retirement Board, Washington, D.C.

Membership: Individuals, 5,323.

Purpose: To advance the ideals, progress, and policies of the public employment service through cooperation and discussion.

Activities: Considers the functions and problems of employment offices; gives especial attention to the guidance of young people.

Publications: Reports of proceedings of annual conventions, available to members only.

NATIONAL COUNCIL ON HOUSEHOLD EMPLOYMENT (1928); Haverford, Pa.; Dr. Amey E. Watson, Executive Secretary.

Formerly the National Committee on Household Employment.

Membership: Individuals, 58, and organizations, 5.

Purpose: To improve the relations between employer and employee in household employment; to develop and promote standards in the field of household employment; and to cooperate with organizations in their efforts to achieve these objectives.

Activities: The council is primarily an educational organization seeking to educate both employers and employees and to secure the extension of social security benefits to the more than 2,000,000 women, of whom a large percentage are under 30 years of age, employed in household service. It acts as a clearinghouse of information, is building up a library, and stimulates and promotes standards of labor relationships. It carries on its work through correspondence, lectures, conferences, symposiums, and study groups. Effort is being made to educate both the employer and the worker to understand their functions. National and regional conferences are planned, and summer camps are served through study groups. Training courses in household employment are stimulated throughout the United States. Local Community Councils on Household Employment are planning to become affiliated.

Publications: The publication of a bulletin is being planned. *Proposals for a Voluntary Agreement in Household Employment*, mimeo.; bibliography, mimeo.

Staff: Several part-time workers, including temporary investigators.

Finances: For the latest complete fiscal year income totaled approximately $4,000, of which $3,500 was derived from gifts and grants and $500 from membership fees.

NATIONAL VOCATIONAL GUIDANCE ASSOCIATION (1913); 425 West 123rd St., New York, N.Y.; Dr. Ralph B. Kenney, Executive Secretary.

Membership: Individuals, 3,000, in 60 branch associations throughout the United States; branches are also located in Hawaii, Puerto Rico, and Canada. Annual dues, $3.50.

Purpose: To further educational and vocational guidance; to stimulate guidance activities in local communities; to encourage community organizations for guidance; to render assistance to state and local school systems concerned with guidance programs; to conduct an annual national convention; and to render any service possible to those interested in programs of vocational guidance and occupational adjustment.

Activities: Studies the problem of occupational information, with a view to placing in the hands of youth accurate information regarding opportunities for work and opportunities for preparation for the different occupations and professions; promotes a special study of standards in the training of vocational guidance counselors. Maintains committees on counseling, placement, scholarship, college guidance, secondary school guidance, out-of-school guidance, special groups, radio, occupational research, and individual analysis. In addition to the national convention held annually in February, the council holds regional conferences throughout the United States. Through its members the council serves youth in schools, colleges, and agencies such as the YMCA, the YWCA, the CCC, and the NYA.

Publications: *Occupations, The Vocational Guidance Magazine*, monthly, October through May; $3.50 a year, free to members; Dr. Harry D. Kitson, editor. Radio committee publishes a series of radio scripts on "America at Work." Also reprints of articles.

Staff: Full-time paid employees, 4.

PSYCHOLOGICAL CORPORATION (1921); 522 Fifth Ave., New York, N.Y.; Paul S. Achilles, First Vice President and General Manager.

Membership: The corporation is not a membership society but lists as research associates qualified psychologists throughout the country who desire to cooperate in various divisions of its activities; about 350 such professional psychologists, located primarily at colleges and universities, are so listed.

Purpose: To further researches for the advancement of scientific psychology; to earn funds for research; to develop opportunities for psychologists to engage in research projects both individually and cooperatively; and to obtain and administer grants for such purposes.

Activities: Conducts consumer surveys on products, advertising effectiveness, sales appeals, and related public opinion problems. Maintains a Psychological Service Center offering examining and counseling services to adults and children on personal, educational, and vocational problems; consulting service on problems of sales, office and factory personnel; sales, publishing, and advisory services on psychological tests, books, and materials. Examines adults, young people, and children with psychological tests and by interviews and helps them work out programs of education or personality development. This service is on a fee basis; an examination usually requires from six to ten hours, and the fee is about $25 or more. Also sells psychological tests to schools and other youth-serving agencies, including Civilian Conservation Corps camps.

Publications: *Journal of Applied Psychology*, bimonthly, $6 a year; *Test Service Bulletin*, occasionally, sent free to users of tests who desire to be placed on mailing list.

Staff: Full-time paid employees at headquarters, 35.

Finances: The income of the corporation is derived entirely from psychological work done for individuals and companies.

SOUTHERN WOMAN'S EDUCATIONAL ALLIANCE

See Alliance for Guidance of Rural Youth (p. 143).

YOUTH SERVICE, INC. (1933); 1045 Worthington St., Springfield, Mass.; Frank W. Barber, Director.

Name changed from American Youth Council, Inc., to present form in 1940.

Membership: Individuals, 2,779, including 2,085 youth between the ages of 16 and 24 who are interested in assisting with the service and who are members of committees operating groups and special activity clubs.

Purpose: To assist young people who are out of school and over 16 years of age in their efforts to keep employable and to make the necessary contacts to secure satisfactory placement; and, secondly, to direct these young people to opportunities to improve themselves in their avocational interests in order to insure more profitable use of leisure time.

Activities: Provides a registry of youth and their achievements; occupational counseling, guidance, and advice through personal interviews; direction to extra training and practice when necessary in order that an individual may become and may remain employable; assistance in securing satisfactory placement; interest programs for development of leadership, talent, and skills in music, dramatics, journalism, homecrafts, art, public speaking, and similar interests. The service, which is not confined to members, was extended to several thousand young people in 1939: new registrations, 1,115; seeking service but previously registered, 1,664; volunteer service for practice and experience, 2,105; attendance at meetings for youth betterment, 2,887; individuals interviewed and given counsel, 2,207; persons recommended for jobs, 1,201; placements, 520. In addition to the regular program, the service sponsors the following activities: United Job Seekers Club, the purpose of which is to make job contacts and secure employment; Youth Talent Mart and an annual Youth Talent Night; monthly program of enjoyment and entertainment for the benefit of all youth in the city.

Publications: *Youth Log*, monthly; free to members, corporation members, and interested friends. Annual community household guide for local distribution.

Staff: Full-time paid employees at headquarters, 2; part-time unpaid workers, 10.

Finances: Value of plant and equipment at national headquarters, $8,000. Estimated annual value of unpaid staff services, $5,610; estimated annual value of space, heat, light, and similar services received without charge, $500. Balance December 31, 1939, $9.94. For the preceding calendar year, operations were as follows:

Income

Gifts and grants	$1,824.04
Membership fees	412.00
Other sources	1,335.57
	$3,571.61

Expenditures

Salaries	$3,056.00
Travel	11.50
Communications	206.01
Office supplies	291.95
Rentals, insurance, etc.	1,418.17
Additions to equipment	140.00
Other purposes	1,563.76
	$6,687.39

Table XVIII

STATISTICS OF ORGANIZATIONS IN THE FIELDS OF GUIDANCE, PERSONNEL, AND EMPLOYMENT

Organization	Year Founded	Approximate Aggregate Membership (individuals)	Number of Members under 25 Years of Age	Total Employees on Headquarters Staff	Aggregate Endowment of National Headquarters	Plant and Equipment (headquarters only)	Approximate Annual Budget (headquarters only)
Alliance for Guidance of Rural Youth	1914	350	...	3	$ ...	$1,160	$ 11,600
American Occupational Therapy Association	1917	1,200	...	3	...	...	10,000
American Vocational Association	1925	23,804[a]	230,000[b]	4	28,613[c]	3,100	31,500
Cooperative Test Service of the Am. Council on Educ.	1930	none	...	27	none[d]	1,079[e]	100,000
Council of Guidance and Personnel Associations	1934	12[f]	...	[g]	...	...	1,300
Engineers' Council for Professional Development	1932	7[f]	...	3	...	...	16,500
Institute of Women's Professional Relations	1928	...	...	28	...	...	...
International Assn. of Public Employment Services	1913	5,323	...	[h]	...	...	...
National Council on Household Employment	1928	58	...	4	...	...	4,000
National Vocational Guidance Association	1913	3,000	...	4	...	...	...
Psychological Corporation	1921	350[i]	none	35	none	...	...
Youth Service	1933	2,779	2,085	2	none	8,000	6,700

a Adult membership only.
b Membership of the Future Farmers of America, organization sponsored by the association.
c Also reserve funds of $6,387.
d The organization has cash reserves of $62,400.
e Distributing office only.
f Number of constituent bodies.
g No paid staff.
h Several part-time workers, including temporary investigators.
i Number of psychologists listed as research associates.

XVIII. Leisure and Recreational Associations

The significance of leisure increases as technological advancement multiplies the productivity of man power and makes possible the release of humanity from long hours of drudgery. Even during extraordinary periods when a prompt speeding up of industrial production may be necessitated by the exigencies of national defense, the social gains inherent in the maintenance of reasonable regulation of the length of the working day and the working week are not likely to be abandoned. At such times the extension of wholesome recreational activities is vital to the morale of the military and industrial forces and of the entire population.

In time of stress no less than in time of calm it is essential that the myriad leisure arts be encouraged. Fortunately the educative value of recreation is increasingly recognized, and throughout the civilized world may be observed the growth of the concept of wise and happy uses of leisure time as an important element in a modern culture.

In America the governmental agencies have made only beginnings in the promotion and encouragement of public recreation. Our cities have public parks and playgrounds, libraries, and museums; our states and federal government maintain great public parks, reserved forests, and game preserves; but none of our states has any major administrative department devoted to the field of recreation as a whole, nor is there any such agency in the federal government.

Progress in demonstrating improved uses of recreational areas is being made by governmental agencies at all levels, but we are still in the stage of preparing public opinion to realize and appreciate the social values that can come from collective effort in this field under public auspices. At such a stage, the indispensable tasks of experimenting, pioneering, and publicizing fall largely, though not wholly, upon voluntary organizations such as are listed and described in the present section.

For our purposes here a broad concept of recreation has been adopted, and the associations described are accordingly widely varied. Among those whose inclusion is obviously appropriate are the organizations concerned with athletics in various forms—hiking, hosteling, and camping. Naturally others concerned with

public parks and nature study appear, and these in turn bear some similarity to another group whose primary concern is with the conservation of natural resources, including timber and wild life. Conservation has fundamental economic implications, but its close relation to resources for public recreation requires that it not be omitted here.

Associations concerned with museums, and others interested in the advancement and extension of music and the fine arts, the theater, and other cultural media, also are present. Many of the organizations described are primarily educational in their aims but belong here because their activities in which young people participate are necessarily designed to fit into leisure time rather than to occupy a portion of the regular working day or school day.

The principal organization taking for its province the whole range of recreation is the National Recreation Association, which dates from 1906 and has behind it some thirty-five years of pioneering in the development and realization in America of a broad concept of public recreation and its values.

Organizations whose membership or clientele consists chiefly of children and youth, as distinguished from those composed largely of persons above the age of 25, are:

> Air Youth of America
> American Youth Hostels
> Junior Americans of the United States
> National Music Camp

Cross references: Section V, General Character-Building Organizations for Youth, pp. 19–30; Section X, Organizations for Research and Social Planning, pp. 70–79; Section XVI, Educational Associations, pp. 112–41, especially American Association for Adult Education, p. 113, American Association for Health, Physical Education, and Recreation, p. 113, American Library Association, p. 121, Bureau of University Travel, p. 125, Federal Radio Education Committee, p. 125, Music Educators National Conference, p. 127, National Advisory Council on Radio in Education, p. 127, National Capital School Visitors Council, p. 129, National Committee on Education by Radio, p. 129, National Education Association, Department of Art Education, p. 133, and Open Road, p. 137; Section XIX, Health and Safety Organizations, pp. 170–83; Section XX, Organizations in the Field of Social Work, pp. 184–95.

AIR YOUTH OF AMERICA, INC. (1939); 30 Rockefeller Plaza, New York, N.Y.; Ernest Gamache, Executive Director.

Membership: National council of approximately 30 members.

Purpose: To render a noncommercial educational service of leader guidance: in recreation, by encouraging model plane building and flying as a wholesome hobby and sport, particularly among youth of limited opportunity; in education, by providing junior aviation materials for use in public and private schools and through the training of teachers and youth leaders; and in vocational guidance, by serving to a limited extent as a source of information for young people who wish to plan careers in aviation.

Activities: Serves as a national center for guidance in junior aeronautics; program centers around the building and flying of model planes. Distributes a series of scientifically graded model airplane kits through regular trade channels; broadcasts radio programs; distributes educational movies; assists in organizing exhibits; provides leadership training; and makes available scholarships to recognized aviation schools. In cooperation with the Museum of Modern Art Film Library, during the summer of 1940 sponsored a conference on aviation and youth, a principal feature of which was the showing of aviation films of educational interest.

Publications: *Air Youth Horizons*, monthly; $1 a year. *An Air Youth Guide*, $1.25; *Model Airplane Contests; How to Build Model Airplanes; An Air Youth Handbook; Junior Aviation Instruction; An Air Youth Manual;* and others.

Staff: Full-time paid employees, 5; part-time paid employees, 4.

Finances: Value of plant and equipment of national headquarters, $2,500. Cash on hand January 1, 1939, $423. For the calendar year 1939, operations were as follows:

Total Income

Gifts or grants	$ 9,021

Expenditures

Salaries	$ 7,827
Travel	810
Communications	315
Office supplies	379
Rentals, insurance, etc.	2,250
Other purposes	3,014
	$14,595

AMATEUR ATHLETIC UNION OF THE UNITED STATES (1888); 233 Broadway, New York, N.Y.; Daniel J. Ferris, Secretary-Treasurer.

Membership: The constituency consists of 8,000,000 individuals (members in active associations consisting of clubs and other bodies of individual members devoted wholly or partially to physical culture or to some specialty in athletics; athletic members who register for competition; veteran members, associate members, and sustaining and life members), including 62,925 registered competing athletes; active members, 41, regional and state associations of Amateur Athletic Union Clubs; allied members, 37, national organizations administering a sports program, such as U.S. Football Association. Annual dues of $10 for member clubs; registration fee of 25¢ for competing athletes.

Purpose: To encourage systematic physical exercise and education in the United States; to improve and promote athletic sports among amateurs; to educate the people to the benefits of recreational sports; to coordinate the activities of, and cooperate with, other athletic organizations in the United States; to establish and maintain throughout the United States a uniform test of amateur standing and uniform rules for the government of all athletic sports within its jurisdiction.

Activities: Takes the lead in America's participation in the Olympic Games, raising the necessary funds and conducting the tryouts; maintains a bureau of records covering all branches of amateur sport in the United States; institutes, regulates, and awards the amateur athletic championships of the United States; sponsors national, state, and local legislation in the interest of the institution of public playgrounds, gymnasiums, swimming pools, and fields for amateur sport.

Publications: *The Amateur Athlete*, monthly; $1 a year.

Staff: Full-time paid employees, 5, of whom 1 spends major time in field work; part-time paid employees, 3.

Finances: Value of equipment at national headquarters, $2,000. Balance October 31, 1939, $40,725. For the fiscal year ending on that date, operations were as follows:

Income

Membership fees	$ 7,892.49
Sports handbooks	131.83
Sanction fees	4,826.47
Reserve funds	1,139.26
National championships, entry fees, and other sources	27,933.84
	$41,923.89

Expenditures

Salaries	$23,428.10
Travel	1,511.93
Communications	2,005.14
Office supplies	314.79
Amateur Athlete (net)	1,784.63
Rentals, insurance, etc.	1,937.10
Athletes' tours, printing, and other purposes	13,914.19
	$44,895.88

AMERICAN ASSOCIATION OF MUSEUMS (1906); Smithsonian Institution, Washington, D.C.; Laurence Vail Coleman, Director.

Membership: More than 275 institutions, including all the leading museums of the country, and nearly 1,000 individual museum workers, trustees, and patrons. Annual dues: individuals, $5; institutions, minimum $10, maximum $250.

Purpose and Activities: The association studies museum conditions and methods and through its publications distributes to members the results of its work and of other studies. These cover a wide range of museum problems, including the financing and administration of museums, their educational work, the preparation and installation of exhibits, and the construction, arrangement, and lighting of museum buildings. The association sponsors the organization of regional museum groups for mutual aid and cooperation and the organization of professional groups among museum workers for similar purposes. It advises on museum problems and has organized and built museums embodying new ideas. It is in touch with museums and kindred organizations throughout the world.

Publications: *The Museum News*, biweekly except in summer; *Publications of the American Association of Museums, New Series*, technical papers issued occasionally. *Handbook of American Museums*, 1932, 787 pp., $5; *Manual for Small Museums*, by L. V. Coleman, 1927, 395 pp., $5; *A Bibliography of Museums and Museum Work*, by R. C. Smith, 1928, 310 pp., $5; *Historic House Museums*, by L. V. Coleman, 1933, 187 pp., $2.50; *The Museum in America* (3 vols.), by L. V. Coleman, 730 pp., $7.50.

Staff: Full-time paid employees at headquarters, 4; part-time paid employee at headquarters, 1.

Finances: General fund endowment, $2,087.22; general fund surplus, $2,989.12; special fund reserves (grants-in-aid, book publication, research, etc.), $9,642.24. Value of plant and equipment of national headquarters, $3,492.33. Estimated annual value of space, heat, and light received without charge, $2,500. Current deficit April 30, 1940, $1,761.34. For the fiscal year ending on that date, income for and expenditures from the general fund were as follows:

Income

Grants	$12,500.00
Membership fees	8,028.47
Publications	228.69
Endowment and interest	190.59
Sale of bonds	471.88
	$21,419.63

Expenditures

Salaries	$17,471.00
Travel	239.09
Communications	609.47
Office supplies, etc.	1,192.85
Publications	2,343.86
Annual meeting	1,324.70
	$23,180.97

AMERICAN CAMPING ASSOCIATION, INC. (1924); 330 South State St., Ann Arbor, Mich.; Ross L. Allen, Managing Executive.

Membership: Individuals, 1,500, in 24 local sections (21 in the United States, 2 in Canada, 1 in Hawaii). Local dues are determined by the sections. National dues for the several classes of members are: associate, $2; active, $3; camp, $5; sustaining, $25. About 100 members are camp counselors between the ages of 19 and 25.

Purpose: To further the interests and welfare of children and adults through camping as an educative, recreative, and character-developing experience.

Activities: Annual three-day conventions; a continuous program of research and study, consisting of the actual performance of certain basic and routine investigations and the identification of special problems and issues which can appropriately be assigned to other competent persons, organizations, and agencies for investigation.

Publications: *The Camping Magazine*, 9 issues annually; Dr. Bernard S. Mason, editor, Cincinnati, Ohio. *Directory of Camps in America*, annually; proceedings of the annual convention; various reprints from the *Camping Magazine*.

Staff: Full-time paid employees, 3; part-time paid employee, 1.

Finances: Value of equipment at headquarters, approximately $1,500. Headquarters budget for the calendar year 1940, approximately $12,000. Cash on hand December 31, 1939, $831.04. For the preceding calendar year, operations were as follows:

Income

Contribution from Chrysler Corporation	$ 6,666.67
Membership fees	3,964.00
Advertising in *Camping Magazine*	2,192.91
Nonmember subscriptions to *Camping Magazine*	1,475.68
1939 convention	2,545.00
Miscellaneous	613.87
	$17,458.13

Expenditures

Salaries	$ 6,688.34
Travel	672.86
Communications	1,130.24
Office supplies	312.38
Publications	3,973.06
Office rent and maintenance	829.97
Studies and education	267.97
1939 convention	1,913.79
Miscellaneous	659.43
	$16,448.04

AMERICAN CHORAL AND FESTIVAL ALLIANCE, INC. (1931); 200 St. Paul St., Brookline, Mass.; Mrs. William Arms Fisher, President.

Membership: Individuals, 8,000.

Purpose: To stimulate choral activities in America; to make surveys of new developments in organization of new choral societies; to provide plans and helps in organizing music festivals; to secure publicity for festivals; to induce radio stations to feature choral singing; to foster musical sportsmanship by choral competitions; to maintain the skills developed in the schools, colleges, and studios.

Activities: Conducts surveys of the growing singing units in the United States and issues plans for festival gatherings to bring about a greater community spirit. Until the outbreak of the present European war, the main activity was to bring foreign societies to America every two years for a joint Festival of Nations.

Publications: *Music Festivals in the United States*, by William Arms Fisher, $1. A new work is now in preparation giving a more complete résumé of festival development, in school as well as church and community.

Staff: Employees, 3.

Finances: Value of equipment at headquarters, $1,000. Approximate annual budget, $4,000.

AMERICAN FEDERATION OF ARTS (1909); Barr Bldg., Washington, D.C.; Robert Woods Bliss, President; Thomas C. Parker, Director.

Membership: The federation consists of more than 485 separate organizations, including smaller study clubs in sparsely settled sections of the country, great museums in metropolitan centers, and regional and national professional organizations. In addition to the individual membership, the federation has an underlying membership of more than 325,000 people. Membership rates are as follows: associate, $5; active, $10; contributing, $25; supporting, $50; sustaining, $100. "Chapter" membership is available to nonprofit organizations.

Purpose: To help the people of America toward a better understanding and a keener appreciation of art that they may enjoy a happier, richer everyday life.

Activities: The federation is a clearinghouse of information. Through its chapters it keeps in touch with activities in all sections of the country. It is equipped to give information on any phase of art activity. Through traveling exhibits, works of art are brought from cities to communities; to date more than 1,460 have been circulated with more than 7,600 engagements. Illustrated lectures are available to smaller organizations, each lecture being in typewritten form and accompanied by illustrative slides; at present there are more than 40 subjects in circulation. The federation cooperates with manufacturers in improving the design of industrial products; assists in planning attractive, orderly communities; sponsors exhibitions of American art in South America and South American exhibitions in

the United States; supervises and promotes intelligent legislation relating to art. A convention is held each year. The federation helps colleges, universities, and schools in the preparation of art-educational programs.

Publications: *American Magazine of Art*, monthly; $5 a year, free to members. *American Art Annual*, biennially; $7, 25 per cent discount to members. *Who's Who in American Art*, biennially; $8, 25 per cent discount to members. *Art School Directory*, biennially; $1.35 to members, $1.75 to others. *American Painting Today*, $3.50 to members, $4.50 to others. Monographs on outstanding artists are published occasionally and are for sale at modest prices.

Staff: Full-time paid employees, 15; part-time paid employee, 1.

Finances: Approximate annual budget, $89,000.

AMERICAN FOLK DANCE SOCIETY (1916); 670 Fifth Ave., New York, N.Y.; Elizabeth Burchenal, President.

Membership: Individuals, approximately 230. Membership in the society automatically carries with it membership in the Folk Arts Center (see p. 158).

Activities: Represents the work of the Folk Arts Center in the field of folk dancing and music. Gives courses and institutes for teachers and laymen at headquarters and in the field (over 40,000 leaders in various fields have been taught); conducts demonstrations, festivals, etc.

For further data, see Folk Arts Center.

AMERICAN FORESTRY ASSOCIATION (1875); 919 17th St., Washington, D.C.; Ovid Butler, Executive Secretary.

Membership: Individuals, approximately 14,000. Annual memberships are of three classes: subscribing, $4; contributing, $10; sustaining, $25. Life members make a single payment of $100, and patrons pay $1,000.

Purpose: To promote the protection, preservation, and wise use of the forest resources of the United States, together with the complementary resources of soil, water, wild life, and outdoor recreational facilities to the end that these resources may contribute in a larger and more permanent way to the social and industrial welfare of the people.

Activities: Initiates campaigns to bring about further state and federal laws designed to protect the public interests in the use and preservation of natural resources; conducts special campaigns to protect trees and forests against devastation by forest fires, tree insects, and tree diseases; conducts group vacation trips to the national forests and national parks during summer months in order to give laymen an insight into the resources of these public reservations; provides the public with information on forest, wild life, and other conservation fields; also provides books, and sporting and travel equipment at special discount. Activities specifically adapted to youth include the sending of *American Forests* to schools and colleges as gift subscriptions from members, promotion of special forestry contests among boys and girls in different states, cooperation with Boy Scouts, 4-H Clubs, and similar youth organizations in the planting of trees, and sponsoring of special educational projects in schools to awaken the younger generation to the need of protecting forests from fire.

Publications: *American Forests*, monthly; $4 a year, 35¢ a copy; Ovid Butler, editor. *Conservation*, bimonthly; 50¢ a year, 10¢ a copy; Erle Kauffman, editor. *American Conservation in Picture and in Story*, edited by Ovid Butler, $2.50; *Knowing Your Trees*, by G. H. Collingwood, $1; *Youth Rebuilds*, edited by Ovid Butler, 189 pp., $1.50; *Rangers of the Shield*, edited by Ovid Butler, 270 pp., $1.50; *Forest Fire and Other Verse*, by John Guthrie, 321 pp., $1.50; *Trees of Washington*, by Erle Kauffman, 90 pp., $1.

Staff: Full-time paid employees, 20.

Finances: Endowment funds at end of calendar year 1939, $281,694.21 (including real estate); also special revolving fund of $9,825.63. Value of plant and equipment at national headquarters, approximately $65,000. For the calendar year 1939, operations were as follows:

Income

Gifts	$ 2,350.16
Membership fees	51,620.24
Publications	12,263.64
Interest	6,118.44
Forester's office	3,584.77
Advertising	13,197.70
Miscellaneous	3,345.32
	$92,480.27

Expenditures

General administration	$24,801.65
Publications	36,404.72
Membership	15,688.00
Forester's office	8,280.77
Educational publicity	7,014.07
	$92,189.21

AMERICAN INSTITUTE OF PARK EXECUTIVES
(1898); Box 422, Tulsa, Okla.; Will O. Doolittle, Executive Secretary.

Membership: Individuals, 500. Branch societies: American Park Society, American Society of Zoological Parks and Aquariums, Midwest Institute of Park Executives, Park Commissioners' Section.

Annual dues: fellows, $10; sustaining members (public commissions or boards), $25.

Purpose: To gather and disseminate facts and information concerning public parks, gardens, and recreation; to aid municipalities in promotion of parks; and to conduct a service bureau for park executives.

Activities: Annual meeting. Committees study and report on such subjects as playgrounds and recreation, conservation and nature study, park and recreation planning, training of park executives, national, state, and provincial parks, zoological exhibits, and horticulture, arboriculture, and botanic gardens.

Publications: *Parks & Recreation*, monthly; $3 a year to nonmembers; Will O. Doolittle, editor. *Roster and Year Book*, for members only. *Soft-Ball or Gun*, by Lieut. John D. Leonard, 1937, 9 pp. Occasional bulletins and leaflets.

Staff: Full-time paid employees, 2, who spend one-fourth of time in field work; part-time paid employees, 3, who spend all of time at home office.

AMERICAN NATURE ASSOCIATION (1922); 1214
16th St., N.W., Washington, D.C.; Richard W. Westwood, Secretary.

Membership: Individuals, approximately 75,000. Dues are $3 for 1 year, $5 for 2 years, or $10 for 5 years. Membership automatically accompanies subscription for *Nature Magazine*.

Purpose: To stimulate public interest in all phases of nature and the outdoors, the conservation of natural resources, the beauty of rural roadways, the national parks and other forest lands, and all useful living creatures.

Activities: Conducts a Conservation Department devoted to conservation of renewable natural resources; carries on campaigns for roadside beautification and elimination of unsightly billboards and other influences destructive of natural beauty; discourages cruel methods of hunting and trapping wild animals and birds; provides at nominal cost illustrated lectures and motion pictures on conservation and wild life.

Publications: *Nature Magazine*, 10 times annually; free to members; Richard W. Westwood, managing editor. *Nature Almanac; Bird and Animal Book; Birds of the States*; special bulletins.

Staff: Full-time paid employees, 21.

Finances: Estimated value of plant and equipment at national headquarters, $75,000. Approximate annual budget, $200,000.

AMERICAN YOUTH HOSTELS, INC. (1935);
Northfield, Mass.; Isabel and Monroe Smith, National Directors.

Membership: In 1940 there were 13,161 passholders eligible to use 243 hostels in eight regions of the

United States and over 5,000 hostels in 20 countries of the world. The youth are about equally divided between boys and girls and represent all of the states and approximately 11 foreign countries. About three-fourths of all hostelers are between the ages of 15 and 25. Annual fees: individual pass, $1 for persons under 21, $2 for persons 21 or over; special organization group pass available to organizations, clubs, school groups, camps, and settlement houses, $5 for a group of eight youth and two adults.

Purpose: To help all persons, especially young people, to a greater knowledge, understanding, and love of the world by providing them with youth hostels in America and by assisting them in their travels both here and abroad; to make possible, through hosteling, wide friendships that will link youth with youth the world over.

Activities: Establishes and maintains hostel chains and networks in eight different regions of the United States: New England, Middle Atlantic, Southeast, Great Lakes, Midwest, Rocky Mountain, Northwest, and Southwest. The hostels, which are located at distances of 15 to 20 miles apart so that young people may hike or bicycle conveniently from one shelter to the next, are available at a cost of not more than 25¢ a person for overnight; they are under the supervision of a resident farmer and his wife as houseparents and contain separate sleeping quarters, washrooms, and kitchen facilities in addition to a common recreation center. During the summer the travel department sponsors foreign and American trips.

Some progressive educators have adopted the plan of youth hosteling during the course of school programs. Thus Roslyn High School on Long Island, making use of youth hostels for the trips, sends students out under the supervision of a teacher to gather firsthand information about economic, social, industrial, and geographical conditions in the United States. Often schools adopt hostels nearby and help to construct them or further the work of hosteling in the community. Organizing councils and committees, upon whose boards serve prominent youth leaders, churchmen, camp directors, teachers, and other interested citizens, sponsor the direction and financing of hostels within their communities.

Publications: *A Y H Knapsack*, quarterly; free to passholders, 15¢ a copy to others; Isabel and Monroe Smith, editors. *A Y H Handbook*, annual directory, 50¢. *Thrill of New Trails*, free information folder; *Travel*, folder listing annual trips, free to inquirers. Posters and other publications. All mimeographed material and lists free upon request.

Staff: Full-time paid employees, 23, including 17 at headquarters and 6 in field work; part-time paid employee, 1.

Finances: Value of plant and equipment of national headquarters, $22,560.11. Total current assets September 30, 1940, $11,652.99. For the fiscal year ending on that date, operations were as follows:

Income

Gifts or grants	$ 8,809.68
Sale of passes	9,558.47
Publications and merchandise	10,592.76
Fees for organization of travel groups	5,833.78
Net income from owned hostels and trading posts	2,254.50
Other sources	2,611.64
	$39,660.83

Expenditures

Departmental expenses	
General administrative	$13,881.43
Supplies	4,150.63
Travel	3,065.42
Publicity and field expenses	8,062.82
Net expense of regional development	9,806.94
Other purposes	279.47
	$39,246.71

ASSOCIATED GLEE CLUBS OF AMERICA, INC.
(1924); 1 Parade Place, Brooklyn, N.Y.; Clayton W. Old, President.

Membership: Male glee clubs, most of which are organized into 13 districts varying in size from 6 to 30 member clubs. Approximate aggregate individual membership, 10,000. Annual dues, 50¢ a singing member.

Purpose: To extend male chorus singing in the United States and Canada and to further cooperative relations among neighbor clubs.

Activities: Brings together glee clubs of a state or city and forms them into compact organizations called "districts," which are composed of at least five neighbor groups. The first "division," consisting of four districts, was organized recently in the Midwest. The association aids the districts in establishing a cooperative musical enterprise and, by such means as furnishing appropriate literature, assists them in the promotional work of establishing clubs in industrial plants, banks, business concerns, and social centers. The clubs thus formed are taken into the district organization and become eligible for participation in the joint concerts and other activities of the group. The national organization also maintains a Service Bureau which advises the clubs on repertoire, organizational methods, and financing. With the aid of a committee of five eminent conductors, the association each year recommends eight compositions as a common repertoire for the clubs and also submits a supplementary list of sixteen compositions.

In order to encourage the establishment of junior glee clubs for boys of post-high school age, the association furnishes to senior clubs without charge full information on how to form a junior group, special lists of songs suitable in range to junior voices, and bylaws insuring orderly procedure. Each junior group is under the sponsorship of a senior club, which lends music from its library and assists in securing a rehearsal hall, conductor, and accompanist, and in finding opportunities to sing for modest fees so that the junior club may become self-supporting. Members of the junior club, on arriving at maturity, are eligible to membership in the senior sponsor group.

Publications: *The Keynote*, spring and fall. Occasional campaign folders and repertoire lists.

Staff: Clerical employee, 1. The executive staff at headquarters all serve without remuneration.

Finances: Income consists of dues from member clubs and fees for advertisements in the *Keynote*. Approximate annual budget, $4,000.

ASSOCIATION OF ART MUSEUM DIRECTORS

(1916); President, Clyde H. Burroughs, Art Institute of Detroit, Detroit, Mich.; Secretary and Treasurer, J. Arthur MacLean, Toledo Museum of Art, Toledo, Ohio.

Membership: Limited to 50 individuals, by invitation. Only chief executive officers of art museums in the United States and Canada having a budget of over $50,000 a year are eligible. Dues are regulated by annual assessments and vary somewhat from year to year.

Purpose: To conduct round-table discussions pertaining to museum maintenance and to the functions of art museum directors.

Activities: Annual meetings, usually about the middle of May. Various museums carry on what is called a museum school where young apprentices are taught the functions of the museum, in the educational, executive, or other departments. Young persons of both sexes are among the clientele served by art museums, and a limited number of young persons are employed in museum work as regular and part-time employees and apprentices.

Publications: Verbatim minutes of the annual meetings. Members of the association were instrumental in aiding the inauguration and financing of the *Art Index*, published by the H. W. Wilson Company in New York City.

Staff: No permanent paid employees.

Finances: Annual dues are the sole regular source of revenue.

ASSOCIATION OF LEISURE TIME EDUCATORS

(1930); 981 Montford Rd., Cleveland, Ohio; H. G. Roberts, Executive Secretary.

Membership: Individuals, 300. The association has five local chapters in Illinois, Tennessee, Georgia, Louisiana, and Virginia; the organization of seven other chapters is pending.

Purpose: To bring together professional directors and leaders of leisure-time education and recreation to (1) promote fellowship, efficiency, and cooperation

among leisure-time educators, (2) share experiences, (3) develop wider professional knowledge, and (4) promote common interests and better mutual understanding.

Activities: Each chapter meets regularly, and the program emphasizes the elements of the stated purpose. Conferences of members are held during national meetings of such organizations as the National Conference of Social Work (see p. 189) and the National Recreation Association (see p. 165) and also during regional meetings of similar groups. Chapters sponsor local training programs of leaders.

Publications: *The Seminar*, 4 issues annually; free to members, $1 a year to others.

Staff: Part-time unpaid workers, 2.

Finances: Balance December 31, 1939, $16.91. For the preceding calendar year, operations were as follows:

	Income	
Gifts and grants		$ 65.00
Membership fees		147.00
Publication refund		60.80
		$272.80

	Expenditures	
Office supplies		$142.80
Publications		109.30
Other purposes		13.90
		$266.00

COOPERATIVE RECREATION SERVICE (1935);

Delaware, Ohio; Lynn Rohrbough, Secretary.

A cooperative clearinghouse on recreational education.

Membership: Members from the central states, 200. Membership is open to all who want recreation services on a nonprofit basis.

Purpose: To discover a sound road to creative leisure; to function efficiently with other agencies having the same interest; to evaluate intelligently the services already in the field; to train leaders for the new recreation; and to apply the practices of consumers' cooperation to leisure spending.

Activities: Provides a bulletin service for members, through which new developments in recreation and related fields are reported, business reports are made, and new members are introduced. Sponsors Recreation Institutes in various parts of the country to train leaders. Recreation materials are handled which can be purchased or produced advantageously for the members.

Publications: *The Recreation Kit*, quarterly. A series of 40 booklets on various aspects of recreation; *Handy*, recreation kits for young people between the ages of 13 and 19, $2.50; *Handy II*, folk recreation of permanent interest, $2.50.

Staff: Full-time paid employees, 4, of whom 1 spends major time in field work.

Finances: Value of plant and equipment at headquarters, $20,000.

FOLK ARTS CENTER (1928); 670 Fifth Ave., New York, N.Y.; Elizabeth Burchenal, Director.

Under the guidance of the National Committee on Folk Arts of the United States (see p. 162).

Membership: Individuals, approximately 500, including members of the American Folk Dance Society (see p. 154), members of the National Committee on Folk Arts of the United States, and the latter's consultants and regional representatives. Annual dues: subscribing, $5; associate, $10; contributing, $50; sustaining, $100.

Purpose: To provide an institution devoted entirely to, and carrying on a service for, the field of folk arts in the United States, including folk dancing, music, and related folklore.

Activities: Serves as the headquarters of the National Committee on Folk Arts of the United States and of the American Folk Dance Society. Loans exhibitions of significant original examples of folk arts in the United States and comparative exhibitions from other countries; maintains a national information bureau and reference service; carries on research in the field of American folk arts; maintains a reference library and archive relating to the field, including collateral data; is in the process of assembling a reference museum in the field; maintains cultural relations with other countries in the field of folk art. Many youth-serving organizations in the country are represented through individual membership; organizations thus represented include the 4-H Clubs, national and local units of the YMCA and the YWCA, Camp Fire Girls, state and regional associations for handicrafts, folk dancing, festivals, etc., and federal projects in recreation, handicrafts, art, music, adult education, etc., in different sections of the country.

Publications: The following volumes, prepared by Elizabeth Burchenal and published by G. Schirmer, Inc., under the auspices of the American Folk Dance Society and the Folk Arts Center: *Folk Dances and Singing Games*, revised 1933, $1.50; *Dances of the People*, revised 1934, $1.50; *American Country Dances*, 1918, $1.50; volumes of folk dances of Finland, Denmark, Ireland, and Germany, $1.50 a volume (except *Folk Dances of Germany*, $2).

Staff: Full-time unpaid administrative officers, 2; part-time unpaid workers, 8.

Finances: Value of equipment at national headquarters, $5,000. Estimated annual value of unpaid staff services, $11,000; estimated annual value of space, heat, light, and similar services received without charge, $2,400. For the fiscal year ending October 31, 1939, income totaled $2,444.03; expenditures for the same period aggregated $1,940.73.

IZAAK WALTON LEAGUE OF AMERICA (1922); 222 North Bank Drive, Chicago, Ill.; Kenneth A. Reid, Executive Secretary.

Membership: Chapters, 400, in 33 states and the District of Columbia. Many chapters also sponsor junior chapters comprised of boys up to 18 years of age.

Purpose: To develop opportunities for the enjoyment of the outdoors as an essential part of the character-building and the spiritual and physical development of the people; to encourage the protection, restoration, and conservation of woods, waters, and wild life; to safeguard public health and conserve aquatic life by the elimination of pollution.

Activities: Engages in legislative activities directed toward sound conservation practices. Two principal objectives at present are: a bill to control stream pollution on a nation-wide basis by watershed; and a measure calling for appropriations to purchase private interior holdings in Superior National Forest in order to bring under public administration a unified lakeland wilderness area. All junior activities are sponsored directly by the individual chapters.

Publications: *Outdoor America*, 10 issues annually; free to members, $1 a year to nonmembers; Kenneth A. Reid, editor.

Staff: Full-time paid employees at headquarters, 6. All national and local officers serve without pay.

JUNIOR AMERICANS OF THE UNITED STATES, INC. (1940); 11 West 42nd St., New York, N.Y.; Dr. Harold Davis Emerson, President; Eli Gottlieb, Executive Vice President; Dr. Goodwin Watson, Director of Education.

Membership: Directors, 7; advisory council members, 15. The organization is designed for boys and girls 8 to 16 years of age. Membership will be free of all costs to youth.

Purpose: To offer to youth who regularly choose the movie theater as their preferred or only means of recreation adequate neighborhood facilities by which they may best present their self-created out-of-school recreational activities under the supervision of paid educator-counselors.

Activities: The organization plans that members shall be entitled to leisure-time guidance, official monthly publication, admission to the Saturday morning movie show, admission to the Saturday morning regular meeting, and participation in radio quiz prizes in each local club. All neighborhood motion picture houses are potential club headquarters. Each club will be furnished with books, games, athletic equipment, radio, etc. A percentage of the organization's gross income will regularly go to the Roy Roger's Foundation, the purpose of which is to grant free scholarships, camp vacations, and club memberships to the underprivileged.

Publications: The organization intends to publish

the *Junior Americans Magazine Monthly*, which will be distributed to members without charge.

Staff: Employees, 4.

Finances: It is estimated that the program will require a weekly expenditure of approximately $17,000 for 1,000 theater clubs. The organization does not collect dues, solicit funds, or accept contributions or donations.

JUNIOR PROGRAMS, INC. (1936); 37 West 57th St., New York, N.Y.; Mrs. Dorothy L. McFadden, Founder-Director.

Membership: Board of 12 directors; advisory board of 53 members. Sponsoring committees, with an aggregate membership of about 2,500, exist in 220 communities in 35 states and British Columbia.

Purpose: To make available to all American youth, at admissions of 25¢ or less, high caliber performances of drama, opera, ballet, and concerts, given by professional adults; to make such performances available through the touring productions of the organization.

Activities: Produces professional opera, ballet, drama, and concerts for youth; tours these productions to all sections of the country; organizes local sponsoring committees of civic, social, and educational groups to help bring these performances to their communities; in connection with forthcoming performances, provides for classroom use correlation materials such as librettos and scores, directions for art work, and games and dances. During the 1939–40 school year 558 performances were given to a total of approximately 1,000,000 young people. Abridged versions of the operas *Bumble Bee Prince* by Rimsky-Korsakoff (Bluebird Records, BC-14, $1.50) and *Haensel and Gretel* by Humperdinck (Victor Records, P-38, $2.50) and the ballet *Robin Hood* (Victor Records, P-35, $2) have been especially produced for children by the Junior Programs Opera Company and Orchestra.

Publications: Annual booklet listing the productions available for the following year and a general description of activities and developments of the organization, issued free to sponsoring committees. *Committee Booklet*, containing comprehensive instructions to sponsoring committees on organizing, promoting, and publicizing a Junior Programs series, 50¢; mimeographed report on outstanding school project activities developed in five different communities, distributed free to educators. *Robin Hood Unit, Adventures of Puck Unit,* and *The Emperor's Treasure Chest Unit* (relating to Brazil), units of study in mimeographed form prepared by Dr. Hugh B. Wood of the University of Oregon, $1 each. *The Bumble Bee Prince* and *Robin Hood*, books for children published by Garden City Publishing Company (New York), 50¢ each.

Staff: Full-time paid employees, 54, of whom 46 spend major time in field work.

Finances: Value of plant and equipment of national headquarters, $25,000. For the fiscal year ending April 30, 1940, operations were as follows:

Income

Gifts and membership fees	$ 35,100.00
Royalties	900.00
Other sources	69,002.17
	$105,002.17

Expenditures

Salaries	$ 54,805.20
Travel	15,880.32
Communications	2,379.65
Office supplies	3,324.15
Publications and publicity	8,556.13
Rentals, insurance, etc.	7,351.99
Productions	12,704.73
	$105,002.17

LEISURE LEAGUE OF AMERICA, INC. (1933); 1309 West Main St., Richmond, Va.; Milton T. Cummings, Jr., Manager.

Membership: A corporation having seven directors.

Purpose: To distribute publications containing the greatest possible selection of hobbies and recreational material.

Activities: Publishes books covering a wide range of worthy interests for the use of leisure time.

Publications: *Care and Feeding of Hobby Horses*, by Earnest Elmo Calkins, 64 pp.; *You Can Write*, by F. Fraser Bond, 112 pp.; *How to Spend Your Husband's Leisure*, by Doris Webster, 96 pp.; *What to Do about Your Invention*, by Edward Thomas, 110 pp.; *Tropical Fish*, by Lucille Quarry Mann, 96 pp.; *Photography for Fun*, by William M. Strong, 96 pp.; *Quilting*, by Elizabeth King, 92 pp.; *Music for Everybody*, by Sigmund Spaeth, 84 pp.; *A Garden in the House*, by Helen Van Pelt Wilson, 112 pp.; *The Life of the Party*, by Fred Menaker and Franklin Folsom, 96 pp.; *How to Sell What You Write*, by Myron M. Stearns, 96 pp.; *How to Design Your Own Clothes*, by Hannah Shelton, 80 pp.; *Stamp Collecting*, by Henry Renouf, 80 pp.; *Hiker's Guide*, by Ben Solomon, 96 pp.; *Interior Decorating*, by Helen M. Daggett, 96 pp.; *Discover the Stars*, by Gaylord Johnson, 112 pp.; *Book of Unusual Pets*, by Lucille Quarry Mann, 96 pp.; *How Smart Are You?* by F. E. Menaker, 64 pp.; *Motor Camping*, by Porter Varney, 96 pp.; *Hunting with the Microscope*, by Gaylord Johnson, 96 pp.; *The Knitting Book*, by Elizabeth King, 96 pp.; *Working with Tools*, by Harry J. Hobbs, 96 pp.; *How to Sail*, by Samuel Carter, 96 pp.; *A Dog's Life: From Puppyhood to Old Age*, by Josephine Z. Rine, 106 pp.; *The Cookery Book*, by L. P. de Gouy, 112 pp.; *Skiing for All*, by Otto Schniebs, 96 pp.; *Creative Handicrafts*, by Mabel Reagh Hutchins, 96 pp.; *Chess in an Hour*, by Frank J. Marshall, 64 pp.; *Reading Character from*

Handwriting, by Dorothy Sara, 80 pp.; *How to Watch a Football Game*, by Mal Stevens and Harry Shorten, 80 pp.; *Drawing for Fun*, by Walter Willoughby, 64 pp.; *How to Make Music on the Harmonica*, by P. V. Planta, 112 pp.

Staff: Full-time paid employees, 4.

Finances: Approximate annual budget, $30,000.

MOTION PICTURE RESEARCH COUNCIL
(1927); 111 Sutter St., San Francisco, Calif.; Dr. Ray Lyman Wilbur, National President; Miss Ione Schlaifer, Executive Secretary.

Membership: Approximately 1,000 individuals and institutions or associations. Chapters are maintained in San Francisco and Boston. Annual dues: organizations, $5; individuals, regular $10, active $5.

Purpose: To educate the public to higher standards in connection with the production and exhibition of motion pictures by means of investigations and research undertaken with a view to instructing, training, and advising parents and others relative to motion pictures suitable for exhibition to children.

Activities: Carries on a campaign for the enactment of legislation to prohibit compulsory block booking and blind selling of films to the end that films desired by the local community may be freely selected by it; maintains a legislative office in Washington, D.C. Holds public meetings for the dissemination of information regarding motion pictures.

Publications: *The News Bulletin*, quarterly, sent to all members regardless of class of membership; *The Cinema Forum*, included in organization membership fee. Series of nine volumes, under the title of Motion Pictures and Youth, prepared under the auspices of the council with the assistance of the Payne Fund and published by the Macmillan Company: *Children's Sleep*, by Samuel Renshaw, Vernon L. Miller, and Dorothy Marquis, $2; *Movies and Conduct*, by Herbert Blumer, $1.50; *Movies, Delinquency, and Crime*, by Herbert Blumer and Philip M. Hauser, $1.50; *Boys, Movies, and City Streets*, by Paul G. Cressey and Frederick M. Thrasher; *How to Appreciate Motion Pictures*, by Edgar Dale, $1.20; and four combination volumes containing two studies each.

Staff: Full-time paid employee, 1; part-time unpaid workers, 3.

Finances: Estimated annual value of unpaid staff services, $750; estimated annual value of space, heat, light, and similar services received without charge, $640. Income is derived entirely from membership fees, contributions, and the proceeds from an annual benefit entertainment.

NATIONAL AMATEUR ATHLETIC FEDERATION, WOMEN'S DIVISION

See American Association for Health, Physical Education, and Recreation (p. 113).

NATIONAL AUDUBON SOCIETY (1905); 1006
Fifth Ave., New York, N.Y.; John H. Baker, Executive Director.

Membership: Individuals, 6,500; affiliated groups and clubs, 150. Also over 200,000 children enrolled in approximately 4,000 Junior Audubon Clubs, consisting of at least 10 members each, in 1939–40 school year.

Purpose: To arouse public appreciation of the beauty and economic value of wild life and to stimulate action to preserve and protect it; to preserve an adequate breeding stock of all native wild life; to preserve environmental conditions of ample food, water, and cover; to fix guardianship responsibility on federal, state, or competent private agencies to safeguard all species threatened with extinction.

Activities: Encourages the establishment of more sanctuaries, the enactment of legislation to eliminate pollution of inland and marine waters, the limitation to emergencies of the use of poison as a method of wild life control, and the regulation of hunting and commercial use; promotes the establishment of permanent primitive areas, combats public works such as draining projects when seriously destructive of wild life and its habitat yet not of clearly demonstrated public benefit, combats wasteful lumbering, opposes overgrazing on public lands; opposes widespread killing of predatory wild life, urges the elimination of the practices of paying bounties, and discourages vermin campaigns; advocates legislation establishing the teaching of nature appreciation and the biological basis of wild life conservation as part of the regular school curriculum, trains teachers and other youth leaders to develop genuine lasting interest in wild life and its conservation, prepares and distributes conservation material and natural science facts among children, and maintains research fellowships at universities as a means of basing conservation policies on biological facts. Maintains the Audubon Nature Camp, at which 985 individuals, including teachers, principals, superintendents, youth group leaders, and camp counselors from 37 states and 4 Canadian provinces have been enrolled since its inauguration in 1936.

Publications: *Audubon Magazine* (formerly *Bird-Lore*), bimonthly; free to members, $1.50 to nonmembers. *News on the Wing*, 4 issues a year; sent to all who form Junior Audubon Clubs.

Staff: Full-time paid employees at headquarters, 25.

Finances: Endowment funds, $1,700,000.

NATIONAL BOARD OF REVIEW OF MOTION PICTURES, INC. (1909); 70 Fifth Ave., New York, N.Y.; James Shelley Hamilton, Executive Director; Helen A. Cahill, Director for Young Reviewers.

Membership: Approximately 1,200 individuals of varied interests, many connected with large welfare organizations or educational institutions; none may be connected with the motion picture industry. Boys and girls aged 8 to 14 in the Young Reviewers Club in New York City, 300; also several hundred 4-Star Clubs throughout the country in schools, libraries, etc., for the study of motion pictures.

Purpose: To help the public clarify and record what it feels about motion pictures; to provide a leadership in expressing appreciation in a practical way of the best that the motion picture screen presents and in supplying effective encouragement to those forces in motion picture production which may be looked to for the development of the screen's great potentialities, both recreationally and educationally.

Activities: Selects the better pictures, publishes descriptive classified lists of them, and builds up support for them through the work of community groups; attempts to further the general use of motion pictures as teaching tools in visual instruction and supplies up-to-date information on suitable available films in the educational field. Maintains a Committee on Exceptional Photoplays, composed of critics and students of the motion picture, which contributes critical discussions of out-of-the-ordinary films and assists community groups to show such films locally.

The basic work of the board, in so far as popular entertainment films are concerned, is carried on by the Review Committee, consisting of over 300 voluntary members who have served a probationary term of service. The committee is divided into subgroups of about 15 each who meet at scheduled times in the projection rooms of producing companies to review films submitted by the latter before release to the country at large; always a secretary from the headquarters staff of the board is present. After discussion of the selection and audience-classification of the picture, the opinions of the members present are recorded on ballots, and the majority opinion becomes the report of the board. Results of the reviews are published in the board's periodicals. A department of the board is the National Motion Picture Council, which serves as a clearinghouse of information on local community activities relating to the motion picture and which affiliates with itself a large number of local councils and individuals in all parts of the country, formed for the purpose of uniting the community in a constructive program for the study, support, and best use of the motion picture.

Since 1931 a junior review committee, known as the Young Reviewers, has functioned in New York City for the purpose of disclosing juvenile tastes in motion pictures and of developing the critical faculties of young people; the procedure used is similar to that employed by the adult committee. This junior activity has been expanded into 4-Star Clubs throughout the country.

Publications: *National Board of Review Magazine*, monthly, $2 a year; *Weekly Guide to Selected Pictures*, $2.50 a year or $1 with the magazine; *4-Star Final*, mimeographed publication of Young Reviewers and 4-Star Clubs, 75¢ a year. Special lists, such as *Selected Book-films, Books on the Motion Picture*, *Non-theatrical Distributors, An Outline of Activities for Motion Picture Councils, One Hundred Questions and Answers on the Motion Picture*, and other miscellaneous materials for community work, 5¢ and 10¢ each; list on request.

Staff: Full-time paid employees, 8.

Finances: The work of the board is largely financed through a pro rata charge of $6.25 to film producers or distributors for every 1,000 feet of film reviewed.

NATIONAL BUREAU FOR THE ADVANCEMENT OF MUSIC (1916); 45 West 45th St., New York, N.Y.; C. M. Tremaine, Managing Director.

Purpose: By means of information and individual assistance in printed material and correspondence, to further interest in music and musical activities, especially those in which large groups can participate.

Activities: Distributes numerous publications.

Publications: *Municipal Aid to Music in America*, 297 pp., $2; *The Utilization of Music in Prisons and Mental Hospitals*, $1; *College Entrance Credits and College Courses in Music*, 1930, $2; *Music in Industry*, by K. S. Clark, 383 pp., $3. Also numerous pamphlets containing music, instructions, or descriptive matter, 5¢ to 20¢.

Staff: Full-time paid employees at headquarters, 4.

Finances: Estimated annual value of space, heat, light, and similar services received without charge, $1,000. For the fiscal year ending June 30, 1939, income and expenditures were $4,000, all of which was received from gifts and grants.

NATIONAL COMMISSION ON THE ENRICHMENT OF ADULT LIFE (1930); 1201 16th St., N.W., Washington, D.C.; President, James A. Moyer, State House, Boston, Mass.

Membership: Individuals, 70, consisting of the executive committee of the Department of Adult Education of the National Education Association (see p. 131) and 25 additional members. The commission has encouraged the formation of subordinate state commissions of 15 to 50 members; some of these commissions have become independent organizations, often with the financial support of the American Association for Adult Education (see p. 113).

Purpose: To promote plans for a wiser use of the leisure hours; to assist in the development of wholesome recreational and cultural avocational interests; and to conduct surveys of special fields of adult education.

Activities: Arranges and executes investigations, suggests lines of research to college and university departments of education and sociology, assembles the opinions of experts and national civic leaders, and seeks to obtain funds to support the work of national and state commissions.

Publications: Committee reports: *Adult Education Techniques*, Robert C. Deming, chairman, 112 pp., 75¢; *Basic English for Adult Education*, Mary L. Guyton, chairman, 67 pp., 75¢; *Delinquency of Second Generation of Adults in America*, G. A. Znamensky, secretary, 61 pp., 75¢. Thirty-four pamphlets and mimeographed reports dealing with various aspects of avocational education, 5¢ each or $1.50 a set.

Staff: Part-time unpaid workers at headquarters, 2.

Finances: Estimated annual value of unpaid staff services, $500; estimated annual value of space, heat, light, and similar services received without charge, $100. For the fiscal year ending May 31, 1940, operations were as follows:

Income

Gifts and grants	$ 40
Publications	100
Department of Adult Education (NEA)	60
	$200

Expenditures

Travel	$ 70
Communications	5
Office supplies	25
Publications	75
Postage	25
	$200

NATIONAL COMMITTEE ON FOLK ARTS OF THE UNITED STATES (1928); 670 Fifth Ave., New York, N.Y.; Elizabeth Burchenal, Executive Chairman.

Membership: Committee members, 8, supported by 31 expert consultants and 25 regional representatives as corresponding members; together these represent practically every section of the United States, Hawaii, Alaska, and Canada; also a representative-at-large in South America and in Europe.

Activities: Serves as the source of information on behalf of the United States for the International Commission on Folk Arts and Folk Lore attached to the International Institute of Intellectual Cooperation. Provides the guidance for the Folk Arts Center (see p. 158).

For further data, see Folk Arts Center.

NATIONAL COMMITTEE FOR MUSIC APPRECIATION (1939); 1221 National Press Bldg., Washington, D.C.; Edward T. Ingle, National Director; Thelma Hood, Secretary.

Membership: National and local committee members, 3,000, in 75 chapters throughout the country.

Purpose: To democratize musical culture in order that the largest possible number of people may be able to have the enjoyment and inspiration of good music.

Activities: The national committee, in its capacity as an advisory body, maintains a subcommittee on the advancement of music appreciation in the schools, studies means of improving the financial condition of orchestras, and has conducted a survey of the status accorded music by periodicals. It aids in the establishment of new symphony orchestras in schools, industry, and unorganized communities; furthers general music education through movies; encourages the advancement of music study courses in schools and conducts series of contests for school children; establishes libraries of recorded music in public libraries and other civic institutions (the first experiments were made in 1939 with the establishment of libraries of symphonic recordings in Newark, Chicago, Evanston, and Washington); encourages additional music columns and features in periodicals and on the radio; and makes an annual award for an original composition and one for cultural service to the community. The 1939 program emphasized symphonic music; the 1940 program is devoted to opera. The committee also assists in the movement to stimulate closer relationships with the Latin American republics in the field of music through artistic reciprocity and through such educational projects as the exchanging of recorded music libraries and the fostering of scholarship students.

The local committees encourage music appreciation in the schools through listening periods of recorded music and the stimulation of local school orchestras; further interest in and attendance at local concerts; and sponsor newspaper appreciation programs, including the low-cost distribution of recorded music. The latter activity is made possible through the waiving of royalties by performers and minimizing of costs by manufacturers and distributors; net proceeds are donated to local symphony orchestras and other musical organizations; for the year ending August 31, 1940, $78,137 was thus distributed by state or city chapters or affiliated musical societies.

Publications: *Projects and Program of the National Committee for Music Appreciation*, annually.

Staff: Full-time paid employees, 4, of whom 3 spend major time in field work; part-time paid employee, 1.

NATIONAL CONFERENCE ON STATE PARKS (1921); 901 Union Trust Bldg., Washington, D.C.; Miss Harlean James, Executive Secretary.

Membership: Individuals, 500. Annual dues: individual, $5; sustaining, $10; organization, $25; contributing, $100.

Purpose: To urge upon local, county, state, and national governments the acquisition of additional land and water areas suitable for recreation, for the study of natural history and its scientific aspects, and for the preservation of wild life, as a form of conservation of natural resources, until there shall be public parks, forests, and preserves accessible to all citizens of the United States.

Activities: Annual meetings of state park executives and civic leaders; advocacy of comprehensively planned and integrated state park systems. Occasional regional conferences. Information service on all questions related to state parks and other public recreational areas.

Publications: *Planning and Civic Comment*, quarterly, Dora A. Padgett, editor; *American Planning and Civic Annual*, Harlean James, editor; both periodicals are published jointly with the American Planning and Civic Association (see p. 71). *State Recreation—Parks, Forests, and Game Preserves*, 1928, $1; *A State Park Anthology*, 1930, $1.

Staff: Part-time employees, 4.

NATIONAL FEDERATION OF MUSIC CLUBS

(1898); Bankers Trust Bldg., Norfolk, Va.; Mrs. Vincent Hilles Ober, President.

Membership: 5,277 clubs in 48 states, District of Columbia, Canal Zone, and Alaska; 263 Student Music Clubs for young people between the ages of 17 and 25, located in 33 states; 2,983 Junior Music Clubs for children up to 18 years of age, located in 47 states, District of Columbia, and Canal Zone. The local units are organized into state federations, which are in turn grouped into 16 districts. Approximate individual membership: Senior Division, 75,000; Student Division, 8,000; Junior Division, 60,000. Annual national dues (divided between the national and local organizations): active (open to organizations assuming active musical service), minimum of 20¢ per capita for members of Senior Division, 15¢ per capita for members of Student Division, 10¢ per capita for members of Junior Division; associate (open to interested civic organizations), $5 to $15 for senior organizations, $4 to $12 for student organizations, $2.50 to $7.50 for junior organizations; special, $3 to $5 for individuals. Life members, $100; subscribers, $500; donors, $1,000; patrons, $5,000.

Purpose: To bring into working relation with one another music clubs and other musical organizations and individuals directly or indirectly associated with musical activity for the purpose of aiding and encouraging musical education and of developing and maintaining high musical standards throughout America; to make music an integral part of the civic, industrial, educational, and social life of the nation; to encourage and advance American creative musical art and to promote American artists.

Activities: The Senior Division has active departments of American music, church music, education, extension, finance, legislation, and publicity; committees within these departments have charge of course of study, young artists' contests, composition contests, choir and choral festivals, music in schools and colleges, rural music, international music relations, motion picture music, opera, radio, civic music, philanthropic music, orchestra and chamber music, American folk music research, library extension, and choral activities. The Student Division encourages the study of music and active participation in it by young people, the work of the clubs being guided by adult advisers; the membership consists of college glee clubs, bands, and college and church choirs, as well as student musician groups; the division conducts student musicians' contests biennially. The Junior Division has committees on education, church music, competitive festivals, orchestras and bands, harmonica bands, and choral work; the membership consists of private classes, school groups, and music study clubs for children; the division provides the same type of training for children as does the Student Division; competitive festivals for children up to 18 years of age are held annually. Student and junior days are included in the program of the national convention and are held in most states.

Publications: *Music Clubs Magazine*, 5 issues annually; $1 a year; Mrs. Paul J. Weaver, managing editor, 320 Wait Ave., Ithaca, N.Y. *Junior Magazine*, reprint of junior section of senior magazine, 25¢ a year. *Book of Proceedings* of biennial conventions, $2 a volume. Numerous pamphlets covering the various fields of interest of the federation.

Staff: Full-time paid employees at headquarters, 4; part-time paid employee, 1. All elected officers serve without remuneration.

Finances: Endowment funds, $22,355.22; Edgar Stillman-Kelley Scholarship Fund, $533.32; reserve funds, $3,000; savings account for special projects and prizes, $2,937.63. Value of equipment at national headquarters, $1,770.18. Balance June 30, 1939 (including reserve funds and savings account for special projects), $18,152.23. For the biennium ending on that date, operations were as follows:

Income

Membership fees	$21,059.17
Publications	18,710.71
Endowment and reserve funds	2,250.02
Contests	7,169.25
Other sources	21,604.39
	$70,793.54

Expenditures

Salaries	$13,861.85
Publications	16,581.83
Other purposes	32,740.58
	$63,184.26

NATIONAL MUSIC CAMP

(1928); Interlochen, Mich.; winter office, 303 South State St., Ann Arbor, Mich.; Joseph E. Maddy, President.

A summer school of music operated by the National High School Orchestra Camp Association, a non-profit, tax-exempt educational corporation.

Membership: Average annual enrollment, 350, of whom 250 to 300 are between the ages of 12 and 24 (about 50 per cent of the college division members and all of the high school division students, who average 15.6 years, fall within this group). Membership is open to high school and college music students and to music teachers and supervisors. The college group consists of students just beyond high school age and those who have completed the camp courses outlined for the high school division; any adult who wishes to study music may enroll in the college division. Camp members come from about 35 states annually, and each yearly enrollment includes members from Hawaii, Alaska, Panama, other outlying territories, and Canada. Fee for attendance at annual camp, $250.

Purpose: To provide a musical center where all the arts—music, radio, drama, dance, and painting—are combined to give equality of opportunity to the youth of America.

Activities: The camp maintains a complete full-time faculty of nationally recognized teachers and musicians. It promotes youthful interests in band, orchestra, piano, choir, composition, conducting, chamber music, radio, drum-majoring, drama, art, and the dance. It provides thorough instruction in all branches of music and on all instruments; private lessons are available for all instruments and in each specialized field. Students may apply for membership in the orchestra, band, or choir, each of which gives weekly broadcasts over a nation-wide hookup as well as concerts in the Interlochen Bowl. Concerts, broadcasts, radio programs, visits to the World's Fair, and scholarship contests are among the added services. All classes and other camp activities are under adult counselor supervision. A hotel, 32 dormitories, the Interlochen Bowl, two beach houses, broadcasting building, hospital, musical library of more than 4,000 titles, and a complete schedule of outdoor sports and social activities are features offered in the woodland center which lies between twin lakes one mile south of the village of Interlochen.

Publications: *Scherzo*, weekly program and magazine, 8 issues during the summer season; *Prelude*, catalog published annually prior to each season. Occasional leaflets and bulletins.

Staff: Full-time paid employees at headquarters, 2. Staff for eight-week camp season: full-time paid employees, 160; part-time unpaid workers, 70.

Finances: Value of plant and equipment, $210,377.53. Estimated annual value of unpaid staff services, $5,600. Cash on hand October 1, 1939, $2,348.83. For the fiscal year beginning on that date, operations were as follows:

Income

Gifts and royalties	$ 174.17
Tuition and private lessons	55,487.37
Concerts	2,334.55
Hotel	9,116.32
Paramount movie	5,000.00
Other sources	5,242.26
	$77,354.67

Expenditures

Salaries	$25,612.57
Travel	678.66
Communications	1,095.34
Office supplies	644.56
Publications	2,512.94
Rentals, insurance, etc.	5,729.24
Additions to plant	890.24
Other purposes, including food, hotel, etc.	26,366.14
	$63,529.69

NATIONAL MUSIC WEEK COMMITTEE (1924); 45 West 45th St., New York, N.Y.; C. M. Tremaine, Secretary.

Membership: Committee of 33 heads of national civic organizations, including the Boy Scouts, Camp Fire Girls, Girl Scouts, YMCA, YWCA, and National Federation of Music Clubs.

Purpose: To make more widespread the enjoyment of music by the general public and to extend the recognition of its value as an individual and a community asset by means of an intensive seven-day drive.

Activities: Organizes the celebration of National Music Week in May, in which many schools, 4-H Clubs, junior music groups, and private teachers and pupils participate. Provides assistance to local Music Week committees and workers.

Publications: Annual letter of suggestions sent to local committees. Numerous pamphlets and publicity materials, 5¢ to 20¢.

Staff: Part-time paid employees at headquarters, 4.

Finances: Estimated annual value of space, heat, light, and similar services received without charge, $1,000. For the fiscal year ending June 30, 1940, income and expenditures were $6,000.

NATIONAL PARKS ASSOCIATION (1919); 1624 H St., N.W., Washington, D.C.; Edward B. Ballard, Executive Secretary.

Membership: Individuals, approximately 600; affiliated organizations, 24; other cooperating organizations, 140.

Purpose: To give the entire nation a voice in maintaining the standards of America's national primeval parks, in protecting those parks against harmful interference, and in supporting the preservation, development, and use of all federal reservations under administration of the National Park Service for the continuing refreshment, education, and inspiration of the American people.

Activities: Distributes information on present and proposed congressional legislation affecting national parks, monuments, etc.; mobilizes public opinion for the maintenance of national park standards; and, through its publications, promotes public appreciation of the true values and functions of all federal reservations under administration of the National Park Service.

Publications: *National Parks Bulletin*, quarterly; subscription price included in all classes of membership; Robert Sterling Yard, editor of publications; Edward B. Ballard, editor of *Bulletin*. *National Parks News Service*, occasional releases issued for use of members, cooperating organizations, and Congress. *National Park Standards*, free pamphlet.

Staff: Full-time paid employees at headquarters, 2; part-time paid employees (occasional), 2.

Finances: Reserve funds, $1,732.50. Balance April 30, 1940, $607.47. For the fiscal year ending on that date, operations were as follows:

Income	
Gifts and grants	$4,405.00
Membership fees	1,889.70
	$6,294.70

Expenditures	
Salaries	$3,452.93
Travel	218.54
Communications	336.09
Office supplies and duplicating service	396.98
Publications	453.83
Rentals	360.00
Membership solicitation	683.55
	$5,901.92

NATIONAL RECREATION ASSOCIATION (1906); 315 Fourth Ave., New York, N.Y.; Howard Braucher, Secretary.

Membership: Individuals, 8,836.

Purpose: To give every child in America a chance to play; to give all persons, young and old, an opportunity to find the best and most satisfying use of leisure time.

Activities: A variety of services to assist urban and rural localities to obtain or develop more and better facilities such as: children's playgrounds, neighborhood playfields, music, drama, and art activities in home and community; recreation buildings and wider use of school buildings for recreational purposes; opportunities for hiking and nature study and for gardening. Efforts to develop better state and local legislation for recreation; better city planning for parks and playfields; better organization and administration of local recreation work, including

better volunteer leadership and trained and competent full-time paid recreation executives. The youth most directly benefited are those who attend local playgrounds and other recreational facilities provided by the municipal agencies in the 48 states and Washington, D.C., which receive personal field service from the association's field workers.

No figures are available to show completely the number of young persons served by these agencies, but figures for 1939 show that in seven different organized games and sports 4,824,264 individuals were reported as participating, of whom probably 3,750,000 were between the ages of 12 and 25. Young persons participate heavily in many of the service activities of the association, such as the training institutes, the National Physical Education Service, park recreation service, local employment service, bureau of colored work, girls' and women's division, and divisions related to music, drama, arts and crafts, nature activities, and other aspects of recreation in home, church, school, and industry.

Publications: *Recreation*, monthly, $2 a year; *Recreation Bulletin Service*, 22 issues annually, $2.50 a year; *Rural Recreation Bulletin Service*, 11 issues annually, $1.50 a year; *Emergency Recreation Bulletin Service*, 11 issues annually, $1 a year; *News-Letter of the National Physical Education Service*, 10 issues annually, $1 a year. A large number of books and pamphlets. Lists available: *Publications on Play and Recreation*, 12 pp.; *Inexpensive Publications on Community Drama*, 6 pp.; *Music Publications*, 4 pp.

Staff: Full-time paid employees (not including secretarial, clerical workers), 21, of whom 14 spend major time in field work.

Finances: Several endowment and reserve funds aggregated $398,348.47 as of December 31, 1939. Value of equipment at headquarters, $4,000. Estimated annual value of unpaid staff services by volunteers, $200,000. For the calendar year 1939, operations were as follows:

Income	
Contributions	$152,354.28
Publications	26,231.87
Other services	3,241.15
Income from endowment	15,149.14
Other sources	10,085.67
	$207,062.11

Expenditures	
Salaries	$138,851.54
Travel	31,021.78
Communications	10,049.71
Office supplies	286.30
Publications	19,781.16
Rentals, etc.	8,612.07
Additional equipment	107.76
Other purposes	6,599.04
	$215,309.36

NATIONAL STORY LEAGUE (1903); 7 East Blackthorn St., Chevy Chase, Md.; Mrs. H. Lyle Campbell, National President.

Membership: Individuals, 2,925 (active members, 2,245; associate members, 500), including 52 boys and 160 girls of junior age in Texas, Ohio, Pennsylvania, West Virginia, Florida, Missouri, and Kansas. There are 125 local leagues in America.

Purpose: To encourage the creation and appreciation of the good and beautiful in life and literature through the art of storytelling.

Activities: Holds a national convention every two years and three district conventions in the alternating years. Each league holds frequent program meetings where members tell the stories they will use in various kinds of service; each league also has a service department from which may be called storytellers to go to hospitals, old peoples' homes, character-building agencies, recreation centers, schools, and civic institutions. A portion of the time of each convention is given to work of the junior leagues, whose members perform similar services in orphanages, homes for the aged, churches, playgrounds, schools, and Scout groups.

Publications: *Story Art*, bimonthly, 50¢ a year; *Year Book*, published in alternate years. About 12 bulletins each year; also bibliographies and storytelling information.

Staff: Part-time unpaid workers, 30, of whom 27 are engaged in field work.

Finances: Value of equipment in president's office, $25. Estimated annual value of unpaid staff services, $3,000; estimated annual value of space, heat, light, and similar services received without charge, $50. Balance December 31, 1939, $239.21. For the calendar year ending on that date, income totaled $1,717.83; expenditures for the same period aggregated $1,478.62.

NATIONAL THEATRE CONFERENCE (1932); Western Reserve University, Cleveland, Ohio; Barclay S. Leathem, Executive Secretary.

Membership: Directors of community and university theaters, 51.

Purpose: To initiate, encourage, and sponsor projects of educational and cultural value and of immediate common significance designed to serve the interests and to raise the standards of the American theater, particularly of the noncommercial theater.

Activities: Collects information on play lending libraries and encourages new playwrights through the reading and distribution of manuscripts. Through collective purchase, obtains reduced royalties on recommended plays; there are two divisions of the royalty project, one for colleges and community theaters combined and one for high schools; a separate list of plays especially suitable for high school production is maintained. Awards fellowships and conducts a free placement service for qualified persons between the ages of 21 and 35. The conference's services are available to all groups in the United States.

Publications: *National Theatre Conference Quarterly Bulletin*, 4 issues annually; free; Frederic McConnell, editor.

Staff: Full-time paid employee, 1; part-time paid employees, 4; part-time unpaid worker, 1.

Finances: The conference has received from the Rockefeller Foundation for the five-year period 1938–43 grants-in-aid of $10,000 for administration, $5,000 for the royalty project, and $25,000 for fellowships. Value of equipment at headquarters, $150. Estimated annual value of unpaid staff services, $1,000; estimated annual value of space, heat, light, and similar services received without charge, $360. Cash on hand July 1, 1939, $1,620.24. For the fiscal year beginning on that date, operations were as follows:

Income

Gifts and grants	$11,000.00
Membership fees	440.00
Service fees for royalty reductions	110.83
	$11,550.83

Expenditures

Salaries	$ 1,275.00
Travel	245.35
Office supplies	596.46
Publications	847.25
Fellowship project	7,434.63
Other purposes	868.46
	$11,267.15

NEW THEATRE LEAGUE (1934); 110 West 47th St., New York, N.Y.; Ben Irwin, National Executive Secretary.

Membership: Affiliated theaters in America, 25; affiliated theaters in Canada, England, and Australia, 10; individual and group members and subscribers, 1,000. Almost all of the groups are composed of young people. Annual fees: individual membership, $1; play-of-the-month service, $5; group membership, $25.

Purpose: To establish a chain of progressive and artistically mature theaters that will be a vital community force in furthering the cause of labor, of peace and democracy, which are essential to the development of any art today; to stimulate the writing and production of progressive plays for an American people's theater; to educate and raise the artistic level of all little and new theater groups.

Activities: Maintains a repertory department and a play criticism service; a production department in New York produces new plays regularly. Maintains the New Theatre School of 175 students in New York, which offers courses in directing, acting, and playwriting. Representatives from the schools and from many of the affiliated theaters and organizations attend the American Youth Congress (see p. 82).

Publications: *New Theatre News*, monthly mimeographed bulletin giving information and news on activities of new theaters; $1 a year, free to affiliated groups; Ben Irwin, editor. *Plays for a People's Theatre*, annual catalog.

Staff: Full-time paid employees, 3; part-time paid employees, 3; part-time unpaid workers, 5.

Finances: Value of equipment at national headquarters, $750. Estimated annual value of unpaid staff services, $1,000. For the fiscal year ending August 31, 1939, operations were as follows:

Income

Gifts and grants	$ 200
Membership fees	1,000
Publications	200
Play criticisms and bookings	700
Tuitions	8,800
Other sources	4,000
	$14,900

Expenditures

Salaries	$ 6,700
Travel	60
Communications	1,100
Office supplies	800
Publications	150
Advertising, publicity, and other purposes	6,190
	$15,000

SOCIETY OF RECREATION WORKERS OF AMERICA (1938); City Hall, Elizabeth, N.J.; Arthur T. Noren, Secretary.

Membership: Full-time professional employees in executive or leadership capacity associated with the recreation movement, and representatives of affili-

ated recreation associations, 330. There are 10 geographical divisions, each having two representatives to the administrative council.

Purpose: To unite in one organization all recreation workers in America; to foster and maintain high standards of professional qualifications and professional ethics; to encourage and promote adequate programs of professional training for recreational workers; to protect the interests of recreation workers as a group in situations where their professional interests are involved; to encourage study and research on matters of professional interest; and to function in any other manner which will further the interests of the recreation movement and its personnel.

Activities: Disseminates information concerning the activities and interests of the organization; cooperates with other agencies or organizations for similar or related objectives; holds annual meeting; awards Joseph Lee Memorial Prize for recreation literature. A Training Committee is conducting a survey of in-service training programs in local, state, and federal recreation agencies; a Nature Study "Project of the Year" Committee is sponsoring a nation-wide project; other committees are concerned with professional ethics and research and study.

Publications: *Quarterly Bulletin.*

Staff: Part-time paid employee, 1; part-time unpaid worker, 1.

Finances: Balance September 30, 1940, $205.08. For the fiscal year ending on that date, operations were as follows:

Total Income

Membership fees	$1,552.94

Expenditures

Salaries	$ 90.00
Office supplies	325.73
Publications	650.00
Conference	289.47
	$1,355.20

TABLE XIX

STATISTICS OF LEISURE AND RECREATIONAL ASSOCIATIONS

Organization	Year Founded	Approximate Aggregate Membership (individuals)	Number of Members under 25 Years of Age	Total Employees on Headquarters Staff	Aggregate Endowment of National Headquarters	Plant and Equipment (headquarters only)	Approximate Annual Budget (headquarters only)
Air Youth of America	1939	30ª	...	9	$ ...	$ 2,500	$ 14,600
Amateur Athletic Union of the United States	1888	b	...	8	none	2,000	44,900
American Association of Museums	1906	1,000	...	5	2,087c	3,492	23,200
American Camping Association	1924	1,500	100	4	...	1,500	17,500
American Choral and Festival Alliance	1931	8,000	...	3	...	1,000	4,000
American Federation of Arts	1909	325,000d	...	16	281,694	...	89,000
American Forestry Association	1875	14,000	...	20	none	65,000	92,500
American Institute of Park Executives	1898	500	...	5	...	...	200,000
American Nature Association	1922	75,000	...	21	...	75,000	...
American Youth Hostels	1935	13,161	9,750	24	none	22,560	39,700
Associated Glee Clubs of America	1924	10,000	...	1	none	...	4,000
Association of Art Museum Directors	1916	50	...	e	...	...	...
Association of Leisure Time Educators	1930	300	...	e	...	...	300
Cooperative Recreation Service	1935	200	...	4	...	20,000	...
Folk Arts Center	1928	500	...	e	...	5,000	2,400
Izaak Walton League of America	1922	400f	...	6	...*	...	...
Junior Americans of the United States	1940	7g	...	4	...	...	...
Junior Programs	1936	2,500h	...	54	none	25,000	105,000
Leisure League of America	1933	7g	...	4	...	...	30,000
Motion Picture Research Council	1927	1,000i	...	1	none	...	...
National Audubon Society	1905	6,500j	200,000k	25	1,700,000	...	...
National Board of Review of Motion Pictures	1909	1,200j	...	8	...	...	...
National Bureau for the Advancement of Music	1916	...	...	4	...	...	4,000
National Commission on the Enrichment of Adult Life	1930	70	none	e	none	none	200
National Committee for Music Appreciation	1939	3,000	...	5	...	...	...

TABLE XIX—Continued

Organization	Year Founded	Approximate Aggregate Membership (individuals)	Number of Members under 25 Years of Age	Total Employees on Headquarters Staff	Aggregate Endowment of National Headquarters	Plant and Equipment (headquarters only)	Approximate Annual Budget (headquarters only)
National Conference on State Parks	1921	500	...	4	$ ...	$ ...	3 ...
National Federation of Music Clubs	1898	149,000	68,000	5	22,888[m]	1,770	35,400
National Music Camp	1928	350	275	2[n]	none	210,400	77,400
National Music Week Committee	1924	33	...	4	...	...	6,000
National Parks Association	1919	600	...	4	none[p]	...	6,300
National Recreation Association	1906	8,836	...	21[q]	398,348[r]	4,000	215,300
National Story League	1903	2,925	212	[e]	none	25	1,700
National Theatre Conference	1932	51	...	5	none	150	11,500
New Theatre League	1934	1,000	...	6	...	750	15,000
Society of Recreation Workers of America	1938	330	none	1	...	...	1,500

a. Number of members on the national council.
b. The organization has a constituency of 8,000,000 individuals, including 62,925 registered competing athletes.
c. Also general fund surplus of $2,989 and special fund reserves of $9,642.
d. Underlying membership of 485 constituent organizations.
e. No paid staff.
f. Number of local units.
g. Number of directors.
h. Aggregate membership of sponsoring committees.

i. Includes organizations as well as individuals.
j. Adult membership only.
k. Number of children enrolled in Junior Audubon Societies.
m. Also reserve funds and special savings account totaling $5,937.
n. In addition there is a full-time paid staff of 160 at the summer camp.
p. The association has reserve funds of $1,732.
q. Not including secretarial, clerical workers.
r. Includes reserve funds.

XIX. Health and Safety Organizations

Within less than a century the average expectation of human life has been much increased. The greatest advance has been made in the reduction of infant mortality, but there is yet room for great improvement in maternal and child health service, both in rural regions remote from health centers and in urban slums. This is in large part a problem of youth, for more than 40 per cent of all births are to mothers under the age of 25.

The general rate of incidence of illness among persons between the ages of 12 and 25 is naturally lower than among the younger or older age groups. But there are certain exceptional diseases of which the rate of incidence is high among youth. These include tuberculosis (excluding cases arising from unfavorable occupational environment) and the venereal diseases.

The toll of tuberculosis among young persons has been reduced, but the disease has not by any means been eradicated. The service of detection by periodic examinations should be made to function for the entire secondary school population and for out-of-school youth. An attack upon the venereal diseases, embracing the extension of clinic service and a revamping of the attitudes of the medical profession and of the public toward this type of disablement, has been in progress for several years under the leadership of the United States Public Health Service, and promises to make control of these diseases the next national public health achievement.

The American Youth Commission recommends that in every school, from the primary grades up through college, there should be regular physical examinations for all students and that comparable facilities should be provided for out-of-school young people. The Commission also emphasizes that sport and athletic programs in schools should be directed not only to the athlete but to the whole student body, so that those without special athletic ability may receive the benefits of regular exercise. The improvement of instruction in physiology and physical and mental hygiene, especially at the secondary school and college levels, should continue.

The control of disease and the promotion of the public health depend not only upon discoveries in medical science but also upon the education of the public in the understanding and appreciation of the practices recommended by experts. Furthermore, new advances in the control of specific diseases have often been preceded by popular campaigns to arouse the interest both of scientists and laymen in the necessity of making a concerted attack upon the particular danger under scrutiny. Private associations in public health often render valuable service in these campaigns of public enlightenment.

There are also certain pioneering and speculative aspects of public health in which private associations provide much of the initial impetus. The tangle of conflicts which surrounds such subjects as birth control and eugenics prevents or delays widespread social action in such matters until a general sentiment has been crystallized after a long period of debate, experimentation, and demonstration. What future developments may be can now be only guessed; but we already find vigorous voluntary societies engaged in pointing out the possibilities.

The joint clearinghouse and coordinating center for national voluntary health agencies is the National Health Council, which numbers among its membership some fifteen national voluntary societies and two national governmental bureaus.

Cross references: Section XXII, Organizations Serving Handicapped Youth, pp. 202–8. *See also:* American Association for Health, Physical Education, and Recreation, p. 113; American National Red Cross, p. 186; Society of State Directors of Health and Physical Education, p. 138.

AMERICAN ASSOCIATION OF MEDICAL SOCIAL WORKERS (1918); 844 Rush St., Chicago, Ill.; Mary M. Maxwell, Executive Secretary.

Membership: Medical social workers, 1,900. About 40 per cent are employed by tax-supported hospitals.

Institutions in America and Canada are eligible. Types of membership: member, $5; junior, $3; associate, $3 and $5; corporate, $25; contributing, $10 and $20; sustaining, $25 or more; honorary.

Purpose: To serve as an organ of intercommunication among medical social workers; to maintain and improve standards of social work in hospitals, dispensaries, special clinics, or other distinctly medical or psychiatric institutions; and to stimulate the intensive and extensive development of medical social work.

Activities: Medical social workers are concerned with the social needs of the individual patient in terms of his medical situation. An annual meeting of the association is held concurrent with the annual meeting of the National Conference of Social Work (see p. 189). There are six standing committees, on membership, ways and means, program, publications, nominations, and education. The Education Committee keeps informed concerning educational facilities for medical social work, fosters the improvement of such education, and recommends to the executive committee educational agencies thought to be worthy of approval by the association.

Publications: *Bulletin*, 8 issues annually; $1 a year.

Staff: Full-time paid employees, 3.

Finances: Approximate annual budget, $17,000.

AMERICAN ASSOCIATION OF SCHOOL PHYSICIANS

See American School Health Association (p. 173).

AMERICAN AUTOMOBILE ASSOCIATION (1902); SAFETY AND TRAFFIC ENGINEERING DEPARTMENT; Pennsylvania Ave. at 17th St., N.W., Washington, D.C.; Burton W. Marsh, Director.

Membership: Individuals, 1,000,000, in 725 constituent motor clubs and branches in the United States and Canada. Annual dues from local clubs to national association, 25¢ an individual member.

Purpose: To promote traffic education, especially among school children.

Activities: Sponsors, with schools and police, safety patrols operating in about 3,250 cities and towns in the United States with nearly 300,000 children serving on these patrols, protecting the lives of 8,000,000 school children; distributes over 150,000 teacher lesson plans each month of the school year through AAA clubs. These lessons are compiled by an assistant superintendent of schools and are grouped into four divisions covering children from kindergarten through junior high school, and children in rural schools. Through AAA clubs also are distributed over 140,000 school safety posters each month of the school year, illustrating timely safe walking and safe bicycling rules to aid teachers in giving instruction to students. Thousands of traffic and safety talks, sometimes accompanied by safety films, are given to school children each year through local arrangement by AAA affiliated clubs. Safety playlets are distributed for assembly presentation by school children. Conferences dealing with the im-

portance of safety education, proved methods, and available materials and their uses are held with educational leaders.

Promotes high school courses in traffic, safety, and driving, reaching at least one-half million students in 8,000 high schools with traffic education in classroom programs; 600 high schools now use dual-control driver training cars for behind-the-wheel training and practice. Has sponsored 50 intensive teacher training courses and cooperates with colleges in summer session courses in driver education and training for teachers. AAA certificates have been received by 2,500 trained teachers.

Conducts annual National Pedestrian Protection Contest for cities and states to improve the convenience and safety of street and highway use for the man on foot. Honor awards signifying national recognition are given for improvement in the pedestrian fatality and injury record and for the excellence of effort to improve traffic facilities.

Publications: Sportsmanlike Driving, in textbook form or series of five text pamphlets, units as follows: *The Driver; Driver and Pedestrian Responsibilities; Sound Driving Practices; Society's Responsibilities; How to Drive. Training New Drivers, Driver Education and Training Manual for High School Teachers*, containing comprehensive list of practical activities for a high school course in driver education and training; *Pedestrian Protection*, based on a three-year comprehensive study and presenting recommendations for reduction of pedestrian accidents; *Speaking for Pedestrian Protection*, a speakers manual; *Standard Rules for Operation of School Safety Patrols*; various safety playlets and other literature of value to teachers on walking and driving safety.

AMERICAN BIRTH CONTROL LEAGUE

See Birth Control Federation of America (p. 175).

AMERICAN EUGENICS SOCIETY, INC. (1926); 1270 Sixth Ave., New York, N.Y.; Rudolf C. Bertheau, Secretary.

Membership: Individuals, 650, including about 25 young persons; one branch in California. Types of membership: subscribing, $5; professional and student, $3; contributing, $10 to $50; supporting, $50 to $100.

Purpose: To interpret a sound democratic eugenics program in America, creating interest in children among competent parents and making it economically possible for an ever increasing number of responsible parents to have larger families; to encourage research in human heredity; to stimulate the medical profession and public health authorities to their proper responsibility for reducing the incidence of hereditary defect.

Activities: Brings together laymen, scientists, and professional workers interested in eugenics and such allied fields as public health and nursing, housing and recreation, church work, and educational work in schools, colleges, and universities. Conducts conferences with groups in these fields and participates in their conferences through group discussions and the presentation of papers. Provides discussion material on eugenics, population trends, marriage, family relations, human heredity, etc., and advocates forum discussions among youth groups. Holds conferences with and conducts prize essay contests among college students; publishes articles and theses by students in the *Eugenical News*.

Publications: *Eugenical News*, quarterly; $3 a year, free to members. *Eugenics Review*, published quarterly in London, England; $3 a year, free to members. Publications written by the directors: *American Eugenics*, 1936, 67 pp., 10¢; *Development of Eugenic Policies*, 1936, 23 pp., 10¢; *Conferences on the Relation of Eugenics to the Fields of Recreation-Nursing-Education and Medicine*, 1937, 38 pp., 10¢; *Practical Eugenics—Aims and Methods of the American Eugenics Society*, 1938, 24 pp., 10¢; *American Eugenics Today*, revised 1940, 20 pp., 10¢.

Staff: Full-time paid employees at headquarters, 2; part-time paid employee, 1; part-time unpaid workers, 24.

Finances: Balance March 31, 1940, $1,925.92. For the fiscal year ending on that date, operations were as follows:

Income

Gifts and grants for current purposes	$ 3,255.00
Special gifts	3,900.00
Membership fees	3,021.89
Publications	173.78
Gift for student's essay contest	397.91
	$10,748.58

Expenditures

Salaries	$ 3,728.00
Conferences	157.27
Communications	96.23
Office supplies	111.59
Publications and membership	3,527.17
Rentals	619.80
Contests	754.67
	$ 8,994.73

AMERICAN HEART ASSOCIATION, INC. (1922); 1790 Broadway, New York, N.Y.; H. M. Marvin, M.D., Acting Executive Secretary.

Membership: Individuals, 2,300; state heart associations, 7; local heart associations, 7; regional heart association, 1; heart committees, 29; cardiac clinics, about 327. The membership is located in the United States and Canada.

Purpose: To collect and correlate facts relating to cardiovascular diseases; to devise and apply preventive measures to lessen impairment of the cardiac structure; to coordinate the work being done in established centers in the fight against diseases of the heart; to furnish the encouragement and assistance requisite for the development of additional centers for cardiac work; to disseminate information in regard to diseases of the heart and the methods to be employed for their prevention and relief; to arouse the public mind to its responsibility and opportunity to assist in the fight against diseases of the heart.

Activities: Maintains a central office as a clearinghouse for the work of the various local associations and committees; gathers information on all phases of diseases of the heart; cooperates with other groups in promoting education concerning the importance of the public health aspects of diseases of the heart.

Publications: *Bulletin*, quarterly, free. *American Heart Journal*, monthly; $10 a year; Fred M. Smith, M.D., editor. *Modern Concepts of Cardiovascular Disease*, monthly; free to active members; bound copies of issues for years 1932–35 and 1936–39, $2 each. *Nomenclature and Criteria for Diagnosis of Diseases of the Heart*, 1939, 282 pp., $2; *Standard Requirements for a Cardiac Clinic* and *Standard Requirements for a Peripheral Vascular Disease Clinic*, free; *Atlas of Congenital Cardiac Disease*, by Maude E. Abbott, M.D., 1936, 72 pp., $5.50. A number of books and pamphlets relating to diseases of the heart, some free and others priced at 5¢ to 35¢ a copy. Films and slides for rental or purchase. Price list upon request.

Staff: Full-time paid employees, 4; part-time paid employee, 1.

Finances: Approximate annual budget, $15,500.

AMERICAN ORTHOPSYCHIATRIC ASSOCIATION (1924); 1790 Broadway, New York, N.Y.; Norvelle C. La Mar, M.D., Secretary.

Membership: Individuals, 369, chiefly psychiatrists, psychologists, and psychiatric social workers engaged in clinical work. Types of membership: members, $6; fellows, $10.

Purpose: To unite and provide a common meeting ground for those engaged in the study and treatment of problems of human behavior; to foster research and spread information concerning scientific work in the field of human behavior, including all forms of abnormal behavior.

Activities: Annual meeting. There are no youth activities other than the regular professional activities of the individual members.

Publications: *American Journal of Orthopsychiatry*, quarterly; $6 a year; Lawson G. Lowrey, M.D., editor, 25 West 54th St., New York, N.Y. *Introduction to the Rorschach Method*, by S. J. Beck, 278 pp., $4; *Studies in Sibling Rivalry*, by David M. Levy, M.D., 96 pp., paper $1, cloth $1.25; *Visual Motor Gestalt Test and Its Clinical Use*, by Lauretta Bender, M.D., 176 pp., $3.50. Also special reprints of groups of papers on particular subjects.

Staff: Part-time paid employees at headquarters, 2.

Finances: Current operations for the calendar year 1939 were as follows:

Income

Membership fees	$1,670.50
Publications	3,826.94
Other sources	2,340.08
	$7,837.52

Expenditures

Salaries	$1,433.00
Publications	3,662.67
Other purposes	1,917.48
	$7,013.15

AMERICAN PUBLIC HEALTH ASSOCIATION

(1872); 1790 Broadway, New York, N.Y.; Reginald M. Atwater, M.D., Executive Secretary.

Membership: Persons engaged or interested in public health work, 6,700, located in the United States, Canada, Mexico, and Cuba; 2 regional branches, western and southern; 22 state affiliated organizations. Types of membership: honorary fellows; fellows, $10; members, $5; sustaining members, $50 or more; life members, $100.

Purpose: To provide a professional society for the public health workers of North America with the objective of controlling preventable disease and providing security of health for all the people; to develop public health standards; to stimulate the recruiting and training of public health personnel; to strengthen the public health profession.

Activities: Makes surveys and appraisals of state and community health work; furnishes information regarding the most satisfactory administrative practices; conducts detailed studies of local health problems; provides a regular consultation and advisory service; keeps a list of openings in public health work and a record of available personnel; prepares standards for the control of communicable diseases and the examination of milk and water; holds an annual meeting which includes a health exposition comprising commercial, scientific, and educational exhibits. Contributes to the advancement of public health through the studies and reports of authorities who serve voluntarily on technical committees conducting research on such topics as the following: professional education; nutritional problems; standard methods for the examination of water, sewage, milk, and shellfish; swimming pools and bathing places; rural sanitation; occupational diseases; hygiene of housing; infant and maternal mortality and school health problems. The association has ten sections, as follows: Health Officers, Laboratory, Vital Statistics, Engineering, Industrial Hygiene, Food and Nutrition, Maternal and Child Health, Public Health Education, Public Health Nursing, and Epidemiology.

Publications: *American Journal of Public Health,* monthly; free to members, $5 to others; Harry S. Mustard, M.D., editor. Yearbook, annually; free to members, $1 to others. *A Half Century of Public Health,* by Mazyck P. Ravenel, 1921, 473 pp., $7.50; *Physical Defects—The Pathway to Correction,* 1934, 171 pp., paper $1, cloth $1.25; *Appraisal Form for Local Health Work,* 1938, 185 pp., $1.60; *Community Health Organization,* by Ira V. Hiscock, 1939 (third edition), 318 pp., $2.50; *Panum on Measles: A Translation from the Danish,* 1940, 111 pp., $2.50; *Bibliography on Public Health and Allied Subjects,* compiled annually, free; *Basic Principles of Healthful Housing,* 1939 (second edition), 32 pp., 25¢; *Control of Communicable Diseases,* 1935, 79 pp., 30¢. *Weight-Height-Age Tables for Boys and Girls from birth to 6 years,* 10¢; *Weight-Height-Age Tables for Boys and Girls from 5 to 18 years,* 5¢.

Staff: Full-time paid employees, 24, of whom 4 are in field work; part-time paid employees in field work, 4.

Finances: Value of equipment at national headquarters, $1,200. Current operations for the calendar year 1939 were as follows:

Income

Gifts	$ 61,150.35
Membership fees	40,023.99
Publications	35,809.21
Other services	17,284.35
Other sources	2,051.45
	$156,319.35

Expenditures

Salaries	$ 81,538.11
Travel	16,583.91
Communications	12,796.06
Office supplies	6,151.44
Publications	25,070.89
Rentals, insurance, etc.	7,269.36
Other purposes	5,888.73
	$155,298.50

AMERICAN SCHOOL HEALTH ASSOCIATION

(1927); Kent State University, Kent, Ohio; A. O. DeWeese, M.D., Executive Secretary-Treasurer.

Name changed from American Association of School Physicians to present form, 1937.

Membership: Physicians, dentists, nurses, and members of other medical science professions, 1,227. There are three local branches. Annual dues, $2.

Purpose: To consolidate the interests and activities of the medical science professions concerned with school health work.

Activities: Issues official publication for the study and evaluation of school health problems.

Publications: *Journal of School Health,* monthly; $1.75 a year.

Staff: Part-time paid employees, 2; part-time unpaid workers, 100.

Finances: Estimated annual value of unpaid staff services, $5,000. Cash balance on hand December 31, 1939, $1,200. For the fiscal year ending on that date, operations were as follows:

Income

Membership fees	$2,500
Publications	1,100
	$3,600

Expenditures

Salaries	$ 200
Travel	100
Communications	200
Office supplies	200
Rent, insurance, etc.	1,700
	$2,400

AMERICAN SOCIAL HYGIENE ASSOCIATION
(1914); 1790 Broadway, New York, N.Y.; Walter Clarke, M.D., Executive Director.

Membership: Individuals, approximately 10,000, affiliations with state and local social hygiene committees and societies, 148. Types of membership: active, $2; library, $3; society, $10.

Purpose: To encourage, strengthen, and preserve American family life. Specifically, to aid in the control and prevention of syphilis and other venereal disease infections; to prevent sex delinquency; to reduce commercialized prostitution; to promote a rational program of sex education that will prepare for successful marriage and family life.

Activities: Cooperates with national, state, and local governmental and voluntary agencies interested in furthering social hygiene; promotes higher standards of medical instruction in social diseases; carries out studies of methods and facilities for the diagnosis, treatment, and public health control of social diseases; provides a consultation and information service; sponsors intensive health education campaigns in selected communities. Distributes special exhibits, motion pictures, talking slide films, and phonograph records. The association has four divisions: Medical and Public Health, Legal and Protective, Educational and Family Relations, Public Information and Extension.

Educational programs are directed toward youth through schools, clubs, group leaders, and organizations of parents. The Youth Service cooperates with local groups of the YMCA and the YWCA, churches, college groups, NYA, etc., in developing and extending social hygiene activity; corresponds with many schools on programs relating to physical education, home economics, and sciences; and initiates cooperative projects with national, state, and city health and welfare officials. Through this program over 2,000 young people's groups in the 48 states,

Canada, and South America are reached. Medical measures are particularly intended to benefit youth, since the ages of highest onset of both syphilis and gonorrhea are between 20 and 25. Protective and legal measures are aimed at eliminating influences dangerous to youth. Directly or indirectly, probably three-fourths of the work of the association is concerned with young people.

Publications: *Journal of Social Hygiene*, 9 issues annually; $3 a year. *Social Hygiene News*, monthly; free to members. *A Classified List of Social Hygiene Pamphlets*, a folder listing the numerous pamphlets published by the association. Several bibliographies relating to special aspects of social hygiene.

Staff: Full-time paid employees, 26.

Finances: The budget for 1940 was as follows:

Public information and extension	$ 39,637
Legal and protective activities	13,424
Medical and public health activities	14,924
Sex education program	11,162
Special projects (including Youth Service)	35,610
Field service	48,693
Committee activities	36,550
Publications service budget	20,000
	$220,000

AMERICAN SOCIETY OF DENTISTRY FOR CHILDREN
(1926); Dr. Frank F. Lamons, President, 503 Doctors Bldg., Atlanta, Ga.; Dr. Ralph M. Erwin, Jr., Secretary, 613 Corbett Bldg., Portland, Ore.

Membership: Dentists, 500; state units, 18.

Purpose: To disseminate knowledge concerning children's dentistry to professional and lay people.

Activities: Promotes children's dentistry in public schools and in dental schools; stimulates pertinent research; helps standardize methods and techniques; conducts programs in dental societies and directs city, state, and national health programs featuring oral health and preventive dentistry.

Publications: *Review of Dentistry for Children*, 4 issues annually; $3 a year; Dr. Samuel D. Harris, editor, 2312 Eaton Tower, Detroit, Mich.

Staff: Part-time paid employees, 2.

Finances: Estimated annual value of space, heat, and light received without charge, $150. Cash balance on hand December 31, 1939, $1,275. For the fiscal year ending on that date, operations were as follows:

Income

Membership fees	$1,600
Publications	142
	$1,742

Expenditures

Salaries	$ 80
Communications	300
Office supplies	100
Publications	800
	$1,280

AMERICAN STUDENT HEALTH ASSOCIATION
(1920); University of Kansas, Health Service, Watkins Memorial Hospital, Lawrence, Kan.; Dr. Ralph I. Canuteson, Secretary-Treasurer.

Membership: Institutions of higher education, 181, each represented by its institutional physician or health officer.

Purpose: To discuss student health problems; to supervise and care for individual student health and illness; to supervise the sanitation of student environment; and to promote the development of physical and mental health.

Activities: Holds annual meetings in December, with presentation of papers on many phases of health work and discussion thereof. Acts as a clearing-house for the promotion of student health services. Serves the student bodies enrolled in the 181 member colleges and universities.

Publications: Papers are published in the *Journal-Lancet*, a monthly, issued at Minneapolis. Two copies of the proceedings of each annual meeting are sent to each member institution.

Staff: No paid staff. Officers are chosen from among student health service workers in the institutions comprising the membership.

Finances: For the fiscal year ending December 31, 1939, total income, from membership fees and the proceedings, was $2,010.75. Total expenditures during the same period were $1,595.15, chiefly for the annual meeting and for the publication and distribution of the proceedings.

BIRTH CONTROL FEDERATION OF AMERICA,
INC. (1921); administration office, 501 Madison Ave., New York, N.Y., D. Kenneth Rose, Executive Vice President; Medical Department, 17 West 16th St., New York, N.Y., Woodbridge E. Morris, M.D., General Medical Director.

Formerly American Birth Control League and Birth Control Clinical Research Bureau until merger in 1939. Also cooperates with Voluntary Parenthood League.

Membership: Member leagues in 30 states and District of Columbia; underlying individual membership, 32,263, national and state.

Purpose: Ultimately, to make medical birth control information available to all who need it. Immediately, to include birth control in maternal health and welfare services of public agencies.

Activities: Maintains following departments: Regional Organization, Public Information, Medical, National Clinic Service, and a medical advisory committee—the National Medical Council on Birth Control. Public education to demonstrate the health, economic, and eugenic value of scientific contraception; medical education through medical colleges, medical societies, and publications for physicians. Educational program carried on by means of literature, films, speakers, exhibits, and posters. Organizes state and local leagues and establishes birth control centers under medical direction and sponsorship of community committees. Advises member leagues and centers in problems of organization, public education, and clinic administration.

Publications: *Service of Information, Bulletin*, and *Newsletter*, free to membership. *Human Fertility*, bimonthly, for medical and scientific professions; $2 a year. Directory of contraceptive clinics and services in the United States, its territories, and Canada. *Technique of Conception Control*, medical text for physicians and medical students. Reprints and professional material for public health and social workers; general educational pamphlets, reprints, and book list.

Staff: Full-time paid employees, 33; part-time paid employee, 1.

Finances: Balance at end of calendar year 1939, $39,337.18. For the corresponding fiscal year, income and expenditures were as follows:

Income

Contributions and memberships	$214,803.98
State league membership dues	2,017.70
Publications	3,133.49
Miscellaneous	178.19
	$220,133.36

Expenditures

Headquarters	$ 25,440.62
Operating expenses	10,708.41
Regional Organization Department	37,669.81
Medical Department	15,958.23
National Clinic Service	6,187.26
Public information	31,625.48
Extension program	25,133.61
Distribution to local organizations participating in campaign	28,072.76
	$180,796.18

FOUNDATION FOR POSITIVE HEALTH (1919);
1790 Broadway, New York, N.Y.; Lenna L. Meanes, M.D., Medical Director.

Membership: Representatives of national lay and professional women's organizations, 48.

Purpose: To create a desire for positive health; to further ways and means for obtaining and maintaining it; to establish the conviction that mental health is generally attainable through individual effort and responsibility; to establish the conviction that mental health is as procurable as physical health.

Activities: Answers inquiries and requests for program suggestions. Has a four-year contract with the New York City Board of Education and makes contracts with schools for the *Handbook on Positive Health*.

Publications: *Handbook on Positive Health*, prepared in cooperation with the Council on Health and Public Instruction of the American Medical Association and the National Board of the YWCA, $1.50. Pamphlets: *Feet, Shoes, and Posture*, 15¢; *Nutrition*, by McCollum, 15¢; *Mental Health*, by White, and *Children and Adolescents*, by Taft (two in one pamphlet), 15¢; *The Heritage of Life*, by Cannon, 15¢; *Recreation Adapted to Individual Needs*, by Lindeman and Betzner, 15¢; *A Wise Woman at the Court of Hygeia*, by Hathaway (one-act play), 35¢. Material for group programs and for individual use.

Staff: Part-time unpaid workers, 2.

MATERNITY CENTER ASSOCIATION (1918); 654 Madison Ave., New York, N.Y.; Hazel Corbin, General Director.

Membership: Individuals, approximately 2,500.

Purpose: To teach the public the vital importance of adequate maternity care; to secure, in cooperation with all existing agencies, such care for all expectant mothers.

Activities: Classes for prospective fathers and mothers and consultation service for those wishing advice as to what constitutes good maternity care and where it may be obtained; most of those benefiting from these services live in the metropolitan area. Public education and information: publications, posters, and lectures by staff members, emphasizing the standards by which adequate care is measured and how obtained and stressing the importance of good maternity care not only for the benefit of the individual but also for its influence upon the family and community. Cooperation with other agencies to promote better maternity care and health. A course in midwifery for graduate nurses; institutes of varying length for nurses to prepare them better for obstetric nursing in the public health field, conducted in New York and throughout the country.

Publications: *Briefs*, 6 issues annually; $1 a year. *Maternity Handbook*, $1; *Getting Ready to be a Father*, $1.25; *Atlas on Growth and Birth of a Baby* (16 life-size charts), $3.50; *Public Health Nursing in Obstetrics*, 50¢. Various pamphlets, posters, and charts.

Staff: Full-time paid employees, 21, of whom 9 spend major time in field work; part-time paid employees, 4, all of whom spend major time in field work.

Finances: Reserve funds, $261,595.37. For the fiscal year ending December 31, 1939, operations were as follows:

Income

Gifts for current expenses	$25,122.94
Membership fees	30,421.95
Publications	327.36
Institute fees	3,350.96
Reserve funds	23,234.78
Benefits, miscellaneous	15,552.72
	$98,010.71

Expenditures

Salaries	$57,762.96
Travel	564.00
Communications	1,379.49
Office supplies	1,680.75
Publications	1,335.83
Rentals, insurance, etc.	5,568.19
Institutes, East Harlem Nursing Service, drugs, miscellaneous	28,352.15
	$96,643.37

NATIONAL COMMITTEE OF HEALTH COUNCIL EXECUTIVES (1926); Secretary-Treasurer, Margaret H. Tracy, Boston Health League, 80 Federal St., Boston, Mass.

Membership: Individuals, about 30, executive officers of national, state, and local health councils. Annual dues, $1.

Purpose: To provide for exchange of experience, consideration of mutual problems, and discussion of suitable activities for health councils; to stimulate extension of the health council idea.

Activities: Two meetings annually, one in connection with the National Conference of Social Work (see p. 189) in the spring, and the other at the time of the meeting of the American Public Health Association (see p. 173) in the autumn.

Publications: *Compilation of Reports of Health Councils in U.S.*, annually. *Health Councils*, 1940, 2 pp. mimeo.

Staff: No paid employees.

Finances: Total annual income, about $30, from membership fees exclusively. Annual expenditures are for mailing, mimeographing, stationery, postage, and office supplies only.

NATIONAL COMMITTEE FOR MENTAL HYGIENE, INC. (1909); 1790 Broadway, New York, N.Y.; George S. Stevenson, M.D., Medical Director.

Membership: Elected members, 750, mostly professional people with a special interest in mental health work. Associate memberships (contributing, subscribing, service, and sustaining members, and patrons) open to the general public. Associate members receive, on request, subscriptions to periodical publications, choice of pamphlets, and reference and loan privileges from the National Health Library (see National Health Council, p. 177).

Purpose: To promote interest and action throughout the United States in the control and prevention of mental disease and the conservation of mental health by improving hospitalization for the mentally ill and defective, by improving and extending clinic services for early diagnosis and treatment, by stimulating psychiatric research, by professional training, and by public education.

Activities: Promotes measures to raise standards of care and treatment of the mentally ill; supports psychiatric and mental hygiene research and is at present conducting a series of original investigations in dementia praecox; advises and assists in the development of psychiatric clinics for children and adults. Cooperates with 60 state and local mental hygiene societies and with national mental hygiene organizations in 35 other countries; assists in the organization and conduct of state and local mental hygiene societies; and works for public understanding and support of organized activities in the broad field of mental health endeavor. Promotes training and placement of professional personnel, with emphasis on improved psychiatric teaching in medical schools and the development of postgraduate training centers in psychiatry; administers fellowships in the training field; conducts experimental studies in teachers colleges and normal schools to secure better selection and training of candidates for the teaching profession and improved mental health practices in public schools; engages in certain aspects of personnel work affecting the training and placement of physicians, nurses, social workers, and other professional workers in psychiatry, mental hygiene, and related fields; and provides vocational guidance for medical students and students of nursing and social work preparing for careers in the mental health field. Encourages child guidance work through the extension of psychiatric clinic services and the cultivation of mental hygiene programs in teacher training institutions; promotes the establishment of mental health services in high schools, colleges, courts, correctional institutions, social agencies, etc.

Publications: *Mental Hygiene,* quarterly journal for professional and lay people; $3 a year; Dr. George S. Stevenson, editor. *Understanding the Child,* quarterly magazine for teachers; 50¢ a year; Dr. Henry B. Elkind, editor, 3 Joy St., Boston, Mass. Occasional newsletter reporting on developments in organized mental hygiene work in general and on the committee's activities in particular. Series of pamphlet publications on mental disease and defect, hospitals and clinics, mental hygiene in education and child training, and the mental health aspects of crime, delinquency, dependency, and other social problems. Also a number of pamphlets dealing especially with mental hygiene in the schools and colleges.

Staff: Full-time paid employees, 18, of whom 4 spend major time in field work; part-time paid employees, 4, all of whom spend major time in field work. NYA workers at headquarters, 7.

Finances: Value of equipment at headquarters, approximately $3,000. Estimated annual value of unpaid staff services, $1,800. Cash balance on hand December 31, 1939, $6,077.35. For the preceding calendar year, operations were as follows:

Income

General administration	$ 49,498.37
Membership	30,391.30
Community clinics	16,811.99
Psychiatric education and fellowships	12,100.00
Extension and field service	6,092.49
Mental hospital service	8,936.11
Dementia praecox research	45,325.06
School studies	703.16
World's Fair exhibit	15,973.67
Survey of research under private auspices	3,800.00
	$189,632.15

Expenditures

General administration	$ 52,014.09
Membership	28,391.30
Community clinics	16,280.10
Psychiatric education and fellowships	11,500.00
Extension and field service	2,822.13
Mental hospital service	8,936.11
Dementia praecox research	45,241.47
School studies	703.16
World's Fair exhibit	15,811.67
Survey of research under private auspices	1,854.77
	$183,554.80

NATIONAL HEALTH COUNCIL, INC. (1921); 1790 Broadway, New York, N.Y.; Thomas C. Edwards, Business Manager.

Membership: Seventeen constituent organizations concerned with major fields of public health work in the United States. Active members: American Heart Association (see p. 172), American Public Health Association (see p. 173), American National Red Cross (see p. 186), American Social Hygiene Association (see p. 174), American Society for the Control of Cancer, American Society for the Hard of Hearing (see p. 204), Conference of State and Provincial Health Authorities of North America, Maternity Center Association (see p. 176), National Committee of Health Council Executives (see p. 176), National Committee for Mental Hygiene (see p. 176), National Organization for Public Health Nursing (see p. 179), National Society for the Prevention of Blindness (see p. 180), National Tuberculosis Association (see p. 181). Advisory members: Children's Bureau, Department of Labor; Public Health Service, Federal Security Agency. Associate members:

Chart VI

THE NATIONAL HEALTH COUNCIL

NATIONAL HEALTH COUNCIL

American Heart Association

American National Red Cross

American Nurses' Association (associate)

American Public Health Association

American Social Hygiene Association

American Society for the Control of Cancer

American Society for the Hard of Hearing

Children's Bureau, Department of Labor (advisory)

Conference of State and Provincial Health Authorities of North America

Foundation for Positive Health (associate)

Maternity Center Association

National Committee of Health Council Executives

National Committee for Mental Hygiene

National Organization for Public Health Nursing

National Society for the Prevention of Blindness

National Tuberculosis Association

Public Health Service, Federal Security Agency (advisory)

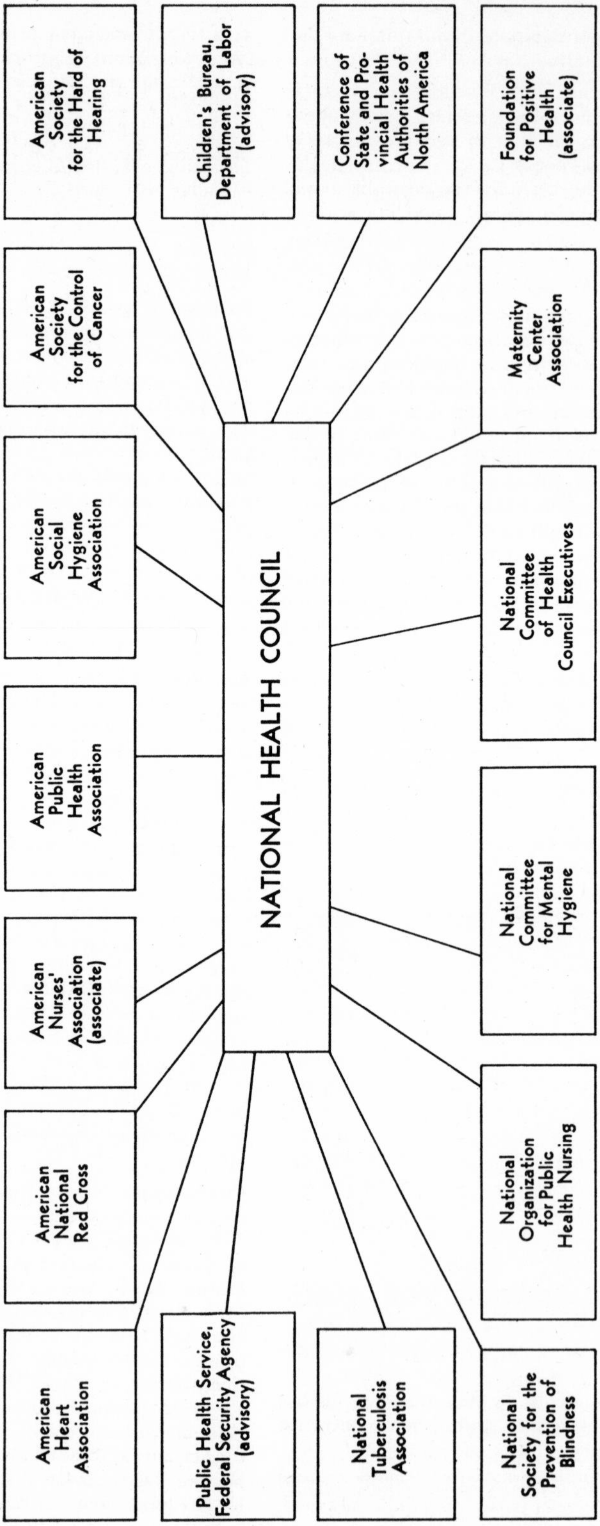

American Nurses' Association, Foundation for Positive Health (see p. 175).

Purpose: To cooperate with official federal, state, and local health authorities, voluntary health agencies, and community groups in promoting better health in the United States.

Activities: Acts as a national clearinghouse for voluntary health agencies; coordinates the operations of its constituent members; sponsors joint projects such as information services regarding motion picture health films, conference dates, health examinations, and health poster lists. Maintains a service department to administer such common services as rental arrangements, shipping, bookkeeping, telephone, multigraphing, proofreading, film distribution, purchase of printing, and other service activities of which the cost may be prorated according to use by the member agencies. Maintains the National Health Library, a cooperative activity of the council, which extends reference and loan privileges and compiles bibliographies. From time to time sets up, as experiments or for temporary purposes, such special services as joint field itineraries, a statistical service, a National Health Congress, a health service for Negroes, and a joint campaign against congenital syphilis.

Publications: *National Health Series*, a set of 20 popular health books assembled and edited by the council and published by Funk and Wagnalls, 35¢ each.

Staff: Full-time paid employees at headquarters, 17; part-time paid employees, 2.

Finances: Operations for the fiscal year ending December 31, 1939 were as follows:

Income		
Publications	$	296.85
Other services		46,026.71
Other sources		70,107.78
		$116,431.34
Expenditures		
Salaries	$	30,856.20
Communications		846.98
Office supplies		532.89
Publications		818.25
Rentals, insurance, etc.		64,991.08*
Other purposes		19,753.07
		$117,798.47

NATIONAL ORGANIZATION FOR PUBLIC HEALTH NURSING, INC. (1912); 1790 Broadway, New York, N.Y.; Dorothy Deming, General Director.

Membership: Individuals, 10,000, including nurses, health officials, physicians, and others concerned

* The rent for the National Health Council proper amounts to $5,000 a year. The remainder of this item is billed to various members and subtenants of the council who participate in the joint housing plan.

with the development of public health nursing as a sound community program; agencies employing public health nurses, 360; state organizations for public health nursing, 19. Types of membership and annual dues: individual, nurse, associate nurse, lay (more than one-eighth of the membership is nonprofessional), $3; life, $100; agency, 1 per cent of the agency's total expenditure for public health nursing during the last fiscal year, with minimum dues of $10 and $25 and maximum of $1,000; associate agency, $5.

Purpose: To assist 23,000 public health nurses, and the board and committee members of the 6,000 agencies employing them, to bring health to families and individuals in the most effective and progressive manner; to develop and promote public health nursing; to act in an advisory capacity to persons engaged or interested in public health nursing; to secure adequate preparation and educational opportunity for the public health nurse; to provide personnel assistance; to assist in the integration of public health nursing into the total social and health programs; to promote understanding of the service of public health nursing among federal departments, national, state, and local health and social agencies, and the general public.

Activities: Furthers cooperation between public health nurses and all those interested in public health work; maintains a clearinghouse of information on accepted practices of public health nursing; furnishes an advisory and consultation service through correspondence, office conferences, and field trips; conducts educational activities such as recommending minimum qualifications for those appointed to positions in public health nursing, endorsing collegiate courses in public health nursing, and encouraging self-education through local institutes, group conferences, and the distribution of reading suggestions. Interprets public health nursing, its standards and goals, to federal, state, and local authorities concerned with unemployment and relief programs; builds up a strong partnership between the professional and nonprofessional groups; carries on statistical studies and other types of surveys; meets biennially. Maintains the following sections: board and committee members, school nursing, industrial nursing.

Publications: *Public Health Nursing*, monthly; $2 a year to members, $3 to others; Purcelle Peck, editor. *P h n*, 4 issues annually; free to members. *Manual of Public Health Nursing* (New York: Macmillan), 529 pp., $2.50; *Board Members' Manual* (New York: Macmillan), 173 pp., $1.50; *Survey of Public Health Nursing* (New York: Commonwealth Fund), 262 pp., $2; *Suggestions for Statistical Reporting and Cost Computation in Public Health Nursing* (NOPHN), 48 pp., single copy free to members, 25¢ to nonmembers; *Personnel Policies in Public Health Nursing*, by Marian G. Randall (New York: Macmillan), 170 pp., $2; *Public Health Nursing in Industry*, by Violet H. Hodgson (New York: Macmillan), 249 pp., $2.

Staff: Full-time paid employees, 30, of whom 7 spend about a third of their time in field work.

Finances: Current operations for the calendar year 1939 were as follows:

Income

Contributions	$ 19,090.50
Membership fees	
Individual	30,837.00
Agency	23,503.70
Public Health Nursing	24,111.65
Earnings	4,256.03
National Foundation for Infantile	
Paralysis	2,497.32
Other sources	4,703.75
	$108,999.95

Expenditures

Correspondence and consultation	$ 29,241.21
Field service	21,884.48
Educational service	9,692.78
Statistical service and studies	11,403.71
Public Health Nursing	24,701.40
Other publications	6,662.19
Community nursing service	1,000.00
National Foundation for Infantile	
Paralysis	2,497.32
	$107,083.09

NATIONAL SAFETY COUNCIL, INC. (1913); 20 North Wacker Drive, Chicago, Ill.; W. H. Cameron, Managing Director.

Membership: Constituent units, 5,000, consisting of industrial corporations and insurance companies, individuals, city, state, and governmental departments, local safety councils, chambers of commerce, automobile clubs, schools, libraries, and other civic organizations. Dues range from $5 to $1,000 or more. Industries, railroads, public utilities, and insurance companies are assessed in proportion to the number of employees or the volume of business; special classifications are effected for municipal departments, libraries, and chambers of commerce.

Purpose: To promote the conservation of human life and the safety, health, and welfare of the individual, the workman, and the general public, particularly through the prevention of accidents and of occupational diseases in industry, in homes, on streets and highways, and in other public places.

Activities: Concerns itself with child safety through the Committee on Public Safety and through the Education Division. The former reaches the child in the home through the civic organizations and other community groups, and the latter through the school members that form the Child Education Section, which has committees on elementary school, secondary school, statistics, program, and state activities. These committees work with safety experts in developing standard methods and procedures.

Publications: *National Safety News*, monthly; *Public Safety*, monthly; *Safety Education*, monthly; *Industrial Supervisor*, monthly; *Safe Worker*, monthly; *Safe Driver*, monthly; *News Letters*, 26 issues monthly; posters, 54 issues monthly; various research reports, bulletins, and pamphlets. List sent on request.

Staff: Full-time paid employees at headquarters, 125.

Finances: Annual budget, $800,000.

NATIONAL SOCIETY FOR THE PREVENTION OF BLINDNESS, INC. (1915); 1790 Broadway, New York, N.Y.; Mrs. Eleanor Brown Merrill, Executive Director.

Membership: Membership fees from 3,000 individuals, agencies, and corporations; also donations from approximately 14,000 individuals, agencies, and corporations during 1939.

Purpose: To endeavor to ascertain, through study and investigation, any causes, whether direct or indirect, which may result in blindness or impaired vision; to advocate measures which shall lead to the elimination of such causes; to disseminate knowledge concerning all matters pertaining to the care and use of the eyes.

Activities: Activities having a more or less direct bearing on the health and protection of the eyes of youth include: stimulating studies and disseminating scientific information regarding hereditary and nutritional factors in eye health; promoting measures to prevent prenatal and natal eye infections, such as those from syphilis and gonorrhea; developing eye-testing procedures and advancing their use in preschool, school, and college groups; cooperating in efforts to abolish the indiscriminate sale and use of fireworks in order to reduce eye and other bodily injuries; promoting the concept of eye protection and eye hygiene, including proper illumination; promoting the establishment of sight-saving classes for children with serious visual handicaps; cooperating in the training of medical social eye workers and of teachers of sight-saving classes, as well as in promoting eye health knowledge among the nursing and teaching professions in general; furnishing publications and posters to young persons in connection with school studies, safety courses, Boy and Girl Scout groups, health clubs, NYA agencies, etc.; and furnishing material to parents about the care and protection of children's eyes.

Publications: *Sight-Saving Review*, quarterly, $2 a year; *Sight-Saving Class Exchange*, 4 issues annually, free; annual report, free; *News Letter*, occasionally, free. Numerous pamphlets and bulletins on various phases of the program for the prevention of blindness and the conservation of vision throughout life; vision test charts; exhibits, stereopticon slides, motion pictures, and talking slide films. Catalog on request.

Staff: Full-time paid employees, 33, of whom about 6 spend some portion of their time in field work; part-time paid employees, 3.

Finances: Endowment funds, $37,740.74; reserve funds, $380,248.85. Cash balance on hand January 1, 1939, $26,393.62. For the fiscal year ending December 31, 1939, operations were as follows:

Income

Gifts and grants	$ 79,214.93
Membership fees	15,779.14
Publications	4,015.13
Films and other services	743.77
Endowment and reserve funds	13,745.21
Estates and trust funds	17,750.13
	$131,248.31

Expenditures

Administration	$ 38,596.68
Education and public information	53,661.69
Field service	16,146.54
Editorial research	9,861.91
Publications	12,001.35
Extension (fund raising)	21,250.39
Cooperative projects	12,972.94
Retirement plan, insurance, etc.	2,590.03
	$167,081.53

NATIONAL TUBERCULOSIS ASSOCIATION

(1904); 1790 Broadway, New York, N.Y.; Kendall Emerson, M.D., Managing Director.

Membership: Individuals, 1,580; "affiliated and represented associations" in every state and territory, in New York City, Chicago, and Puerto Rico, which direct the work of approximately 1,600 municipal, county, and district associations and 800 smaller committees. The state and local associations have their own membership and cooperate with affiliated agencies of many kinds. The national office deals directly with the state associations; the respective state offices handle the local groups. Types of membership: member, $5; life, $100; corporate, $5; representative, $5; honorary; associate, $10; sustaining, $20 or more. Each member, life member, corporate member, and representative member is entitled to one vote at the annual and special meetings of the corporation held in Portland, Me.

Purpose: To study tuberculosis in all its forms and relations; to disseminate information concerning its causes, treatment, and prevention; to stimulate, unify, and standardize the work of the various antituberculosis agencies throughout the country, especially the state and local associations; to cooperate with other health organizations in the coordination of health activities; to promote international relations in connection with health activities in the study and control of tuberculosis.

Activities: Conducts programs of health education for the general public and for such special groups as physicians, nurses, medical students, and tuberculosis patients; develops higher standards of work among the affiliated units and among nurses, physicians, technicians, sanatoria, dispensaries, and other agencies engaged in tuberculosis work; evaluates existing health laws and studies the need for further legislation; cooperates with federal agencies dealing with health problems; forwards a program of research into the medical and social problems of tuberculosis; serves as a forum for presenting and interpreting to lay and medical groups the results of research; acts as a clearinghouse for information on statistical, technical, medical, and other aspects of the tuberculosis problem; counsels and guides the development of state and local associations. Every spring since 1928 has been carrying on an intensive campaign called the "Early Diagnosis Campaign" for the specific purpose of discovering early cases of tuberculosis. Sponsors an annual Christmas seal sale for fund-raising purposes and authorizes the state and local organizations to participate under standards laid down and specified by the national association; 5 per cent of the gross proceeds goes to the national association, and the other 95 per cent remains in the state where it was raised.

Urges closer relationship and coordination of child health activities among local and state groups; maintains a Child Health Education Service which is concerned with parent education, health education in schools, including colleges and universities, and a cooperative health program with youth-serving organizations outside of the schools; this service works closely with the American Association for Health, Physical Education, and Recreation (see p. 113), financing its assistant in health education, with the American Student Health Association (see p. 175) in the promotion of college hygiene, and with the National Congress of Parents and Teachers (see p. 130) through participation in the Summer Roundup of Children. The association also carries on a special program of health education for Negroes in the high schools and colleges.

Publications: *Bulletin*, monthly; free to members; D. C. McCarthy, editor. *American Review of Tuberculosis*, monthly; $8 a year; Max Pinner, M.D., editor. *Tuberculosis Abstracts*, monthly publication for physicians; H. E. Kleinschmidt, M.D., editor. Transactions of annual meetings, annually; free to members, current issue $3 to others. *News Letter*, sent monthly to affiliated associations. *Fifteen Years of Child Health Education by the National Tuberculosis Association, 1917–1932*, by Louise Strachan, 54 pp., 50¢; *Tuberculosis from 5 to 20*, 8 pp., single copy free; *Teaching Unit for High Schools on Preventing Tuberculosis*, 16 pp., single copy free; *Health in Colleges* (Proceedings of the Second National Conference on College Hygiene), 1937, 112 pp., $1; *Health Education Material for Teachers*, revised 1938, 8 pp., single copy free; *A Study of Tuberculosis Mortality among Young Women*, by Edna E. Nicholson, 60 pp., 50¢; *Death Rates by Occupations*, by Jessamine S. Whitney, 32 pp., $1;

1,000 Questions and Answers on Tuberculosis, by Fred H. Heise, M.D., 232 pp., 75¢. Several hundred pamphlets, reprints, and reports, some free, others priced at 5¢ to $2. List on request.

Staff: Full-time paid employees, 50, of whom one-third spend part of their time in field work.

Finances: The balance sheet as of December 31, 1939 showed assets of $398,325.81 and liabilities of $377,209.89. Assets included $28,626.16 in cash, $223,822.05 in investments, and $6,115.92 in depreciated book value of furniture and equipment. For the calendar year 1939, operations were as follows:

Income

Percentage on the 1938 seal sale	$262,086.32
Donations and grants	11,166.80
Dues	7,781.50
Interest, dividends, discount	8,436.13
American Review of Tuberculosis	18,486.55
Miscellaneous	1.00
	$307,958.30

Expenditures

General health education	$ 30,923.81
Child health education	8,402.14
Personnel training and publications	31,478.88
Public relations	23,624.65
Library and archives	3,517.27
American Review of Tuberculosis	21,992.00
Membership	6,067.25
Statistical	16,250.50
Social research	5,855.41
Medical research	39,915.96
Rehabilitation	12,239.51
Cooperation with other agencies	10,042.14
Organization and field service	6,345.31
Study of tuberculosis among Negroes	11,961.43
Administration	44,537.61
Field accounting service	3,061.98
Seal sale	26,979.06
	$303,194.91

General service and office expenses were $43,239.56. This sum is distributed among and included in the expenses for the activities shown under "expenditures" in the above tabulation.

Table XX

STATISTICS OF HEALTH AND SAFETY ORGANIZATIONS

Organization	Year Founded	Approximate Aggregate Membership (individuals)	Number of Members under 25 Years of Age	Total Employees on Headquarters Staff	Aggregate Endowment of National Headquarters	Plant and Equipment (headquarters only)	Approximate Annual Budget (headquarters only)
American Association of Medical Social Workers	1918	1,900	...	3	$ ...	$ ...	$ 17,000
Am. Automobile Assn., Safety and Traffic Engrg. Dept.	1902	1,000,000[a]	275,000[b]	...			...
American Eugenics Society	1926	650	25	3			10,700
American Heart Association	1922	2,300	...	5			15,500
American Orthopsychiatric Association	1924	369	...	2			7,800
American Public Health Association	1872	6,900	...	28	...	1,200	156,300
American School Health Association	1927	1,227	...	2	none	none	3,600
American Social Hygiene Association	1914	10,000	...	26			220,000
American Society of Dentistry for Children	1926	500	...	2			1,700
American Student Health Association	1920	181[c]	none	[d]			2,000
Birth Control Federation of America	1921	32,263	...	34	none	...	220,000
Foundation for Positive Health	1919	48[e]	...	[d]	...	...	
Maternity Center Association	1918	2,500	...	25	261,595	...	98,000
National Committee of Health Council Executives	1926	30	...	[d]			30
National Committee for Mental Hygiene	1909	750[f]	...	22	...	3,000	190,000
National Health Council	1921	17[c]	none	19	none	none	117,800[g]
National Organization for Public Health Nursing	1912	10,000	...	30	...	...	109,000
National Safety Council	1913	5,000[e]	...	125			800,000
National Society for the Prevention of Blindness	1915	3,000[h]	...	36	37,741[i]	...	167,000
National Tuberculosis Association	1904	1,580	...	50	[j]	...	308,000

a Adult membership of the entire association.
b Membership in school safety patrols.
c Number of constituent bodies.
d No paid staff.
e Representatives of national lay and professional women's organizations.
f Elected members only.

g Includes about $60,000 in rent billed to various members and subtenants participating in the joint housing plan.
h Includes agencies and corporations as well as individuals; in addition approximately 14,000 donors contributed to the organization in 1939.
i Also reserve funds of $380,249.
j The organization reports investments totaling $223,822.

XX. Organizations in the Field of Social Work

The area of service within the province of social work is broad and varied. The national associations in this area consist of many types. Among the oldest and best known are those in whose activities social service is combined with religious evangelism, such as the Salvation Army, the Volunteers of America, and the Seamen's Church Institute of America.

Also of long standing, and maintaining closer relationships with governmental agencies than do most voluntary organizations, is the American National Red Cross, which overshadows all other organizations in this field in point of membership and financial resources and carries on a large volume of service in disaster relief and numerous other functions in time of peace and in time of war.

Another class of national organizations consists of more or less loose federations of local service units located in cities in various parts of the country. In some cases the national headquarters is an agency of research and publication on a considerable scale, while in others it is scarcely more than a message center for the exchange of information, and its constituency is essentially a group of autonomous local institutions.

On another hand social service workers in various branches of this profession have banded themselves together into professional societies having for their aim the elevation of the standards of social work, the improvement of the conditions under which workers are employed, and the general advancement of the profession.

The vast increase in the social work load throughout the United States within the past decade, and the necessary participation of governmental agencies on a scale hitherto unprecedented, have greatly modified the task of private social agencies and caused a new uncertainty regarding the definition of their functions in the future. It is easily seen, however, that no diminution of the volume of their work is in prospect. Only a redirection of their efforts into new sectors of need is indicated. They will long be able to perform distinctive services which are not likely to be undertaken by governmental agencies. They furnish an outlet for philanthropic impulses which might otherwise easily be thwarted. They permit religious and welfare work to go hand in hand—a combina-

tion often favored by charitable donors but not susceptible of execution through governmental channels.

Broadly speaking, the tendency is away from emphasis on the mere palliative meeting of minimum material necessities, typified by the bread line and the flophouse, and toward stimulating the clientele to develop and enjoy the benefits of educational and character-building activities, including creative work and the fostering of appropriate avocational arts. In these undertakings invidious distinctions based on economic status tend to be minimized, and social work becomes a direct service to all classes of the public, rather than solely a salvage job for the economically unfortunate, as it was once regarded.

One class of organizations devotes attention to the welfare of migrant or transient families and individuals, and some are especially concerned with the welcoming of refugees from Europe. The present book does not purport to describe all national organizations concerned with refugees; but an authoritative directory of such agencies, published late in 1940, is entered in the bibliography.[1]

If one looks for nuclei about which national organizations in the field of social work are clustered, his eye will fall upon the National Conference of Social Work, dating from 1870. Its annual meetings have long attracted professional and lay leaders from many places, and the concurrent meetings of forty or more "associate and special groups" make it a veritable congress of the whole field.

Another nucleus is the National Social Work Council, having as constituent members twenty-nine national organizations in social work and closely related fields.

Cross references: Section V, General Character-Building Organizations for Youth, pp. 19–30; Section XIX, Health and Safety Organizations, pp. 170–83; Section XXI, Child Welfare Associations, pp. 196–201; Section XXII, Organizations Serving Handicapped Youth, pp. 202–8; Section XXIII, Associations for the Prevention and Treatment of Delinquency and Crime, pp. 209–11. *See also:* American Association of Visiting Teachers, p. 116; American Friends Service Committee, p. 32; Council of Jewish Federations and Welfare Funds, p. 57; National Catholic Welfare Conference, p. 48; Na-

---

[1] See p. 223, "National Agencies . . . ."

tional Conference of Catholic Charities, p. 51; National Council of Jewish Juniors, p. 60; National Jewish Welfare Board, p. 62; National Urban League for Social Service among Negroes, p. 100: Protestant Episcopal Church, Department of Christian Social Relations, p. 41.

AMERICAN ASSOCIATION OF SOCIAL WORKERS (1921); 130 East 22nd St., New York, N.Y.; Walter West, Executive Secretary.

Membership: Individual social workers, 11,500, in all parts of the United States. There are 84 local or state-wide chapters and 6 councils. Qualifications are, approximately, college education and a year of graduate study plus two years of experience, although the requirements may be met by completion of two full years in a graduate school of social work. Annual dues are from $6.50 up (including chapter dues).

Purpose: To advance professional standards in social work.

Activities: Provides a national working channel and local machinery for the cooperative activities of professional social workers; encourages proper and adequate basic preparation and training and fosters a homogeneous group which can develop a competent social work opinion; formulates and seeks to establish satisfactory conditions of employment and retirement for personnel so as to attract competent professional workers and enable them to function effectively; influences social planning and legislation for modernized welfare services and improved living standards; disseminates information concerning social work as a profession, encourages and conducts appropriate investigations, and publishes materials related to the experience of social work practitioners and therefore of special value to the advancement of professional social work.

Publications: *The Compass*, 11 issues annually; free to members, $1 a year to others. Books: *Unemployment and Its Treatment in the United States*, by Dorothy C. Kahn, $1; *This Business of Relief*, $1; *Social Case Work*, $1; *Social Work Ethics*, 50¢; and others. Numerous pamphlets and reprints on social work as a career, 5¢ to 15¢, including *Social Work Scholarships and Fellowships for 1940–41*, 10¢. *Platform of AASW on Public Social Services*, 1940, free.

Staff: Full-time paid employees, 14.

Finances: For the fiscal year ending December 31, 1939, operations were as follows:

Income	
Membership fees	$64,244.50
Publications	1,033.59
	$65,278.09

Expenditures	
Salaries	$39,619.71
Travel	7,847.89
Rent and office supplies	9,626.19
Publications	4,643.40
Other purposes	1,410.64
	$63,147.83

AMERICAN ASSOCIATION FOR THE STUDY OF GROUP WORK (1936); 670 Lexington Ave., New York, N.Y.; Charles E. Hendry, Chairman.

Membership: Men, 359, and women, 465, in 41 states, Canada, Hawaii, Puerto Rico, and South America; 59.5 per cent of the members are connected with national organizations, 25.6 per cent are engaged in local service, and 14.7 per cent work with educational and coordinating agencies; a majority of the members are officially related to the work of youth-serving organizations.

Purpose: To encourage the study of group work as a method in recreation, education (especially informal education), and social work.

Activities: Organizes and stimulates voluntary local study groups; prepares and distributes study aids; acts as a medium of exchange for such undertakings; and serves as a center of information on group work. Conducts regional and national conferences. Carries on specialized studies through national committees on local study groups, on current practices and problems in the professional education of group workers, and on group work in state, regional, and national conferences, and through commissions on such topics as objectives of group work, formulating standards in group work, training of group leaders, and record keeping in group work.

Publications: *The Group*, bimonthly; free to members; Thomas Nelson, editor-in-chief. Proceedings, annually. *Suggestions for the Study of Group Work in the Field of Camping*, 1939, 32 pp. mimeo., 25¢; *Let's Discuss Our Problems Together*, a manual for local study groups, 1940, 21 pp. mimeo., 25¢; *Five Study Outlines*, 1940, mimeo.; *Leisure: A National Issue*, by Eduard C. Lindeman, 1939, 50¢; *Group Education for a Democracy*, by William H. Kilpatrick, 1940, 232 pp., $2; *Group Work 1939* (proceedings and third annual report), 50¢; *Group Workers in the Present Emergency*, 15¢.

Staff: Full-time paid employee, 1. NYA workers, 2.

Finances: Reserve funds, $744.98. Value of equipment at national headquarters, $200. Estimated annual value of unpaid staff services, $780; estimated annual value of space, heat, light, and similar services received without charge, $300. Balance June 30, 1940, $285.02. For the fiscal year ending on that date, operations were as follows:

Income	
Membership fees	$2,268.03
Publications	423.70
Royalties	123.80
Other sources	13.33
	$2,828.86

Expenditures

Salaries	$1,474.22
Communications	367.15
Office supplies	258.18
Publications	811.60
Equipment	115.51
National conference	165.81
Other purposes	96.35
	$3,288.82

AMERICAN NATIONAL RED CROSS (1881); 17th and D Sts., N.W., Washington, D.C.; Norman H. Davis, Chairman, Central Committee.

Membership: Individual adults, 7,139,263, in 3,721 chapters and 6,585 branches of chapters located throughout the United States and possessions. Annual dues of $1 to $25, of which 50¢ for each member is forwarded to the national organization, are paid through the chapters. Life and patron memberships at $50 and $100, respectively, are credited in full to the national endowment fund. See also American Junior Red Cross (p. 20).

Purpose: To furnish volunteer aid to the sick and wounded of armies in time of war; to perform all the duties devolved upon a national society by each nation which has acceded to the Treaty of Geneva (August 22, 1864); to act in matters of voluntary relief and in accord with the military and naval authorities as a medium of communication between the people of the United States of America and their army and navy; to continue and carry on a system of national and international relief in time of peace and to apply the same in mitigating the sufferings caused by pestilence, famine, fire, floods, and other great national calamities, and to devise and carry on measures for preventing such disasters; to educate young people for intelligent participation in humanitarian activities on a local, national, and international scale.

Activities: The domestic operations of the organization are carried on in the following major divisions: (1) Home Service to men of the military and naval services, claims work, and information for veterans of all wars, (2) Disaster Preparedness and Relief, (3) Civilian Relief, (4) Nursing, (5) Other Health Service, (6) First Aid and Accident Prevention, (7) Life Saving and Water Safety, (8) Junior Red Cross, and (9) Volunteer Special Services. An indication of the scope of these activities is afforded by the following statistics for the year ending June 30, 1940:

Disaster relief operations in United States and possessions	154
Emergency relief operations in foreign countries	5
Assisted by camp, hospital, and liaison workers	
Ex-service men or families	58,505
Service men or families	53,365
Recreation and entertainment events in camps and hospitals	5,079
Assisted through Red Cross chapters	
Ex-service men or families	140,357
Service men or families	12,155
Nursing service	
Visits by public health nurses	1,038,363
Cases under care	334,194
Children inspected by doctor or nurse	618,623
Home Hygiene Certificates issued	61,855
First Aid Certificates issued	379,860
Highway Emergency First Aid Stations in operation	2,892
Mobile First Aid Units in operation on highways	3,030
Life Saving Certificates issued	94,246
Beginners and Swimmers qualified	182,697
Home and farm accident prevention, number of chapters conducting local programs	1,659
Volunteer Special Services	
Garments made (including 897,000 layette garments)	2,098,571
Surgical dressings made	9,958,201
Calls made by motor corps	66,379
Pages of Braille transcribed by hand	462,857
Pages of Braille printed by duplicating process	683,106
Volunteers reported by chapters under Volunteer Special Services	540,207
Volunteers in other Red Cross services (estimated)	579,708

Senior members are engaged in nation-wide production of garments for refugees in the war-affected areas of Europe, and junior members in contributing to the National Children's Fund of the American Junior Red Cross, through which other war relief is extended to European children. The domestic activities in first aid and life saving and in home hygiene and care of the sick deal largely with young persons under the age of 25.

Publications: *Red Cross Courier*, monthly; $1 a year; Alwyn W. Knight, editor. Numerous bulletins, among which are the following: *Accident Causes—How They May Be Prevented* (ARC 1023); *The Red Cross on the Highway* (ARC 1026); *Annual Report* (ARC 501); *Story of the Red Cross* (ARC 626); *Are You Helpless When Illness Invades Your Home?* (ARC 729); *Health Ahead* (ARC 732); *Keeping the Public Informed* (ARC 737); *Writing for the Blind* (ARC 419); *Program of the American Red Cross with the Military and Naval Services and for Disabled Veterans* (ARC 296). The complete *Check-List of Red Cross Publications* (May 1940) is identified as ARC 89.

Staff: Full-time paid employees, 935, of whom 134 spend major time in field work; part-time paid employees, 6.

Finances: The American National Red Cross Endowment Fund, managed and controlled by a board of nine trustees in accordance with an act of Congress (June 23, 1910), on June 30, 1940 amounted to $14,647,446.47. On the same date the resources of the general and restricted funds (distinct from the endowment fund just noted) were $22,581,061.97. For the fiscal year ending on that date, operations of the national organization were as follows:

Income

Membership fees	$ 3,569,644.21
Contributions for foreign war relief	10,594,927.90
Contributions for disaster relief	367,893.47
Interest on investments	663,694.19
Other sources	232,852.52
	$15,429,012.29

Expenditures

Military and naval welfare service $	658,539.88
Disaster relief	840,533.02
Foreign war relief	2,662,333.35
Civilian relief	22,045.10
Nursing services	225,842.19
First aid, life saving, and accident prevention	382,307.01
American Junior Red Cross	152,383.85
Other services	192,074.99
General service and assistance to domestic chapters	705,588.71
Public information, Roll Call, and fund raising	717,132.52
General executive and finance	337,308.71
	$ 6,896,089.33

During the same year the local chapters are estimated to have received $8,473,000 and expended $7,828,000.

AMERICAN PUBLIC WELFARE ASSOCIATION

(1930); 1313 East 60th St., Chicago, Ill.; Fred K. Hoehler, Director.

Membership: Individuals and agencies, approximately 3,000. Membership is open to all persons and agencies actively interested in public welfare services and work. Annual dues: regular, $2; associate, $2; contributing, $5; agency, $25.

Purpose: To provide technical, consultant, and advisory services to legislative and administrative authorities and to public welfare officials; to act as a clearinghouse for the exchange of thought and experience in the public welfare field and to make available information and reports of value to those actively engaged in this field; to develop high standards of public welfare personnel; and to inform public opinion of the fundamental importance of welfare work in present-day government.

Activities: Holds annual meetings. Maintains close contact with public welfare developments in various sections of the country and with federal welfare and relief programs; makes surveys, plans organization and administration, occasionally loaning a member of the staff; assists in securing trained personnel; and participates in regional and state conferences. Operates two sections known as the National Council of State Public Assistance and Welfare Administrators and the National Council of Local Welfare Administrators.

Publications: *Public Welfare News*, monthly; free to members. Numerous pamphlets and bulletins ranging in price from 5¢ to $1.50.

Staff: Full-time paid employees, 16, of whom 2 spend major time in field work; part-time paid employees, 3.

Finances: Estimated annual value of unpaid committee services, $5,000. For the calendar year 1939, income totaled $70,000 and expenditures aggregated $68,000.

ASSOCIATION OF CHURCH SOCIAL WORKERS

(1934); 1441 Cleveland Ave., Chicago, Ill.; Ruth Erwin, Executive Secretary.

Membership: Individuals, 730, in 44 states, the District of Columbia, Hawaii, and 3 foreign countries. Initial registration fee, $3; annual dues, $2 (in 1942 and thereafter, $3).

Purpose: To establish and uphold professional standards; and to certify accredited church social workers.

Activities: Formulation of standards for the certification of social workers employed under church auspices. Annual meeting at same time and place as National Conference of Social Work (see p. 189).

Publications: *Church Social Worker* (mimeo.), quarterly; free; Ruth Erwin, editor. *1940 Report and Directory*, 52 pp., 15¢.

Staff: Part-time paid employee, 1.

Finances: Estimated annual value of space, heat, light, and similar services received without charge, $200. Balance April 1, 1940, $433.40. For the period June 15, 1939 to April 1, 1940, operations were as follows:

Total Income

Membership fees	$1,529.00

Expenditures

Salaries	$ 718.96
Travel	33.67
Communications	195.90
Office supplies	151.63
Other purposes	408.05
	$1,508.21

FAMILY WELFARE ASSOCIATION OF AMERICA

(1911); 122 East 22nd St., New York, N.Y.; Linton B. Swift, General Director.

Membership: Individuals, 706; family welfare agencies, 220, including public agencies and private sectarian and nonsectarian agencies; affiliated private state agencies, 2. Annual dues: 2 per cent of an agency's family service expenditures exclusive of relief.

Purpose: To offer to public and private family welfare agencies two types of opportunity: (1) to contribute to the development of the field of family social work as a whole; (2) to obtain a wide variety of services which are important to the functioning of a member agency in its own community.

Activities: Directs field service, educational programs, Information Exchange (Department of Studies and Information), and personnel placement. Member agencies are concerned mainly with social case work with maladjusted families. Frequently the focus of this service is on the children or adolescents who are members of the family group.

Publications: *The Family, Journal of Social Case Work*, monthly except August and September, $1.50 a year; *Highlights*, monthly except August and September, $1 a year; Maurine Boie La Barre, editor. List of other publications on request.

Staff: Full-time paid employees, 35, of whom 5 spend major time in the field.

Finances: Balance on hand December 31, 1939, $3,835.37. For the calendar year ending on that date, operations were as follows:

Income

Gifts or grants	$ 40,482.07
Membership fees	55,674.20
Publications	29,069.69
Other services	910.00
	$126,135.96

Expenditures

Salaries	$ 87,972.11
Travel	8,602.41
Communications	1,106.52
Office supplies	3,152.70
Publications	17,305.09
Rent, taxes, insurance	6,726.40
Other purposes	1,146.15
	$126,011.38

INTERNATIONAL MIGRATION SERVICE, AMERICAN BRANCH (1924); 122 East 22nd St., New York, N.Y.; Patrick Murphy Malin, American Director.

Membership: No individual membership except by financial contribution. National branches now in the United States, France, Switzerland, and Greece (others operating temporarily on reduced scale); bureaus or correspondents in most other countries. International headquarters in Geneva, Switzerland.

Purpose: As a private, permanent, world-wide organization specializing in international social case work, to aid people, including young people, whose problems require skilled assistance simultaneously in more than one country.

Activities: During the fiscal year ending June 30, 1940 the American branch served 6,806 families, estimated to have included about 7,500 persons aged 12 to 24 inclusive. Within each country the work is done through local units of other agencies, private or public, chiefly by means of voluminous correspondence. Missing relatives are located, official documents are obtained, nationality questions are answered. Naturally much of the current work is concerned with those among the refugee groups whose problems particularly require the service. Though war has hampered some of the normal activities, the organization continues as one of the very few functioning across battle lines. New tasks have also been assumed, such as the organization during the summer of 1940 of the Migration Division of the U. S. Committee for the Care of European Children and the lending of the services of the international director, George L. Warren, as executive secretary of the President's Advisory Committee on Political Refugees since 1938. The normal work includes assisting parents in one country to fulfill their obligations toward children in another, helping young migrants to adjust themselves in their new circumstances, and in cases where the death of one or both parents has occurred, facilitating the repatriation of children to relatives in the country of origin, where necessary.

Staff: Full-time paid employees, 10; part-time paid employee, 1.

Finances: Balance June 30, 1940, $8,356.90. For the fiscal year ending on that date, operations were as follows:

Total Income

Gifts for current expenses	$36,485.01

Expenditures

Salaries	$ 9,165.68
Travel	287.54
Communications	777.97
Office supplies	412.65
Printing and publicity	1,011.93
Rent, insurance, etc.	2,043.32
Refugee children work in Germany	3,534.37
International headquarters	14,109.77
Other purposes	420.59
	$31,763.82

NATIONAL ASSOCIATION OF GOODWILL INDUSTRIES, INC. (1905); 89 Shawmut Ave., Boston, Mass.; Oliver A. Friedman, Executive Secretary, 2102 West Pierce St., Milwaukee, Wis.; John B. McGee, Young People's Director at Morgan Memorial, 89 Shawmut Ave., Boston.

Membership: Local organizations in 99 cities in the United States and 6 cities in Canada. The local units are generally incorporated in the state of their domicile and are autonomous institutions whose financial and other affairs are wholly distinct from those of the national organization, which is not a controlling agency.

Purpose: To provide employment, training, and rehabilitation for handicapped persons, helping them to attain the highest physical, intellectual, vocational, social, moral, and cultural usefulness of which they are capable.

Activities: The autonomous local units operate various small nonprofit industries, generally involving hand work or the use of simple tools or machinery, and frequently devoted to the salvage of used or worn articles and materials in need of repair or renovation. Some of them also operate homes for transients. Commonly provision is made for religious and recreational exercises, and extensive general relief work is carried on, partly by donating useful products of the industries to those in need of them. The extent of service to youth varies in different localities. For example, the Boston local unit, incorporated as the Morgan Memorial Corporation Industries and Stores, Inc., maintains a house for young men and a settlement house for underprivileged children; participates in summer camp and city fresh-air activities for the welfare of children; and engages in medical, dental, and legal welfare work for both old and young persons.

Publications: *The Goodwill*, quarterly, free. *A Manual of Goodwill Industries* (Boston: Morgan Memorial Goodwill Press, 1935); *Purposes and Policies of Goodwill Industries*, 1936, 65 pp., 25¢.

Staff: Full-time paid employees, 2, of whom 1 spends major time in the field.

Finances: For the calendar year 1939 the budget was approximately $4,475,000. For the same year, 77 cities reported paying an aggregate of $2,883,159 in wages. The Boston unit showed assets and liabilities of $1,770,191; its operating budget for that year was $841,090.

NATIONAL CONFERENCE OF SOCIAL WORK

(1870); 82 North High St., Columbus, Ohio; Howard R. Knight, General Secretary.

Membership: Individuals interested in social work, approximately 7,000; local institutions, about 400. Institutional members pay dues of $25 a year. Individual memberships are of four classes: contributing, dues indeterminate above $10; sustaining, $10; regular, $5 or $3, depending on services desired (see publications).

Purpose: To facilitate discussion of the problems and methods of practical human improvement; to increase the efficiency of agencies and institutions devoted to this cause; and to disseminate information. The conference does not formulate platforms.

Activities: Annual national conventions for the discussion of a wide variety of social problems and issues. There are now five permanent sections: Social Case Work, Social Group Work, Community Organization, Social Action, and Public Welfare Administration. There are special committees for the 1940 meeting on the following subjects: delinquency, education for social work, interstate migration, national health program, older children, refugees, social aspects of housing, social work in rural communities, and unmarried parenthood. The annual convention is accompanied by meetings of numerous "asssociate and special groups," including the following in 1940:

American Association for Applied Psychology; American Association of Medical Social Workers (see p. 170); American Association on Mental Deficiency (see p. 202); American Association of Personal Finance Companies, Committee on Social Relations; American Association of Psychiatric Social Workers; American Association of Schools of Social Work; American Association of Social Workers (see p. 185); American Association of Social Work Students; American Association for the Study of Group Work (see p. 185); American Association of Visiting Teachers (see p. 116); American Council on Community Self-Help Exchanges; American Foundation for the Blind (see p. 204); American Home Economics Association (see p. 120), Social Welfare and Public Health Department; American Legion, National Child Welfare Division (see p. 196); American National Red Cross (see p. 186); American Public Welfare Association (see p. 187); American Social Hygiene Association (see p. 174).

Association of the Junior Leagues of America (see p. 106); Association of Leisure Time Educators (see p. 157); Big Brother and Big Sister Organizations of the United States and Canada; Birth Control Federation of America (see p. 175); Child Welfare League of America (see p. 197); Church Conference of Social Work; Conference on Immigration Policy; Council of Women for Home Missions; Episcopal Social Work Conference; Family Welfare Association of America (see p. 187); Homemaker-Housekeeper Service; Indian Forum; Joint Committee of Trade Unions in Social Work; Legal Aid Group; Life Insurance Adjustment Bureau.

National Association for Aid to Dependent Children (see p. 197); National Association of Day Nurseries (see p. 198); National Association of Goodwill Industries (see p. 188); National Association of Training Schools; National Board, Young Women's Christian Associations (see p. 28); National Child Labor Committee (see p. 199); National Committee for Mental Hygiene (see p. 176); National Committee on Volunteers in Social Work; National Council on Naturalization and Citizenship; National Council for the Physically Handicapped (see p. 206); National Council, Young Men's Christian Associations (see p. 27); National Girls Work Council; National Institute Conference on International Institutes, Local Councils, and Leagues for the Foreign-Born; National Probation Association (see p. 210); National Society for Crippled Children (see p. 206); National Society for the Prevention of Blindness (see p. 180); National Travelers Aid Association (see p. 193); National Tuberculosis Association (see p. 181); Salvation Army (see p. 193); Social Service Exchange Committee; Social Work Publicity Council; Social Work Today.

Publications: *Conference Bulletin*, quarterly; 50¢ a year, free to members. Annual proceedings, free to members paying annual dues of $5 or more, $3 a copy to other purchasers.

Staff: Full-time paid employees, 7.

Finances: Approximate annual budget, $45,000.

NATIONAL FEDERATION OF SETTLEMENTS, INC. (1911); 147 Avenue B, New York, N.Y.; Lillie M. Peck, Secretary.

Membership: Consists of 156 local settlement houses or similar institutions in 24 states; 11 state and city federations; 168 individuals who subscribe $5 yearly to obtain publications; and 104 individuals who subscribe $2 yearly for staff membership.

Purpose: To federate the existing social settlements, neighborhood houses, and similar organizations for the purpose of promoting the welfare of the settlements and of the neighborhoods in which they are located; to establish, maintain, and encourage the development of social settlements in conjunction with the people of the various neighborhoods; to organize and maintain conferences, groups, investigations, studies, and similar activities; to act in an advisory capacity to social settlements and neighborhood houses throughout the world.

Activities: Maintains central office for collection and compilation of material; aids departments and divisions in joint study and conference; renders consultation service; issues publications; organizes annual and regional conferences and institutes; promotes field service. Serves youth through constituent members and through the Boys' and Girls' Work Division. Maintains a Music Division, a Social Security Department, and committees on camp, housing, participation of young people, peace education, race relations, and visual arts. Holds annually a national conference and regional conferences of the Boys' and Girls' Work Division. Holds membership in the National Education-Recreation Council. The federation brings together the staff workers responsible for the activities of young people in the Boys' and Girls' Work Division for conference and study, furnishes advisory service to settlements, and promotes interchange of experience in work with youth. The Committee on Participation of Young People promotes the organization of young people's groups in various cities, intersettlement councils, and exchange of visits. In 1939, 150 representatives of young people's groups met together at the conference of this organization. Member settlements operate 78 camps for adults and young people.

Publications: *Round Table* (publication of the Boys' and Girls' Work Division) and general bulletins, mimeographed publications issued monthly to members only. *The Neighborhood in Nation Building*, by Robert A. Woods, 1923, 348 pp., $1; *Settlement Primer*, by Mary Kingsbury Simkhovitch, revised 1936, 68 pp., 50¢; *Health Insurance with Medical Care: The British Experience*, by Dr. Douglass W. Orr and Jean Walker Orr, 1938, $2.50; *Adventures in Camping*, 1940, 48 pp., 50¢.

Staff: Full-time paid employees, 3, of whom 1 spends part time in field work. NYA workers, 2.

Finances: Endowment fund, $500. Value of equipment at national headquarters, $650. Estimated annual value of unpaid services, $2,000 to $3,000. Balance on hand December 31, 1939, $2,322.09. For the calendar year ending on that date, operations were as follows:

Income

Gifts or grants	$ 90.00
Membership fees	7,819.57
Publications	153.35
Other services	600.35
Other sources	15.80
	$8,679.07

Expenditures

Salaries	$6,758.09
Travel	503.79
Communications	459.82
Office supplies	204.41
Publications	136.04
Rentals	300.00
Other purposes	475.44
	$8,837.59

The foregoing covers the general fund only. Departments having separate budgets, of the approximate size indicated, are: Board of Directors, $500; Social Security Department, $158; Boys' Work Division, $22. The aggregate unexpended balances of the general fund and the separate departments, as of December 31, 1939, were $3,142.07.

NATIONAL FLORENCE CRITTENTON MISSION (1882); 408 Duke St., Alexandria, Va.; Dr. Robert S. Barrett, President.

Membership: Sixty-five Florence Crittenton Homes located throughout the United States, with a total capacity of 1,635 girls and 1,331 babies.

Purpose: To provide necessary and suitable maternal and infant care for unmarried girl mothers and their babies.

Activities: Unmarried girl mothers are given maintenance, care, and training, usually for a period of six months, and assisted in finding satisfactory places thereafter. During 1939 the homes cared for a total of 4,359 girls and 2,811 babies; there were 2,011 births.

Publications: *Bulletin*, quarterly; annual reports (the 1939 report is a pamphlet of 20 pages). *Fifty*

Years' Work with Girls, 1883–1933, by Otto Wilson and Robert S. Barrett, 1933, 513 pp.

Staff: All national headquarters work is done by the officers and staff of the local unit at Alexandria, Va., which functions as a national headquarters.

Finances: At the end of 1939 the aggregate value of real estate for the 65 homes was reported as $3,440,569.50. The aggregate of invested funds was $2,423,007.74. For the calendar year 1939 aggregate income was $727,208.72, and aggregate expenditures $721,208.72. The same items for the National Mission (headquarters) were as follows: real estate, $30,549.57; invested funds, $398,292.22; income $21,260.95; expenditures, $18,374.57.

NATIONAL INFORMATION BUREAU, INC.
(1918); 330 West 42nd St., New York, N.Y.; Leonard J. Cushing, Secretary.

Membership: A nonprofit corporation having 30 directors and a membership of 676 foundations, community chests, chambers of commerce, trade associations, firms, corporations, and individuals.

Purpose: To cooperate with all persons philanthropically inclined, in an effort to make gifts and contributions produce maximum social benefits, by means of a system of accrediting and approving national, interstate, and international nongovernmental social agencies and civic and philanthropic enterprises which fulfill certain standards regarding organization, responsibility, and efficiency.

Activities: Furnishes its members with impartial reports concerning the purposes and practices of specific organizations within the scope of its field; encourages standardization of business and accounting practices by these organizations; declines to approve organizations using any one of several unethical methods of soliciting or collecting funds or of advertising their activities. Operates to protect the public from fraudulent, wasteful, or unnecessary appeals for charitable gifts.

Publications: *Giver's Guide to National Philanthropies* (21 pp.), a descriptive directory of more than 100 approved national organizations, published annually; free to members. Descriptive leaflets and periodic press releases.

Staff: Full-time paid employees, 8; part-time paid employees, 2, of whom 1 spends major time in the field.

Finances: Value of equipment at national headquarters, $1,500. Balance on hand December 31, 1939, $4,534. For the calendar year ending on that date, operations were as follows:

Total Income

Gifts or grants $18,255

Expenditures

Salaries	$14,466
Travel	193
Communications	290
Office supplies	287
Publications	92
Rent, taxes, insurance	1,000
Additions to equipment	158
Other purposes	144
	$16,630

NATIONAL SOCIAL WORK COUNCIL (1920); 50 West 50th St., New York, N.Y.; David H. Holbrook, Secretary.

Membership: Constituent national organizations, 29: American Association for Labor Legislation; American Country Life Association (see p. 90); American National Red Cross (see p. 186); American Public Welfare Association (see p. 187); American Social Hygiene Association (see p. 174); Boy Scouts of America (see p. 21); Boys' Clubs of America (see p. 22); Camp Fire Girls (see p. 23); Child Welfare League of America (see p. 197); Community Chests and Councils; Council of Jewish Federations and Welfare Funds (see p. 57); Family Welfare Association of America (see p. 187); Girl Scouts (see p. 24); National Association of Legal Aid Organizations; National Jewish Welfare Board (see p. 62); National Travelers Aid Association (see p. 193); National Board, Young Women's Christian Associations (see p. 28); National Child Labor Committee (see p. 199); National Committee for Mental Hygiene (see p. 176); National Conference of Catholic Charities (see p. 51); National Society for the Prevention of Blindness (see p. 180); National Consumers League (see p. 215); National Council, Young Men's Christian Associations (see p. 27); National Health Council (see p. 177); National Organization for Public Health Nursing (see p. 179); National Probation Association (see p. 210); National Recreation Association (see p. 165); National Tuberculosis Association (see p. 181); Social Work Publicity Council.

Purpose: To help national social work agencies, groups of such agencies, and formal organizations of such agencies representing social interests to exchange information more readily; to provide for regular conference between leaders; to provide, through its committees, for the investigation and study of common problems.

Activities: Conducts monthly meetings and committee meetings of representatives of the constituent organizations at which information is exchanged between the members. The council has sponsored a few committees, such as the Committee on Care of Transient and Homeless.

Publications: *A Study of the Services and Support of Eleven National Agencies*, prepared by Committee on Contributions to National Agencies from Com-

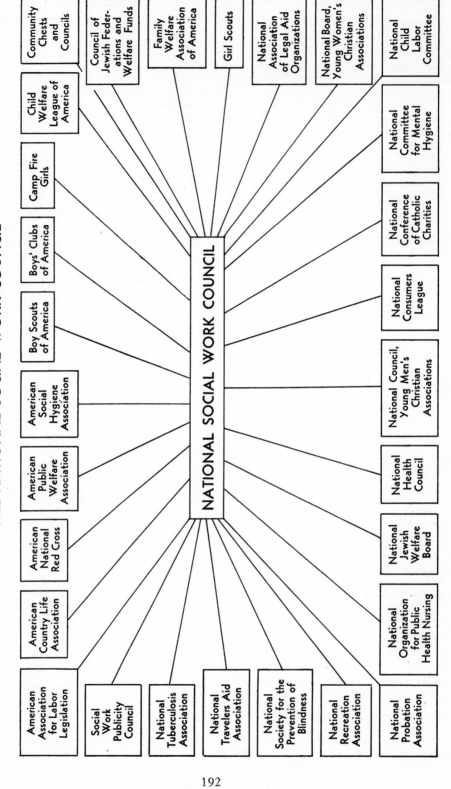

Chart VII
THE NATIONAL SOCIAL WORK COUNCIL

NATIONAL SOCIAL WORK COUNCIL

Community Chests and Councils

Council of Jewish Federations and Welfare Funds

Family Welfare Association of America

Girl Scouts

National Association of Legal Aid Organizations

National Board, Young Women's Christian Associations

National Child Labor Committee

Child Welfare League of America

Camp Fire Girls

Boys' Clubs of America

Boy Scouts of America

American Social Hygiene Association

American Public Welfare Association

American National Red Cross

American Country Life Association

American Association for Labor Legislation

Social Work Publicity Council

National Tuberculosis Association

National Travelers Aid Association

National Society for the Prevention of Blindness

National Recreation Association

National Probation Association

National Organization for Public Health Nursing

National Jewish Welfare Board

National Health Council

National Council, Young Men's Christian Associations

National Consumers League

National Conference of Catholic Charities

National Committee for Mental Hygiene

192

munity Chest Cities, 39 pp.; circulated from the office of the council.

Staff: Full-time paid employees, 2.

Finances: Value of equipment at national headquarters, $1,000. Balance on hand December 31, 1939, $234.08. For the calendar year ending on that date, operations were as follows:

	Income
Gifts or grants	$12,470.00
Publications	377.83
	$12,847.83

	Expenditures
Salaries	$10,100.00
Travel	525.16
Office supplies	636.86
Publications	714.37
Rent, taxes, insurance	1,433.13
Additions to equipment	175.55
	$13,585.07

NATIONAL TRAVELERS AID ASSOCIATION
(1917); 425 Fourth Ave., New York, N.Y.; Bertha McCall, General Director.

Membership: Travelers Aid Societies covering 509 cities, 97; cooperating representatives giving intercity service in 1,374 cities with a population of 2,500 or over, 1,040; Canadian, Mexican, and foreign representatives, 339. The above figures are as of March 1940.

Purpose: To stimulate the development and coordination of essential community services for moving, nonresident people, including case work service, temporary relief, public assistance, medical care, employment opportunity, and travel service; to study transiency and the causes and effects of mobility.

Activities: Renders individualized assistance and counseling for the protection of inexperienced and handicapped travelers and clients of other social agencies arriving, departing, or in transit through the city; investigates local juveniles having difficulty in other cities and expedites their return after the difficulty causing the transiency has been identified; stimulates community planning to prevent youth transiency; assists local parents in finding children who have run away.

Publications: *The Transient*, quarterly; 50¢ a year.

Staff: Full-time paid employees, 10, of whom 3 spend a major part of the time in the field.

Finances: Approximate annual budget, $35,000.

SALVATION ARMY, THE (1865); 120–130 West
14th St., New York, N.Y.; Commissioner Edward J. Parker, National Secretary.

Membership: Individuals in the United States,

242,449, including the membership of the following junior organizations: Life-Saving Scouts of the World (boys aged 12 to 16), 2,069; Life-Saving Guards of the World (girls aged 12 to 16), 6,233; Young People's Legion (boys and girls, 11 to 18), 32,904; Corps Cadet Brigade (boys and girls, 13 to 18), 9,857.

Purpose: To lead men and women into a proper understanding of their relationship to God, with particular regard for the erring, the bewildered, and the unfortunate; to effect the spiritual and moral reformation of all who need it and the reclamation of the vicious, criminal, dissolute, and degraded; to visit the poor and lowly and sick and to preach the gospel and disseminate Christian truth by means of open-air and indoor meetings.

Activities: Maintains an evangelical organization, with a military form of government, including a vast and diversified system of social service, embracing in the United States 4,464 officers, 1,641 constituent units, and 300 institutions of various types, including 36 maternity homes for unmarried girl mothers, 11 young women's residences for self-supporting girls, 9 children's homes and hospitals for orphans, and many homes for the aged, hotels for working people (some for men and some for women), and other types of social institutions and services. Boys' clubs provide group and individual athletics, hiking, vocational training, artcraft, community service activities, nature study, instrumental and vocal music, civics, and first-aid instruction. The junior organizations mentioned under membership also provide instruction and practice in handcrafts, drawing, woodcraft, games, group singing, and religious training under competent leadership. Many of the city centers have gymnasiums and swimming pools. There are 38 summer camps for boys and girls, generally located within convenient access of cities.

Publications: *The War Cry*, weekly; $3.50 a year; issued in four regional editions from New York, Chicago, Atlanta, and San Francisco, with a total circulation of approximately 240,000. *The Young Soldier*, weekly; $1 a year. Numerous books and pamphlets, free or at nominal prices. List on request.

Finances: The national office is supported by appropriations from the four regional headquarters.

SEAMEN'S CHURCH INSTITUTE OF AMERICA
(1907); 281 Fourth Ave., New York, N.Y.; Eugene V. Myers, President; Ruth W. Talmage, Secretary.

Membership: Individuals, 103 contributing members; local affiliated institutes, 14, in Philadelphia, San Francisco, Newport, San Pedro, Port Arthur, Houston, New Orleans, Boston, Tampa, Mobile, Charleston, Honolulu, Stockton, and in the federal hospital at Fort Stanton in New Mexico.

Purpose: To promote religious and philanthropic work among seamen and boatmen in all parts of the

United States of America and its dependencies and protectorates.

Activities: The 14 local institutes serve seamen coming ashore at their respective ports, providing such services as lodging, care of mail, checking of baggage, deposit of money for safekeeping, religious services, entertainments, employment service afloat and ashore, visiting by chaplains on shipboard and in hospitals and jails, distribution of reading matter, distribution of clothing, relief loans and free meals to the destitute. The hospital at Fort Stanton, N.M., is maintained for seamen disabled by tuberculosis contracted in line of duty; a chaplain ministers to their religious and social needs. Several of the local institutes set aside special rooms to be used for reading and social purposes by young sailors.

Publications: The national office publishes only occasional free descriptive leaflets. The Seamen's Church Institute of Philadelphia has an annual publication called the *Crow's Nest*, 15¢ a copy; Rev. P. R. Stockman, editor, 211 Walnut St., Philadelphia, Pa. *Seamen's Church Institute of America* is a mimeographed leaflet describing the organization.

Staff: Part-time paid employee, 1.

Finances: Estimated annual value of unpaid staff services, $1,060. Endowment funds, $6,800. Balance on hand December 31, 1939, $61.01. For the calendar year ending on that date, operations were as follows:

Income

Gifts or grants	$ 513.50
Membership fees	47.00
Other services	598.54
Other sources	449.98
	$1,609.02

Expenditures

Salaries	$ 940.00
Travel	41.05
Office supplies	70.40
Rent, taxes, insurance	75.00
Addition to equipment	111.82
Other purposes	430.00
	$1,668.27

VOLUNTEERS OF AMERICA (1896); 34 West 28th St., New York, N.Y.; Gen. Ballington Booth, Commander-in-Chief; Col. Charles B. Booth, National Secretary.

Membership: Local service units, 104 stations or missions; industrial branches and homes, 74.

Purpose: To serve the poor and unchurched in evangelistic and welfare effort.

Activities: Provides mission services, homes for children, homes and clubs for girls, emergency homes for stranded families, maternity homes for girls, homes for the aged, day nurseries, and industrial homes for men. Operates 18 summer health camps for tired mothers and young children. Sunday School and Christian Companionship League activities have an enrollment of approximately 4,300. Cares for prisoners' families and for paroled and discharged men through a subsidiary organization known as the Volunteer Prison League.

Publications: *Volunteers' Gazette*, monthly; $1 a year.

Staff: Full-time paid employees at headquarters, 11.

Finances: The annual aggregate expenditures of the national organization and its local units are about $1,400,000.

TABLE XXI

STATISTICS OF ORGANIZATIONS IN THE FIELD OF SOCIAL WORK

Organization	Year Founded	Approximate Aggregate Membership (individuals)	Number of Members under 25 Years of Age	Total Employees on Head-quarters Staff	Aggregate Endowment of National Headquarters	Plant and Equipment (headquarters only)	Approximate Annual Budget (headquarters only)
American Association of Social Workers	1921	11,500	...	14	$ ...	$ ...	$ 65,300
American Association for the Study of Group Work	1936	824	...	1	none[a]	200	3,300
American National Red Cross	1881	7,139,263[b]	8,588,398[c]	941	14,647,446[d]	...	15,400,000
American Public Welfare Association	1930	3,000[e]	...	19	none	...	70,000
Association of Church Social Workers	1934	730	...	1	...	...	1,800
Family Welfare Association of America	1911	222[f]		35	...	...	126,100
International Migration Service, American Branch	1924	...		...	...	...	36,500
National Association of Goodwill Industries	1905	105[f]		2	...	...	4,475,000[g]
National Conference of Social Work	1870	7,000		7	...	...	45,000
National Federation of Settlements	1911	156[f]		3	500	650	9,500
National Florence Crittenton Mission	1882	65[f]	...	h	i	30,550[j]	21,300[j]
National Information Bureau	1918	676[e]	...	10	none	1,500	18,300
National Social Work Council	1920	29[f]	...	2	...	1,000	13,600
National Travelers Aid Association	1917	97[f]	...	...	...	...	35,000
Salvation Army	1865	242,449	51,063[k]	...	...	...	...
Seamen's Church Institute of America	1907	103	...	1	6,800	...	1,700
Volunteers of America	1896	178[f]	...	11	...	...	1,400,000[g]

a The organization has reserve funds of $745.
b Adult membership only.
c Membership of the American Junior Red Cross.
d Also general and restricted funds totaling $22,581,062.
e Includes agencies as well as individuals.
f Number of constituent bodies.

g Aggregate of all local units.
h National headquarters work is carried on by the staff of the local unit in Alexandria, Va.
i The National Mission at Alexandria, Va., has invested funds of $398,292.
j Figures for the National Mission at Alexandria, Va.
k Members up to 18 years of age only.

XXI. Child Welfare Associations

Child welfare work was once conceived of as consisting exclusively of the care and education of orphans or dependent children of tender age. Today it assumes a broader meaning, to include concern for the welfare of all children, even though their parents be living and their family relationships not disrupted.

Industrial and social changes have made inroads upon the family as a unit for the care of children, especially among the lower-income classes. The entrance of the mothers of young children into gainful employment necessitates the existence of some social agency to provide for the care of children during working hours.

Such institutions as day nurseries and nursery schools are now rapidly developing and probably face an expansive future—for there is need for agencies well equipped to assume responsibility for the child during a part of his waking hours at an age much earlier than that at which the regular public schools now undertake their educative function.

Relatively recent studies in psychology, psychiatry, and mental hygiene have demonstrated that the care and education of the child in his earliest years have greater influence on his subsequent development than was formerly supposed. The character and ability of the adult population a generation hence can be profoundly affected by provision for scientific and sympathetic child care in our time.

The evils of child labor, long widespread and long denounced by far-visioned social workers, have been reduced somewhat in recent years by industrial changes and by legislation. But the child labor amendment to the United States Constitution still awaits ratification by a few states before adoption, and harmful drudgery for children still persists in many places, particularly in certain types of commercialized agriculture where families of transient laborers are employed to do a heavy volume of tedious hand work at short rush seasons, as in sugar-beet production, berry growing, and fruit farming.

There is still much socially undesirable activity of underprivileged children in the so-called street trades which verge upon mendicancy. There is still opportunity for the withdrawal of children from occupations which render childhood drab and which deprive it of precious time and energy which might otherwise be spent in healthful, joyous, and educative pursuits which are the birthright of every child.

Cross references: Section XIV, Commercial and "Service" Clubs, pp. 102–5; Section XX, Organizations in the Field of Social Work, pp. 184–95; Section XXII, Organizations Serving Handicapped Youth, pp. 202–8, especially National Society for Crippled Children, p. 206. *See also:* American Association of Visiting Teachers, p. 116; American Camping Association, p. 153; American School Health Association, p. 173; American Society of Dentistry for Children, p. 174; Association for Childhood Education, p. 124; Catholic Students' Mission Crusade, p. 46; Christ Child Society, p. 46; National Kindergarten Association, p. 135.

AMERICAN LEGION, NATIONAL CHILD WELFARE DIVISION (1925); 777 North Meridian St., Indianapolis, Ind.; Emma C. Puschner, Director.

Membership: The National Child Welfare Committee consists of representatives from each of the 58 state and territorial departments of the American Legion (see p. 81). In each department there is a child welfare chairman and committee, usually made up of representatives of the American Legion, the American Legion Auxiliary, the Forty and Eight, and the Eight and Forty. Within each department there are district, county, and post child welfare organizations similarly composed. Thus the organization functions on the national, state, county, and community levels.

Purpose: To educate the membership within the Legion and the citizens at large to the conditions and needs of children in the United States and to bring to their attention the best information concerning standards for child care and protection; to assist Legion organizations in the states to secure enactment and improvement of state child welfare laws and provisions; to give temporary service and aid to children, not alone children of veterans, whose needs are not being supplied by local, state, or federal facilities.

Activities: Makes studies of child welfare conditions throughout the United States and disseminates the facts, through the 58 departments of the American Legion, to the 11,691 local posts of the Legion and the 8,000 units of the American Legion Auxiliary.

During the year ending June 30, 1939, actual service was rendered to 442,489 children, of whom 395,342 were children of World War veterans, at a cost of $1,968,632.99, supplementary to the existing programs of aid from governmental and charitable sources. Gives attention to the prevention and treatment of juvenile delinquency and aid and support to the best standards for juvenile court and probation procedure. Inspects and surveys state institutions for the care of delinquent youth and makes recommendations for improvement. Cooperates with existing agencies of child welfare and assists them in the proper performance of their functions.

Publications: The two monthly periodicals of the American Legion. *A Guide for Child Welfare Procedure*, revised annually, 100 pp.; annual report of the National Child Welfare Committee and Division. Booklets: *Our Children's Future*, on the formation and functioning of community coordinating councils; *Building Asset Citizens*, on recommended objectives for state training or industrial schools; *Insurance of Child Health through a Program of Immunization.*

Staff: Full-time paid employees at national headquarters, 6.

Finances: The annual budget of the division is approximately $112,000. About $81,000 of the annual income is derived from the American Legion endowment funds, and about $31,000 is derived from gifts for current expenses. The annual expenditures include about $16,000 for salaries and about $2,000 for travel.

CHILD WELFARE LEAGUE OF AMERICA, INC.
(1921); 130 East 22nd St., New York, N.Y.; Howard W. Hopkirk, Executive Director.

Membership: Constituent agencies, 168.

Purpose: To band together in a national movement agencies, institutions, public departments, and individuals for promotion of better standards of protection and care of children whose families are inadequate or who require foster care; and to act as spokesman for the interests of disadvantaged children.

Activities: Field service; studies of community programs in child welfare and of single agencies; community planning in children's work; assistance to non-social service groups; intersociety and international service; case work training; information and correspondence service; regional conferences; institutes for executives; and lending libraries. Has no direct contact with children, but strives to increase the efficiency of its member organizations, which deal with children from infancy to 18 years of age.

Publications: *Bulletin*, monthly; $1 a year. *Child Welfare Services under Social Security Act*, 40 pp.; *A Study Home: Its Program and Function*, by Richardson L. Rice, 18 pp.; *Directory of Members*,

50¢; *Health Program for Children in Foster Homes*, revised 1939, 24 pp., 40¢; *Purpose and Form of Organizations in the Field of Child Care and Protection—For Governing Boards*, 1938, 23 pp., 35¢. Numerous other bulletins, pamphlets, and reprints ranging in price from 10¢ to 75¢.

Staff: Full-time paid employees, 9.

Finances: Operating balance December 31, 1939, $377.53. For the calendar year ending on that date, operations were as follows:

Income

Gifts or grants	$ 9,003.96
Membership fees	17,582.77
Publications	2,944.90
Other services	998.54
Contributions	12,701.96
Other sources	636.77
	$43,868.90

Expenditures

Salaries	$27,152.82
Travel	2,301.12
Communications	595.91
Office supplies	5,642.99
Publications	3,774.15
Rentals	2,205.96
Other purposes	295.25
	$41,968.20

MOTHERS' AID ASSOCIATION
See National Association for Aid to Dependent Children (p. 197).

NATIONAL ASSOCIATION FOR AID TO DEPENDENT CHILDREN
(1920); 1208 State Office Bldg., Columbus, Ohio; Esther McClain, Chairman.

Originally known as the Mothers' Aid Association.

Membership: Individuals, 150; annual dues, $1.

Purpose: To set forth those principles that need to be known and used to build a sound program of child care and protection and to interpret the needs and trends within the field; to prepare and distribute literature that will aid in the development of standards.

Activities: Arranges programs of an educational nature at national and state conferences. Various committees of the organization are actively engaged in such matters as (1) arranging a program and exhibits at the National Conference of Social Work (see p. 189), (2) preparation of educational material and issuing of quarterly bulletins, (3) study and promotion of adequate legislation, and (4) securing key people in the various states to promote standards of child care and to develop programs on these matters at state welfare conferences.

Publications: Educational leaflet, *Aid to Dependent Children.*

Staff: The 14 executive committee members and 34 state representatives all contribute their services to the association.

Finances: Approximate annual budget, $150, which is spent for educational material, printing, and postage.

NATIONAL ASSOCIATION OF DAY NURSERIES, INC. (1938); 122 East 22nd St., New York, N.Y.; Elizabeth Woodruff Clark, Executive Director.

This organization was known as the National Federation of Day Nurseries prior to November 1938 when the Association of Day Nurseries of New York City was merged with it.

Membership: Voting agency members, 97; associate, 10; and provisional, 6.

Purpose: To coordinate the work of day nurseries and develop a national strength which will raise the standards of child care throughout the country.

Activities: Through field counseling with member and nonmember agencies, promotes better services to children and their families. Conducts conferences, meetings, and discussions; distributes bulletins, pamphlets, exhibits, and other pertinent materials on child care; carries on research in the day nursery field.

Publications: *The Day Nursery*, 9 issues annually; free to members, $1 a year to nonmembers; Agnes E. Benedict, editor. *List of Furnishings and Equipment for a Day Nursery of 40 Children*, 15¢; *Place of the Day Nursery in the Community Welfare Program*, by Winifred Allen, 15¢.

Staff: Full-time paid employees, 9, of whom 1 spends major time in the field; part-time paid employees, 2.

Finances: Reserve funds, $14,866.42. Value of equipment at national headquarters, $749.91. Operating balance September 30, 1939, $749.95. For the fiscal year ending on that date, operations were as follows:

Income

Gifts or grants	$ 7,645.80
Membership fees	2,504.01
Publications	221.19
Other services	416.16
Investments	1,056.50
Other sources	7,464.35
	$19,308.01

Expenditures

Salaries	$14,545.14
Travel	376.24
Communications	851.01
Office supplies	1,139.45
Publications	747.45
Rent, taxes, insurance, etc.	1,011.00
Additions and repairs	613.27
Other purposes	1,086.58
	$20,370.14

NATIONAL ASSOCIATION FOR NURSERY EDUCATION (1925); Publications Distribution Center, West 514 East Hall, State University of Iowa, Iowa City, Iowa; Christine Glass, Secretary-Treasurer, Glass Nursery School, 829 Union Ave., St. Louis, Mo.

Membership: Individuals, 450, throughout the entire United States and a few in Canada. Membership dues: life, $100; active, $2; associate, $1.

Purpose: To disseminate information about nursery schools and to provide a medium for the exchange of ideas concerning the education and developmental welfare of early childhood.

Activities: Biennial national conferences. The work of the organization is carried on through the following committees: publications, publicity, research, legislative, standards and values, nursery school building, related interests, special studies, housing, and membership.

Publications: *Proceedings of the 7th Conference, 1937*, 40¢. *Minimum Essentials of Nursery School Education*, 30¢; *A Bibliography of Nursery School Education, 1935–39*, 40¢; *Nursery School Teaching*, 25¢; *How to Start Publicity for Nursery School Education in Your Community*, 25¢; and numerous mimeographed pamphlets.

Staff: One clerk in the Distribution Center.

Finances: Balance on hand October 18, 1939, $914.74. For the fiscal biennium ending on that date, operations were as follows:

Income

Membership fees	$1,135.00
Publications	159.29
Other services	114.50
	$1,408.79

Expenditures

Salaries	$ 15.00
Travel	327.95
Communications	57.62
Publications	650.13
Office supplies	79.42
Other purposes	571.63
	$1,701.75

NATIONAL BOYS AND GIRLS WEEK COMMITTEE FOR THE UNITED STATES (1924); 35 East Wacker Drive, Chicago, Ill.; S. Kendrick Guernsey, Secretary.

Membership: Individuals, 100.

Purpose: To encourage the observance of an annual Boys and Girls Week (usually in April or May) in communities throughout the United States for the purpose of focusing attention upon the boys and girls and of furthering activities tending to develop them into useful citizens.

Activities: Publicizes the annual observance of Boys and Girls Week; distributes literature designed to assist local committees in carrying through local observances. The celebration of Boys and Girls Week as observed in most communities includes eight days of parades, exhibitions, pageantry, and various other programs calling attention to the importance of various aspects of boy and girl life, such as religion, vocation, education, recreation, citizenship, health, home life, and outdoor life. Among specific results are the creation of permanent commissions on boy and girl life and the establishment of playgrounds, boys' and girls' clubs, summer camps, community centers, and Scout troops.

Publications: *Advance Herald*, announcing dates and program of the week, annually in January; *Manual of Suggestions for Daily Programs*, annually in January. These are furnished free of charge.

Finances: The chief expenses in connection with promoting the 1940 observance of Boys and Girls Week were about $210 for printing 13,000 copies of the *Manual of Suggestions for Daily Programs*, $636 for printing 72,000 copies of *Advance Herald*, and about $90 for stationery. These costs were met by Rotary International (see p. 104). Rotary also contributed the part-time services, valued at approximately $1,000, of two or three members of its staff for editorial and secretarial work.

NATIONAL CHILD LABOR COMMITTEE (1904);
419 Fourth Ave., New York, N.Y.; Courtenay Dinwiddie, General Secretary.

Membership: Individuals, 15,000.

Purpose: To protect children from harmful employment; to improve working conditions for young people; to assist in efforts to train young people for employment and to develop suitable work opportunities for them.

Activities: Works for state and federal legislation to establish a 16-year minimum age for employment during school hours, an 18-year minimum for hazardous occupations, and regulation of hours, night work, and conditions of employment. Aids efforts, legislative and otherwise, to adapt education of youth to meet modern industrial and social conditions and to promote counseling and placement services. Has had a large part in the passage of state and federal legislation which has reduced yearly employment of children under 16 by over 1,000,000. Investigates child labor and related subjects in special industries and special areas. Has recently conducted several studies of migratory agricultural workers and promoted legislation dealing with migrants. Cooperates with public and private agencies and with employers desiring to improve conditions of training or employment for children or youth. Maintains information and exhibit service.

Publications: *American Child*, 9 issues annually; free

to members; Mrs. Gertrude Folks Zimand, editor. *Pick for Your Supper*, by James E. Sidel, 67 pp., 35¢; *Children in Strawberries*, by Raymond G. Fuller, 22 pp., 25¢; *A Summer in the Country*, 39 pp., 25¢; *Child Labor Facts, 1939–1940*, by Gertrude Folks Zimand, 38 pp., 25¢; *Federal Child Labor Amendment*, 1940, 8 pp., free. List of other publications on request.

Staff: Full-time paid employees, 18, of whom 2 spend major time in the field. NYA workers, 4.

Finances: Value of plant and equipment at national headquarters, $1,308. Estimated annual value of unpaid staff services, $1,056. Reserve funds, $12,037.91. Operating balance September 30, 1939, $2,546.35. For the fiscal year ending on that date, operations were as follows:

Income

Gifts or grants	$11,583.68
Membership fees	57,810.20
Publications	320.76
Reserve funds	864.68
	$70,579.32

Expenditures

Salaries	$51,499.11
Travel	2,646.84
Communications	1,542.63
Office supplies	1,001.89
Publications	3,180.58
Rent, taxes, insurance, etc.	2,020.51
Additions to equipment	114.00
Other purposes	18,986.76
	$80,992.32

NATIONAL COUNCIL FOR MOTHERS AND BABIES (1938); 1710 Eye St., N.W., Washington, D.C.; Mrs. Gordon Wagenet, Executive Secretary.

A council and clearinghouse for organizations interested in working toward better care for mothers and babies.

Membership: National agencies and organizations, 60, including health and medical organizations and religious groups, trade unions, agricultural groups, Negro organizations, commercial and service clubs, women's clubs, educational associations, organizations in the field of social work, and child welfare associations.

Purpose: To bring to the national problem of providing better care for mothers and babies the combined strength, knowledge, and understanding of diversified national organizations in order to secure cooperation in applying economic, sociological, nutritional, and medical knowledge.

Activities: Provides consultation service and assistance with programs to state groups; distributes teaching materials from its member organizations and other sources; holds meetings of members and joint meetings with other organizations; reports to its members significant projects in the field of maternal and infant health.

Publications: *Clearing House Notes*, semimonthly; free.

Staff: Full-time paid employees, 4.

NATIONAL FEDERATION OF DAY NURSERIES

See National Association of Day Nurseries (p. 198).

SAVE THE CHILDREN FEDERATION (1932); 1 Madison Ave., New York, N.Y.; John R. Voris, President and Executive Director.

Formerly known as Save the Children Fund of America.

Membership: A nonprofit corporation of approximately 100 members, having a governing board of 27 members and in addition 20 "national sponsors" and about 12,000 contributing friends. Nonsectarian.

Purpose: To serve underprivileged children, regardless of race, color, or creed, especially in neglected and undeveloped areas where no adequate private agencies exist for the general welfare of children; to study the needs of children in America and other lands; to provide information and to arouse public opinion respecting child needs.

Activities: Works in close cooperation with the rural public schools in 50 southern mountain counties, distributing clothing to enable needy children to attend school, helping to provide hot daily lunches, sponsoring mountain demonstration schools, organizing school garden projects, and conducting vacation schools. These services touch about 50,000 children. Has national school relations committee headed by John W. Withers. Organizes mountain county committees composed of school superintendent, health officer, agricultural agent, county judge, clergy, and representatives of various organizations. Conducts county social welfare conferences. Its policy is to coordinate all available local forces to carry on social welfare work.

Publications: *Child Service Quarterly*, 10¢ a year. *Eighth Annual Report*, by John R. Voris, 1940, 12 pp.; *Saving Our Human Resources*, by Samuel J. Crumbine, M.D., 1940, 16 pp. Copies free on request.

Staff: Full-time paid employees at headquarters, 9; part-time paid employees, 3. There are 30 employees in the field in southern mountain counties.

Finances: Current balance December 31, 1939, $1,736.45. For the fiscal year ending on that date, operations of the entire organization (headquarters and field) were as follows:

Income

Gifts (cash)	$ 72,887.68
Gifts (commodities)	131,355.83
	$204,243.51

Expenditures

Salaries	$ 40,104.89
Field expenses	20,455.35
Printing and stationery	6,177.33
Letter shop work	1,502.32
Postage	6,627.93
Distribution of commodities	126,655.50
Other purposes	983.78
	$202,507.10

TABLE XXII

STATISTICS OF CHILD WELFARE ASSOCIATIONS

Organization	Year Founded	Approximate Aggregate Membership (individuals)	Total Employees on Headquarters Staff	Aggregate Endowment of National Headquarters	Plant and Equipment (headquarters only)	Approximate Annual Budget (headquarters only)
American Legion, National Child Welfare Division	1925	...	6	...	$ ...	$112,000
Child Welfare League of America	1921	168[a]	9	none	...	43,900
National Association for Aid to Dependent Children	1920	150	[b]	none	...	150
National Association of Day Nurseries	1938	113[a]	11	none[c]	750	20,400
National Association for Nursery Education	1925	450	[b]	...	...	850
National Boys and Girls Week Committee for the United States	1924	100	[d]	...	...	1,900[d]
National Child Labor Committee	1904	15,000	18	none[e]	1,308	81,000
National Council for Mothers and Babies	1938	60[a]	4	none	...	...
Save the Children Federation	1932	100[f]	42	...	...	204,200[g]

a Number of constitutent agencies.
b No paid staff.
c The organization has reserve funds of $14,866.
d All expenditures for staff and other purposes paid by Rotary International.

e The organization has reserve funds of $12,038.
f In addition about 12,000 donors contribute to the organization.
g Includes all field operations.

XXII. Organizations Serving Handicapped Youth

The blind, the deaf, and the crippled have long been the subject of public solicitude, and institutions and organizations for their education and vocational adjustment are well developed. Fortunately it is now generally realized that what such persons need most of all is opportunity to participate in so far as possible in the same educational advantages, the same recreational enjoyments, and the same vocational pursuits as their fellows who are without major physical handicaps.

To a remarkable extent these needs can be supplied. The blind can read Braille and engage in a variety of activities requiring manual and mental skill; the deaf are enabled to communicate without inconvenience and to make themselves useful and happy in a thousand places. Much credit is due to long-established societies of teachers and other workers in behalf of the handicapped, whose members strive sedulously to improve further the opportunities open to their charges.

An aspect of the problem of physical and mental handicaps which has only lately begun to receive attention is concerned with the large percentages of the population having sensory or other defects in relatively slight degree. The incidence of such slight defects may usually be detected in childhood or in early life, and they may often be either entirely eliminated or minimized by proper measures promptly taken.

It has been authoritatively estimated that three million of the thirty million school children in the United States have impairment of hearing in sufficient degree to constitute a greater or lesser handicap. A vast amount of psychic and economic loss could be averted if all such cases were detected, examined, and intelligently treated at the earliest moment. Comparable or even more alarming is the situation with regard to the impairment of vision.

Public concern for physical handicaps must be broadened beyond the small groups suffering complete sensory losses to include the much larger numbers who suffer varying degrees of sensory impairment. This is one of several factors which give point to the recommendation of the American Youth Commission that regular, periodic physical examinations should be given to all children in the schools and that a similar service should be provided for out-of-school youth.

Cross references: Section XX, Organizations in the Field of Social Work, pp. 184–95, especially National Association of Goodwill Industries, p. 188. *See also:* American Automobile Association, Safety and Traffic Engineering Department, p. 171; American Occupational Therapy Association, p. 143; National Congress of Parents and Teachers, p. 130; National Safety Council, p. 180; National Society for the Prevention of Blindness, p. 180; National Tuberculosis Association, p. 181.

AMERICAN ASSOCIATION OF INSTRUCTORS OF THE BLIND (1853); Josef G. Cauffman, Secretary-Treasurer, Lansing, Mich.

Membership: Five delegates from each residential school for the blind, three from each public school system having an enrollment of 25 or more blind pupils, one from each library for the blind, and associate, honorary, or corresponding members as elected at any meeting of the association. Annual fees, $5 an organization, plus pro rata assessment on basis of number of pupils enrolled.

Purpose: To consult regarding all problems relating to the education of the blind; to foster and promote all movements having as their aim the improvement of the means of such education.

Activities: Biennial conventions at one of the state schools for the blind, having attendance of approximately 300 delegates, with papers and addresses on various aspects of the education of the blind.

Publications: Proceedings, biennially.

Finances: Membership fees support the publication of the proceedings of the biennial convention.

AMERICAN ASSOCIATION ON MENTAL DEFICIENCY (1876); Elwyn, Pa.; Dr. E. Arthur Whitney, Secretary-Treasurer.

Membership: Individual, associate, and honorary memberships aggregate over 650.

Purpose: To study all phases of the problem of mental retardation; to advocate universal identification and registration of mental defectives in each state and county; to conduct research into the medical, psychological, and sociological aspects of the problem; to foster legislation such as marriage laws and selective sterilization.

Activities: Directs parents and child-caring agencies for mentally retarded children to the proper institutions, schools, or clinics caring for such children. Maintains committees on research (Dr. Edgar Doll, chairman, Vineland, N.J.) and education (Dr. Elise Martens, chairman, Washington, D.C.). Through committees on collaboration, public relations, standards and policy, and statistics, the association serves all children of low mentality.

Publications: From 1896 to 1940 the *Journal of Psycho-Asthenics* was published. This was succeeded in 1940 by a *Quarterly Journal;* Dr. Edward Humphreys, editor, Thiells, N.Y. Pamphlets are released from time to time.

Staff: Part-time paid employee, 1; part-time unpaid workers, 2.

Finances: Estimated annual value of unpaid staff services, $700. Cash on hand at the beginning of fiscal year, $982.18. Operations from May 1938 to May 1939 were as follows:

Income

Membership fees	$2,382.14
Publications	390.79
Other services (advertising)	255.50
Other sources	884.99
	$3,913.42

Expenditures

Salaries	$ 300.00
Communications	16.56
Publications	2,171.21
Other purposes	443.47
	$2,931.24

AMERICAN ASSOCIATION TO PROMOTE THE TEACHING OF SPEECH TO THE DEAF (1890); 1537 35th St., N.W., Washington, D.C.; Josephine B. Timberlake, Executive Secretary.

Membership: Individuals, 2,200, chiefly teachers and parents of deaf children, teachers of lip reading to the hard of hearing, and the hard of hearing themselves. Active membership fee is $2 a year.

Purpose: To promote the teaching of speech to the deaf; to aid in improving the education and social adjustment of the deaf and hard of hearing; to increase and diffuse knowledge relating to the handicap of deafness and ways by which the handicap may be overcome.

Activities: Controls the Volta Bureau, established by Alexander Graham Bell in 1887; maintains the largest library on deafness in the United States, which includes reports of all schools for the deaf, organizations for the hard of hearing, and publica-

tions on the education of the deaf in many languages; examines and reports on artificial aids to hearing; maintains an employment bureau for teachers of the deaf. The association sponsors a correspondence club for the parents of deaf children, members of which, located throughout the country, discuss their problems in "roundabout" letters; cooperates with service and health organizations; advises deaf and hard of hearing young persons regarding employment, social adjustment, and education; encourages and gives publicity to Boy and Girl Scout work for the deaf and hard of hearing; and encourages camps for deaf and hard of hearing children.

Publications: *Volta Review,* monthly; $2 a year, free to members; Josephine B. Timberlake, editor.

Staff: Full-time paid employees, 5.

Finances: Endowment fund, $258,956. For the calendar year 1939 the total income was $19,394.37, of which $8,671.54 was from endowment funds. Expenditures amounted to $18,268.21.

AMERICAN ASSOCIATION OF WORKERS FOR THE BLIND (1895); Winnetka, Ill.; Alfred Allen, Secretary-General.

Membership: Individuals, 292, in 48 states, Canada, and Hawaii.

Purpose: To consider and promote all phases of work for and in the interest of the blind and in the prevention of blindness throughout the whole of North America and the territorial and insular possessions of the United States.

Activities: Blind youth, particularly the 6,500 children in 61 residential schools for the blind, are indirect beneficiaries of the work of the association; in their interests the association has a standing Vocational Guidance Committee cooperating with a similar committee representing the American Association of Instructors of the Blind (see p. 202). Engages in efforts toward the general amelioration of blindness, the prevention of blindness, and the education of the public toward its responsibility to the blind, both young and old. Holds biennial meetings at which some time is given to consideration of the needs of young blind persons. Maintains a legislative committee and a joint finding committee, both of which cooperate with similar committees of the American Association of Instructors of the Blind.

Publications: Proceedings, issued biennially in odd-numbered years, each issue a book of about 300 pages, $3 a copy.

Staff: Headquarters and field work is unpaid. Two officers give part-time service; other officers and committee members give service as required.

Finances: Endowment fund, $363.42. Balance on hand at the end of the fiscal biennium June 21, 1937 to June 30, 1939, $3,464.02. Operations for that period were as follows:

Income

Membership fees	$1,817.00
Publications	469.75
Endowment fund	35.45
Miscellaneous	21.93
	$2,344.13

Expenditures

Travel	$ 245.57
Special awards	131.85
Office supplies	81.67
Publications	710.96
Other purposes	538.99
	$1,709.04

AMERICAN FOUNDATION FOR THE BLIND, INC. (1921); 15 West 16th St., New York, N.Y.; Robert B. Irwin, Executive Director.

Membership: Any person actively engaged in work with the blind in the United States or Canada is eligible for professional membership; any person interested in the welfare of the blind is eligible for other classes of membership.

Purpose: To promote the interests of the blind throughout the United States by means of close cooperation with all local organizations and agencies having similar objectives.

Activities: Conducts research, consultation, and field service on behalf of blind individuals and of institutions and organizations for the blind. Promotes the employment of the blind. Provides information service on legislation for the blind and on statistics of blindness. Develops mechanical appliances useful to the blind, such as improved Braille typewriter and talking books; manufactures talking books for the blind. Gives scholarships for vocational preparation to promising blind students. Maintains a reference library of 7,500 books and pamphlets relating to the blind and their welfare.

Publications: *Outlook for the Blind*, 5 issues annually; inkprint edition, 50¢ a copy or $2 a year; Braille edition (slightly abridged), 20¢ a copy or 40¢ a year. *Teachers Forum for Instructors of Blind Children*, 5 issues annually; inkprint and Braille editions, 20¢ a copy or $1 a year. *Talking Book Topics*, 4 issues annually; inkprint edition, free; recorded edition, $1 a year. *Braille Book Review: A Guide to Braille and Talking Book Publications*, 11 issues annually; Braille edition, free. Extensive list of books and pamphlets on various phases of the education, vocational adjustment, and other problems of the blind; some free and others priced at 15¢ to $3.50 a copy.

Staff: Full-time paid employees, 55.

Finances: Approximate annual budget, $110,000.

AMERICAN INSTITUTE FOR THE DEAF-BLIND (1932); 2332 Bryant Ave., Evanston, Ill; Robert H. Gault, Director General.

Membership: A nonprofit corporation having a board of 10 directors. Annual fee for regular member-

ship, $5; sustaining membership, $50. Life members pay up to $1,000 or more in a lump sum.

Purpose: To conduct fundamental research relating to the education and social amelioration of the deaf, the blind, the deaf-blind, and of those who are weak in vision or hearing or in both.

Activities: Conducts technical psychologic laboratory research aimed at: (1) enlarging the usefulness of the senses of touch and vibration; (2) discovering the intelligence and vocational aptitudes of deaf children; (3) personality studies of deaf children; (4) improving the science and art of teaching academic subjects to deaf children; and (5) establishing lip-reading ability and speech habits in deaf children. The number of persons whom the institute has attempted to serve directly to date aggregates 500, all between the ages of 4 and 20. Of these, 200 are between the ages of 12 and 20. Four hundred have been studied in the Illinois State School for the Deaf and at the institute's laboratories, 100 in the Infants' Hospital in London, England.

Publications: Reprints from scientific journals: *Experiments in the Academic Education of Adolescent Deaf Pupils*, by Louise Ebeling Dean, I (1934, 15 pp.), II (1935, 12 pp.), III (1936, 15 pp.); *On the Effect of Simultaneous Tactual-Visual Stimulation in Relation to the Interpretation of Speech*, by Robert H. Gault, 1930, 24 pp.; *A Method of Using the Gault-Teletactor to Teach Speech Rhythms*, by Raymond Carhart, 1935, 4 pp.; *Enriching the Vocabulary*, by Margaret C. Letzter, 1935, 8 pp.; *Tactual Perception of Musical Intervals*, by Louis D. Goodfellow, 1933, 6 pp.; *Implications of Vibro-Tactile Phenomena*, by Robert H. Gault, 1936, 2 pp.

Staff: Full-time paid employee, 1; part-time paid employees, 3; part-time unpaid workers, 10.

Finances: For the fiscal year April 1, 1939 to March 31, 1940, operations were approximately as follows:

Total Income

Gifts for current expenses	$4,475

Expenditures

Salaries	$3,600
Office supplies	50
Laboratory expenses	825
	$4,475

AMERICAN SOCIETY FOR THE HARD OF HEARING (1919); 1537 35th St., N.W., Washington, D.C.; Betty C. Wright, Executive Director.

Membership: Individuals, 7,000, in 122 local societies for the hard of hearing in the United States.

Purpose: To act in the national and international fields of social work for the deaf; to encourage the founding of local organizations; to spread national propaganda in the interests of the deaf and in the prevention of deafness.

Activities: Cooperates with educators, social workers, scientists, physicians, and parent-teacher groups to the end that the hard of hearing in business and social life may receive a square deal in spite of their impairment; gives advice on vocations suitable for the hard of hearing and works with leaders in vocational rehabilitation; encourages the study of lip reading. Friendship and advice are given the isolated through a correspondence club for the hard of hearing called "The Everywhere League." The society has formulated and promoted the following programs: (1) hearing tests of school children with the 4-A Audiometer; (2) retests of those believed to have a defect; (3) reports to parents of ear conditions of those children finally considered to have impaired hearing; (4) recommendations that those having ear trouble be sent to the family physician or ear clinic; (5) establishment in the schools or hospitals of otological clinics for those children unable to have private care; (6) periodic instruction in lip reading for hard of hearing children in connection with their regular grade studies; (7) special classes for the very hard of hearing in cities where large school populations warrant them. The Young People's Group of the Washington chapter offers a scholarship to a hard of hearing boy or girl. Biennial conferences are held at which there is always a young people's session.

Publications: *Hearing News*, monthly; free to members; Laura Stovel, editor. Proceedings of national conferences. Numerous pamphlets and posters, ranging in price from 5¢ to $1, on the following subjects: employment, hard of hearing children, hearing aids, inheritance of deafness, lip reading, and medical problems.

Staff: Full-time paid employees, 5; part-time paid employee, 1; part-time unpaid workers, 3.

Finances: Aggregate endowment funds, $10,847.47. Value of equipment at national headquarters, approximately $2,000; value of unpaid staff services, $200. Balance on hand January 1940, $1,150.63. Operations for the preceding year were as follows:

Income

Gifts or grants	$ 5,781.11
Membership fees	8,362.55
Publications	1,584.85
Other services	953.90
Endowment funds	355.75
Other sources	89.00
	$17,127.16

Expenditures

Salaries	$ 9,366.26
Travel	53.80
Communications	951.56
Office supplies	518.10
Publications	2,652.75
Rent	720.00
Additions to plant and equipment	34.52
Other purposes	1,693.05
	$15,990.04

AMERICAN SPEECH CORRECTION ASSOCIATION (1925); 419 Boylston St., Boston, Mass.; Samuel D. Robbins, Secretary.

Membership: Individuals, 325.

Purpose: To raise existing standards of practice among workers in the field of speech correction; to furnish this profession with responsible and authoritative leadership; and to stimulate among educators, physicians, and the general public a deeper, more intelligent interest in problems of speech correction.

Activities: Annual convention with papers and addresses by the members on their experiences in the improvements of methods of correcting speech defects.

Publications: *Journal of Speech Disorders*, quarterly; G. Oscar Russell, editor, Columbus, Ohio. Proceedings of annual conventions. *A Dictionary of Terms Dealing with Disorders of Speech* (temporarily out of print).

Staff: Part-time unpaid workers, 4, of whom 2 spend major time in the field.

Finances: Estimated annual value of unpaid staff services, $1,000. For the calendar year 1938, the approximate operations were as follows:

Income

Membership fees	$ 900
Publications	100
	$1,000

Expenditures

Communications	$ 50
Office supplies	50
Publications	800
	$ 900

INTERNATIONAL COUNCIL FOR EXCEPTIONAL CHILDREN (1922); 1221 Boston Ave., Flint, Mich.; Mrs. Beulah S. Adgate, Membership Secretary; Dorothy E. Norris, President.

Membership: Teachers, supervisors, school administrators, psychologists, and nurses, 4,600, in 82 chapters in 30 states, Canada, and Hawaii. Annual dues, $2.

Purpose: To promote the welfare and education of all types of exceptional children, including the handicapped and the gifted.

Activities: Annual conventions for the discussion of projects dealing with the social welfare and adjustment of atypical children and problems common to teachers of these classes of children.

Publications: *Journal of Exceptional Children*, 8 issues annually, October to May inclusive; free to members; Harley Z. Wooden, editor.

Staff: Full-time paid employee, 1.

Finances: Estimated annual value of unpaid staff services, $1,500.

NATIONAL COUNCIL FOR THE PHYSICALLY HANDICAPPED (1933); 2102 West Pierce St., Milwaukee, Wis.; Oliver A. Friedman, President.

A joint activity and clearinghouse of national agencies concerned with persons having physical impairments.

Membership: Eight organizations: American Society for the Hard of Hearing (see p. 204), American Occupational Therapy Association (see p. 143), Convention of American Instructors of the Deaf, National Association of the Deaf, National Association of Goodwill Industries (see p. 188), National Society for the Prevention of Blindness (see p. 180), National Rehabilitation Association (see p. 206), National Tuberculosis Association (see p. 181).

Purpose: To act as a coordinating agency and serve as a clearinghouse for member organizations.

Activities: Holds annual meetings. Assembles information and prepares the way for joint action by member agencies on policies relating to the physically handicapped. Conducts legislative activities and research in behalf of the physically handicapped. Education, vocational guidance, and employment of physically handicapped young persons are some of the problems which the member organizations as a unit are trying to solve.

NATIONAL REHABILITATION ASSOCIATION, INC. (1923); U.S. Office of Education, Federal Security Agency, Washington, D.C.; President, H. V. Bené, Arizona State Bldg., Phoenix, Ariz.; Secretary-Treasurer, Homer W. Nichols, State Capitol, Frankfort, Ky.

Membership: Individuals, 50,000. Memberships are classified as follows: individual, $1 a year; professional, $3 a year; contributing, $25; life, $100.

Purpose: To promote national and state programs of guidance, physical restoration, training, and placement in employment for all groups of handicapped persons.

Activities: Serves as a national forum in which persons engaged in work for the handicapped, representatives of organizations engaged in the promotion of the interests of special groups of the handicapped, public officials, and interested individuals may meet on common ground to assemble, study, discuss, and disseminate information concerning the problems involved in the vocational adjustment of the handicapped; seeks to enlighten people throughout the United States concerning the justice and economy of providing for the vocational adjustment of the handicapped; holds annual meetings at which persons who are authorities in their respective fields bring to the membership the best experiences along their particular lines; promotes a spirit of cooperation and a unity of purpose among the various public and private agencies and individuals interested or engaged in work for the handicapped.

Publications: *National Rehabilitation News*, 6 issues annually; $1 a year; Mrs. Kathryn D. Lewis, editor, Room 708, 600 South Michigan Ave., Chicago, Ill. The proceedings of the annual meetings are printed for distribution to the membership.

Staff: No paid staff.

Finances: Income is derived from membership fees.

NATIONAL SOCIETY FOR CRIPPLED CHILDREN (1921); 314 Masonic Temple Bldg., Elyria, Ohio; E. Jay Howenstine, Executive Secretary.

Membership: Affiliated state societies representing the active voting membership, 38; institutional members, 75. Institutional membership fee, $10 a year.

Purpose: To create state societies and cooperate with agencies, governmental and private, in establishing and carrying out a program for the care and education of the crippled child and to assist in the work in behalf of crippled adults; to direct a campaign to eliminate the preventable causes of crippling.

Activities: Holds annual conventions. Conducts campaigns for the sale of seals to help finance work for crippled children; studies and advocates state and federal legislation in behalf of crippled children and physically handicapped persons; endeavors to correlate the work of all private agencies in the field. Among the activities of the local societies are finding the crippled child, transporting him to hospitals and clinics, providing convalescent care, and developing a program of education, vocational guidance, and placement.

Publications: *The Crippled Child*, bimonthly magazine; $1 a year; Vivian M. Hackett, editor-in-chief. *Round Robin*, monthly during school year for school children, 50¢ a year; *The Crippled Child*, monthly bulletin, free to general mailing list; *Institutional Bulletin*, monthly, free to institutional members; *Bulletin on Current Literature*, monthly, free to institutional members; proceedings of annual convention. Other publications include a Loan Packet Library, issued by the Bureau of Information, containing 20,000 catalog subjects; pamphlets and booklets on federal and state legislation, hospitals and institutions, and mimeographed copies of special speeches.

Staff: Full-time paid employees, 10, of whom 1 spends major time in the field.

Finances: For the fiscal year July 1938 to July 1939, operations were as follows:

Income		*Expenditures*	
Membership fees	$ 3,228.60	General office	$10,136.04
Publications	3,444.44	Publications	11,611.49
Seal account	42,983.89	Extension and seals	19,866.14
Miscellaneous	1,229.04	Miscellaneous	2,837.64
		Social work	4,766.33
		Conventions and conferences	1,983.16
	$50,885.97		$51,200.80

Table XXIII

STATISTICS OF ORGANIZATIONS SERVING HANDICAPPED YOUTH

Organization	Year Founded	Approximate Aggregate Membership (individuals)	Total Employees on Headquarters Staff	Aggregate Endowment of National Headquarters	Plant and Equipment (headquarters only)	Approximate Annual Budget (headquarters only)
American Association of Instructors of the Blind	1853	...	...	$ ...	$ ...	$ ...
American Association on Mental Deficiency	1876	650	1	none	...	4,000
American Association to Promote the Teaching of Speech to the Deaf	1890	2,200	5	258,956	...	19,400
American Association of Workers for the Blind	1895	292	a	363	...	1,200
American Foundation for the Blind	1921	...	55	...	...	110,000
American Institute for the Deaf-Blind	1932	...	4	10,847		4,500
American Society for the Hard of Hearing	1919	7,000	6	none	2,000	17,100
American Speech Correction Association	1925	325	a	...	...	1,000
International Council for Exceptional Children	1922	4,600	1	...	...	...
National Council for the Physically Handicapped	1933	8b	...	...	...	...
National Rehabilitation Association	1923	50,000	a	...	...	...
National Society for Crippled Children	1921	113b	10	...	...	51,200

a No paid staff.
b Number of constituent bodies.

XXIII. Associations for the Prevention and Treatment of Delinquency and Crime

Crime and the exploits of criminals have always tended to be greatly overplayed in the press and on the platform. Likewise in much of the consideration which has hitherto been given to the welfare of youth, the relatively few young persons who have fallen afoul of the law have received much more than their proportionate share of attention. The problem of law violation, serious though it may be, is but a tiny fraction of the entire situation involving youth welfare; and if law violation should miraculously cease, there would be but a slight diminution of the total problem. This is true because the vast bulk of injustice, inequity, and underprivilege lies without the scope and beyond the reach of the criminal law.

It is true that a surprisingly large percentage of convicted criminals are youthful; but this may be more of an indictment of our social and economic system than of the individuals involved. On every hand there are evidences of the growth of an enlightened attitude toward youthful crime and delinquency, recognizing that the ultimate answer must be the provision of a decent minimum of housing, food, clothing, education, health service, and recreational opportunity for every boy and girl.

Most of the national organizations devoting their attention to this field are promoting the understanding and acceptance of this attitude and its translation into forms of action which will erase from the American scene the intolerable environments in which criminal tendencies have their origin and in which boys and girls fall into the ways of the delinquent for sheer want of opportunity for more wholesome and socially acceptable activity.

Cross references: American Legion, National Child Welfare Division, p. 196; Boy Rangers of America, p. 21; Brotherhood of St. Andrew in the United States, p. 33; Coordinating Councils, p. 74; Pathfinders of America, p. 26.

CONFERENCE OF SUPERINTENDENTS OF CORRECTIONAL INSTITUTIONS FOR WOMEN AND GIRLS (1930); State Training School for Girls, Chalkville, Ala.; Mrs. Mary H. Fowler, Business Manager.

Membership: Superintendents of institutions for delinquent women and girls, representing 18 states. No dues.

Purpose: To discuss problems of mutual interest and to promote good standards of work in the custody and training of delinquent females.

Activities: Annual meeting in Hotel Pennsylvania in New York City. Study of all phases of corrective training and treatment for socially maladjusted individuals, including medical, psychological, and psychiatric treatment and vocational and academic training.

Publications: No national publication, but nearly all the local institutions represented publish their own local periodicals.

NATIONAL CONFERENCE OF JUVENILE AGENCIES (1915); Woodbine, N.J.; E. L. Johnstone, Secretary-Treasurer.

Membership: Institutional workers, juvenile court attachés, and other individuals dealing directly with youthful offenders, 160, representing 47 states, Canada, and Great Britain.

Purpose: To accumulate and disseminate valid information on the care, treatment, and education of delinquent and dependent children and those at odds with the existing social environment; to promulgate programs of institutional and community care of socially unadjusted children.

Activities: Holds annual conferences. Maintains advisory service with representatives in every state. Promotes special studies on principles and philosophies of personnel, program, and plant in child-caring institutions and agencies. Distributes literature bearing on identification, control, and treatment of delinquency and antisocial conduct.

Publications: *Proceedings*, quarterly; free to members, independent subscription rate $1.50 a year; E. L. Johnstone, managing editor.

Staff: Part-time unpaid worker, 1.

Finances: Reserve fund for the publication of the *Proceedings*, $400. Value of equipment at national headquarters, $500; estimated annual value of unpaid staff services, $5,000. Balance on hand October 6, 1939, $76.88. Operations for the fiscal year ending on that date were as follows:

Total Income

Membership fees and publications	$329.58

Expenditures

Communications	$ 93.35
Office supplies	13.75
Publications	135.60
Other purposes	10.00
	$252.70

NATIONAL PROBATION ASSOCIATION, INC.
(1907); 1790 Broadway, New York, N.Y.;
Charles L. Chute, Executive Director.

Membership: Probation officers and contributors,
16,938. There is one branch, located at 110 Sutter
St., San Francisco, Calif. Annual dues, $2 to $100,
according to grades of membership.

Purpose: To develop juvenile and domestic relations
courts; to establish standards in probation and parole work; to secure effective treatment of delinquency and prevention of crime throughout America.

Activities: Conducts city and state surveys of courts
and probation systems; drafts juvenile court and
probation laws and assists in securing their enactment; promotes the appointment of carefully selected probation and parole officers and assists in
their training; aids judges and local authorities in
improving the administration of probation and parole; publishes practical literature which is available
to all probation workers and other interested persons; carries on research work and serves as a
clearinghouse for information in this field for the
entire country. Holds national and regional conferences.

Publications: *Probation*, bimonthly except August;
20¢ a copy, $1 a year, free to members. Yearbook
(proceedings of annual conference); $1.25 each, free
to members. Miscellaneous pamphlets, survey reports, and reprints including: *Directory* of probation
officers in the United States and Canada, 1940,
$1.25; *Juvenile Court Laws of the United States*,
summarized, $1.25; *Adult Probation Laws*, summa-
rized, $1.25; *State Administered Adult Probation and
Parole System—A Model Act*, 25¢; *A Standard
Juvenile Court Law*, 15¢.

Staff: Full-time paid employees, 24, of whom 2 spend
major time in the field; part-time paid employees, 4.

Finances: Total reserve fund as of March 31, 1940,
$64,651.15. Value of equipment at headquarters,
$2,000. Balance on hand April 1, 1939, $15,813.88.
Operations for the fiscal year ending March 31,
1940 were as follows:

Income

Dues and contributions	$103,637.86
Publications	2,433.05
Reserve funds	1,522.98
Other sources	539.14
	$108,133.03

Expenditures

Salaries	$ 61,573.59
Travel	7,424.13
Communications	9,449.89
Printing	15,980.06
Office supplies	2,308.92
Rent	5,749.25
Other services	2,640.48
Equipment	158.78
Other purposes	1,895.97
	$107,181.07

OSBORNE ASSOCIATION (1921); 114 East 30th
St., New York, N.Y.; Austin H. MacCormick,
Executive Director; William B. Cox, Executive
Secretary.

Membership: Individuals, approximately 1,800.
Annual dues vary from $5 to $25, according to grades
of membership.

Purpose: To promote effective methods of dealing
with juvenile delinquents and adult criminals, from
arrest to release on parole and final discharge; to
collect and disseminate facts about American penal
and correctional institutions; to work for such an
administration of criminal justice and such a correctional system as will give society the greatest
protection.

Activities: Holds annual meetings. Conducts regional
and nation-wide surveys of prisons and adult re-
formatories and of institutions for juvenile delinquents; conducts special surveys of probation and
parole and other phases of correctional work; cooperates with responsible officials and agencies in
the promotion of approved correctional programs.
Provides limited lodgings, meals, clothing, and cash
relief to discharged prisoners from state and federal
prisons and endeavors to assist them in obtaining
employment.

Publications: *News Bulletin*, bimonthly; $1 a year.
*Handbook of American Institutions for Delinquent
Juveniles* (first edition), Vol. I, 1938 (West North
Central States), Vol. II, 1940 (Kentucky and Ten-
nessee), $1.25 each. List of other publications on
request.

Staff: Full-time paid employees, 10.

Finances: Approximate annual budget, $50,000.

Table XXIV

STATISTICS OF ASSOCIATIONS FOR THE PREVENTION AND TREATMENT OF DELINQUENCY AND CRIME

Organization	Year Founded	Approximate Aggregate Membership (individuals)	Total Employees on Headquarters Staff	Aggregate Endowment of National Headquarters	Plant and Equipment (headquarters only)	Approximate Annual Budget (headquarters only)
Conf. of Superintendents of Correctional Inst. for Women and Girls	1930	...	...	...	$ ...	$ ...
National Conference of Juvenile Agencies	1915	160	[a]	none[b]	500	300
National Probation Association	1907	16,938	28	none[c]	2,000	108,200
Osborne Association	1921	1,800	10	none	...	50,000

a No paid staff.
b The organization has a reserve fund of $400.

c The organization has a reserve fund of $64,911.

XXIV. Associations Advocating Peace, Consumers' Cooperation, Temperance, and Humane Education

American history has been, from one viewpoint, largely a series of waves of reform. To mention only a few, we may recall the movement for "manhood suffrage" which culminated about 1840, the antislavery crusade which ended in the sanguinary sixties, the campaign for woman suffrage which reached its height and its final victory in the second decade of the present century, and the mighty battle against the demon rum which gave us a dozen years of national prohibition.

Major movements of this type often spread over two or three generations. Commonly they are first espoused by a sparse group of noisy and persistent advocates who become the butt of ridicule but whose tenacity gradually commands respect and attracts converts to their ranks. Finally, by means of ceaseless campaigning and cumulative pressure on state and national legislators, the wishes of the reformers are written into the law of the land. Again and again it has been observed that this does not necessarily solve the problem aimed at nor miraculously banish the social ills complained of. But usually it does constitute a sort of step forward, at least to the extent of aligning official public policy on the side of humanitarianism.

Humane impulses generally supply the motive power which enables these movements to proceed and grow. This circumstance endows them with an innate dignity and worth which cannot be wholly destroyed by the unfortunate fact that their conduct is often characterized more by wishful and woolly thinking than by prudence and practicality and that their stronger adherents are almost inevitably pulled into a regrettable narrowness and intolerance, which has been said to deter many from joining their cause.

The present age, true to form in at least this respect, has its great popular reform crusades, some in the incipient stage and some further advanced. Who shall say that their names may not be written large when the history of the twentieth century is completed? These movements make their appeal to young persons and capture the enthusiastic support of some among them. They are among the influences affecting youth in a way which is most significant for the future—the molding of social attitudes. Whether their influence is for good or ill, it must be counted as a force in the lives of youth.

The one organization in this section whose membership consists chiefly of young persons, as distinguished from those composed wholly or largely of persons above the age of 25, is Allied Youth.

Cross references: Section XI, Patriotic, Political, Fraternal, and Labor Organizations, pp. 80–89. *See also:* American Friends Service Committee, p. 32; Cooperative Recreation Service, p. 157; Foreign Policy Association, p. 125.

ALLIED YOUTH, INC. (1931); 1201 16th St., N.W., Washington, D.C.; W. Roy Breg, Executive Secretary.

Membership: Young persons aged 14 to 30, approximately 10,000, in more than 100 chartered posts in high schools, colleges, and communities located throughout the United States, Hawaii, and Alaska.

Purpose: To promote and aid effective alcohol education and recreation among American young people. The platform is: "We stand for the liberation through education of the individual and society from the handicaps of beverage alcohol."

Activities: Promotes field assistance and supplies materials and program aids to high school assemblies and college convocations. Aids locally led (usually school-sponsored) posts to present a month-by-month organized program of alcohol education and of recreation. Post activities include study courses, group observation tours, regular bimonthly programs including discussions and question-and-answer periods, and recreational events conducted by the post for its own members and other youth of the school and community. "Alcohol-free companionships and good times are provided in addition to the fact-finding and educational elements of the program." Maintains a speakers bureau.

Publications: *Allied Youth*, 8 pp. illustrated, 11 issues annually; $1 a year, special rate to clubs; Nettie Allen Thomas, editor. *Alcoholfax Educational Service*, monthly during the school year; $10 a year;

W. Roy Breg and Bert H. Davis, editors. *Youth Faces the Liquor Problem*, by Bert H. Davis, 25¢ a copy. Numerous other publications and manuals; list sent upon request.

Staff: Full-time paid employees, 7; part-time paid employee, 1.

Finances: For the calendar year 1939, operations were as follows:

Income

Contributions	$15,686.68
Publications and other services	1,728.39
	$17,415.07

Expenditures

Salaries	$ 9,308.35
Communications	225.15
Other purposes	6,117.50
	$15,651.00

AMERICAN HUMANE ASSOCIATION (1877); 135 Washington Ave., Albany, N.Y.; Eric H. Hansen, Secretary and General Manager.

Membership: Approximately 8,000 individuals in 582 societies, of which 47 are children's societies. Membership fees are as follows: supporting, $2; annual, $5; associate, $10; contributing, $25; life, $500; patron, $1,000; benefactor, $5,000; founder, $25,000.

Purpose: To protect children and animals throughout the country; to create societies for the prevention of cruelty to children and animals and to coordinate the activities of such societies.

Activities: Holds annual meetings; maintains field service for local humane societies; sponsors programs to protect children against cruelty; and supports needed legislation. The National Humane Poster Contest has aroused thousands of young people to a better appreciation of the rights and needs of children and animals. The association has established a Wild Life Department which engages specifically in the conflict against cruel trapping and distributes educational literature, tending to prevent needless cruelty to animals.

Publications: *National Humane Review*, monthly; $1 a year, 75¢ to teachers, school children, Scout masters, libraries, and clergymen. Numerous pamphlets on the care of animals; leaflets on the correlation of humane education with other school subjects, on delinquent parents, and on other pertinent subjects. Complete list sent on request.

Staff: Full-time paid employees, 16.

Finances: For the fiscal year ending August 31, 1939, operations were as follows:

Income

Donations and contributions	$ 4,450.31
Membership fees	16,306.05
Other services	100.00
Investments and legacies	34,710.01
Periodical publication	1,862.40
Sale of literature	4,084.24
	$61,513.01

Expenditures

Administration	$30,888.83
Travel	2,518.25
Communications	3,276.76
Office supplies	948.72
Publications	10,073.09
Printing, literature	5,389.10
Rental, insurance, etc.	2,155.54
Other purposes	8,916.43
Miscellaneous	2,578.80
	$66,745.52

AMERICAN HUMANE EDUCATION SOCIETY (1889); 180 Longwood Ave., Boston, Mass.; Guy Richardson, Secretary.

Membership: Individuals, approximately 5,000. Rates of membership are as follows: active life, $100; associate life, $50; sustaining, $20; active annual, $10; associate annual, $5; annual, $1; children, 75¢. The society sponsors the American Band of Mercy, which has 250,000 units in the United States and several foreign countries, enrolling a total of approximately 7,000,000 children.

Purpose: An organized effort to promote peace on earth, kindness, justice, and mercy to every living creature by carrying humane education into American schools and homes, aiding humane societies, and organizing Bands of Mercy, or Junior Humane Societies, in all parts of the world.

Activities: Distributes humane literature to almost every country; advocates the enactment of laws requiring the teaching of humane education in public schools. Twenty-six states have already passed laws to this effect. Sponsors "Humane Day" observances in schools and prize competitions for the extension of humane education; furnishes films illustrating humane work which may be done for exhibition in schools. The members of the various units, called Bands of Mercy or Junior Humane Societies, put on plays, hold exercises in schools with recitations and readings illustrating kindness to animals, report kind deeds done to needy animals, make scrapbooks on cats and dogs, hold parades and pet shows. Contests are held from time to time. The Jack London Club, an organization sponsored by the society to protect the cruelty incident to the training of animals for stage and screen, has a membership of 770,982.

Publications: *Our Dumb Animals*, monthly; free to first-year Bands of Mercy; Guy Richardson, editor.

Teacher's Helper in Humane Education, by Francis H. Rowley, 32 pp.; *An Early Start to Kindness*, by Lucia Fessenden Gilbert, 48 pp.; *Humane Education, An Activity of the National Congress of Parents and Teachers*, by Francis H. Rowley, 11 pp.; 100 other pamphlets.

Staff: Full-time paid employees, 10, all of whom spend major time in the field; part-time paid employee, 1, who spends major time in the field.

Finances: Endowment funds, $434,116.48. Estimated annual value of space, heat, light, or similar services received without charge, $5,000. Operations for the calendar year 1939 were as follows:

Income

Gifts or grants	$ 100.50
Publications	1,695.45
Endowment and reserve funds	14,490.61
	$16,286.56

Expenditures

Salaries	$12,860.10
Travel	914.20
Office supplies	704.00
Publications	2,083.94
Other purposes	211.00
	$16,773.24

COMMITTEE ON MILITARISM IN EDUCATION

(1925); 2929 Broadway, New York, N.Y.; Edwin C. Johnson, Secretary.

Membership: An executive board of 18 members; a national council of 59 members; a mailing list of about 1,600 interested persons, chiefly adults, but including some college students.

Purpose: To promote campaigns against militarism in education, particularly against compulsory military training in schools and colleges and against the inclusion of military drill in CCC camps; to promote the establishment of physical education courses and courses in problems of world citizenship as alternatives to military training courses.

Activities: Cooperation by correspondence and personal conference with organizations and individuals interested in planning programs directed toward the objectives outlined for the committee; preparation and distribution of publicity materials; participation in the programs of the National Council for Prevention of War (see p. 216) and the National Peace Conference (see p. 216). The youth-serving phase consists of building sentiment against training for war and particularly of efforts to relieve young men in schools and colleges from the necessity of accommodating themselves to compulsory military instruction and exercises.

Publications: *Militarizing Our Youth*, by Roswell P. Barnes, 48 pp., 5¢; *So This Is War!* by Tucker P. Smith, 48 pp., 10¢; *Military Training in the Schools*

and Colleges of Illinois, by Howard P. Becker and E. J. Webster, 1929, 36 pp., 5¢; *What Do Educational Authorities Say about Military Drill?* 3¢; *Frills and Thrills That Bind and Blind Youth*, 3¢; "Main Issues in the Junior R.O.T.C. Controversy," by Edwin C. Johnson, 14-page reprint from the *Harvard Educational Review*, 10¢; "School Military Training Re-considered," by Edwin C. Johnson, 8-page reprint from *School and Society*, 5¢; "An Introductory Course: The Pacific Solution of International Problems," by George M. Stratton, 8-page reprint from the *Journal of Higher Education*, 5¢; "A Course in International Relations," by Leo Litzky, 8-page reprint from *Social Education*, 5¢; "Educating for World Citizenship," by Russell T. McNutt, 8-page reprint from *Social Education*, 5¢.

Staff: Full-time paid employees, 2.

Finances: Value of plant and equipment at national headquarters is estimated at $10,000. For the calendar year 1939, operations were as follows:

Income

Gifts	$7,760.21
Publications	9.25
	$7,769.46

Expenditures

Salaries	$4,794.54
Travel	102.00
Communications	553.26
Office supplies	249.78
Publications	1,604.70
Rentals, etc.	403.40
Other purposes	101.93
	$7,809.61

COOPERATIVE LEAGUE OF THE UNITED STATES

(1916); 167 West 12th St., New York, N.Y.; E. R. Bowen, General Secretary. Also national offices at 608 South Dearborn, Chicago, Ill., and 726 Jackson Place, Washington, D.C.

A national union of consumers' cooperative societies.

Membership: Individuals, approximately 1,041,000. There is a board of directors of 15 members. Campus cooperatives enroll about 100,000 students at approximately 160 colleges.

Purpose: To promote the development of consumers' cooperatives in the United States.

Activities: Several regional cooperative associations are active in educational programs designed to reach young people. The Cooperative Youth Councils in Ohio enroll over 2,000 young people in a program of recreation, study, and cooperative action. The Northern States Cooperative Youth League has more than 1,000 members engaged in cooperative study, play, and action. Summer institutes for young people are sponsored each year by regional cooperative associations in Indiana, Ohio, Minnesota, Wisconsin, and New York, and thousands of young people attend these conferences. During the last year a Pacific Coast Federation of Campus Cooperatives (2315 Dwight Way, Berkeley, Calif.) and a Midwest Federation of Campus Co-ops (5471 Ellis Ave., Chicago, Ill.) have been formed to aid in the extension of campus cooperatives, in the belief that they perform useful economic and educational functions.

Publications: *Consumers' Cooperation,* monthly; *Campus Co-op News Bulletin,* monthly. *Campus Co-ops,* by William Moore, 34 pp., 5¢; *Co-ops on the Campus,* by Bertram B. Fowler, 3¢.

Staff: Staff at the three national offices, 11.

Finances: Income is derived from dues of the affiliated cooperatives, which pay 5¢ a year for each member. Approximate annual budget, $17,500.

LEAGUE OF NATIONS ASSOCIATION (1923); 8 West 40th St., New York, N.Y.; Clark M. Eichelberger, Director; Mrs. Harrison Thomas, Educational Secretary.

Membership: Individuals, 10,000, in 21 branches located in 20 states. There are four youth sections, in Massachusetts, New York, New Jersey, and Pennsylvania, with an aggregate membership of 150 persons.

Purpose: To cultivate public opinion in order to influence the government of the United States to cooperate to the fullest extent practicable in the activities of the League of Nations and to enter the League of Nations at the earliest possible date.

Activities: Promotes a general educational program on the need of a community of nations and of participation of the United States in it; cooperates with the Commission to Study the Organization of Peace; sponsors radio programs with emphasis on world economic cooperation. Promotes model League of Nations assemblies in colleges and secondary schools; furnishes literature to young people in schools, colleges, and organized groups; conducts student contests on the League of Nations, for which the first prize is a trip to Europe or South America; 6,000 students representing 1,210 high schools participated in the 1939–40 contest.

Publications: *New World,* monthly; $1 a year, student rate 50¢ for 9 months; Clark M. Eichelberger, editor. *International Scene,* weekly summary and interpretation of international news; $3 a year, student rate $2 for 8 months. Numerous pamphlets and booklets priced from 1¢ upward.

Staff: Full-time paid employees, 15; part-time unpaid worker, 1.

Finances: Budget for the calendar year 1939 was approximately $56,000.

NATIONAL COMMITTEE ON CAUSE AND CURE OF WAR (1925); 1949 Grand Central Terminal, New York, N.Y.; Josephine Schain, Chairman.

Membership: Ten national women's organizations, representing 5,000,000 women: American Association of University Women (see p. 115); General Federation of Women's Clubs (see p. 107); National Board of the Young Women's Christian Associations (see p. 28); National Council of Jewish Women; National Federation of Business and Professional Women's Clubs (see p. 108); National League of Women Voters (see p. 109); National Women's Christian Temperance Union; National Women's Trade Union League of America (see p. 85); National Committee of Church Women; National Women's Conference of the American Ethical Union.

Purpose: To develop an intelligent and informed public opinion in the field of international relations, beginning with the members of the cooperating organizations and reaching toward their friends and the public at large.

Activities: The member organizations direct the work among their individual members and hold a conference annually to report progress and decide on the program for the coming year. Local, state, and regional conferences are held throughout the year, their programs guided by the recommendations of the national committee. Small local discussion groups known as Marathon Round Tables are also organized throughout the country.

Publications: Various pamphlets describing the program and suggesting ways of adapting committee methods individually or within existing groups. The Marathon Round Tables Committee publishes each year a *Basic Study Kit* and a *Current Issues Folio,* containing comprehensive material on the developing world situation as it relates to the recommended program of the national committee.

Staff: Full-time paid employees, 4.

Finances: Approximate annual budget, $15,000.

NATIONAL CONSUMERS LEAGUE (1899); 114 East 32nd St., New York, N.Y.; Mary Dublin, General Secretary.

Membership: Individuals, 15,000, including the membership both of the national organization and of the 18 affiliated leagues in 16 states. Annual dues: general, $2; association, $5; contributing, $10; sustaining, $25; donor, $100.

Purpose: To awaken consumers' interest in their responsibility for conditions under which goods are made and distributed; to promote fair labor standards through investigation, education, and legislation.

Activities: Supports minimum wage and maximum hour legislation, the elimination of sweatshop labor and the labor of children, the promotion of measures to strengthen state and federal labor departments, the protection of consumers against adulterated foods and dangerous drugs, the promotion of health insurance, the support of the principle of collective bargaining, the promotion of conscientious enforcement of labor laws, and the extension of labor law coverage to include those now exempt from the Federal Fair Labor Standards Act, the Social Security Act, and other state and federal labor laws.

Publications: *National Consumers League Bulletin*, quarterly; 50¢ a year to nonmembers, free to members. *Supreme Court and Minimum Wage Legislation*, 267 pp., $1; *National Consumers League Standard Minimum Wage Bill for Women and Minors; Defense of the Fair Labor Standards Law from Attack*, by Representative Mary T. Norton, 1939, 12 pp. mimeo.; *Wages and Hours Legislation and the Child Labor Problem*, by Dorothy W. Douglas, 1939, 5 pp. mimeo.; *National Health Program: Next Great Social Goal*, by Dr. C.-E. A. Winslow, 1939, 4 pp. mimeo. Numerous other pamphlets ranging in price from 5¢ to 50¢.

Staff: Full-time paid employees at headquarters, 3; part-time unpaid workers, 3.

NATIONAL COUNCIL FOR PREVENTION OF WAR (1921); 532 17th St., N.W., Washington, D.C.; Frederick J. Libby, Executive Secretary.

Membership: Participating national organizations, 15; cooperating national organizations, 11.

Purpose: To work for progressive world organization, world-wide reduction of armaments by international agreement, and world-wide education for peace.

Activities: Carries on educational activities focused on political action to keep America out of war, to remove the causes of war, to promote peace by peaceful means, and to preserve and strengthen democracy. Specifically, during 1939, the council conducted campaigns to prevent the fortification of Guam, to retain the existing neutrality bill, and to stop the drift of the United States towards involvement in the European war; to achieve these objectives, the council worked with and distributed literature to Protestant and Catholic churches, farm groups, and labor organizations. The council regularly distributes literature and furnishes advice to young people in schools, colleges, Sunday schools, Epworth Leagues, Christian Endeavor groups, Girl Scouts, Camp Fire Girls, etc., in all parts of the country.

Publications: *Peace Action*, monthly news bulletin; 50¢ a year or special club rate of 10 subscriptions for $3 when sent at one time; Frederick J. Libby, editor. *Washington Information Letter*, legislative service issued biweekly when Congress is in session; $1 a year; Warren D. Mullin, editor. Numerous kits and pamphlets containing background material on current problems, material on political action, material for rural and labor groups and for work with boys and girls; posters and programs; bibliographies and lists.

Staff: Full-time paid employees, 16; part-time paid employees, 5; part-time unpaid workers, 6.

NATIONAL PEACE CONFERENCE (1935); 8 West 40th St., New York, N.Y.; Walter W. Van Kirk, President.

Membership: Constituent societies, 65, including local peace councils and 40 national organizations having as their primary aim or as one of their objects the promotion of better international relations. Of the constituent societies, six are youth organizations: American Youth Congress (see p. 82); International Society of Christian Endeavor (see p. 37); National Board of Young Women's Christian Associations (see p. 28); National Council of Young Men's Christian Associations (see p. 27); National Student Federation of America (see p. 68); and United Student Peace Committee.

Purpose: To serve (1) as a council board at which members exchange their views on American foreign policy and formulate and clarify policies and issues; (2) as a clearinghouse to receive, record, and publicize views of its affiliated organizations to the public and the government; (3) as a publisher and program servicing agency to provide its member organizations and the general public with objective, nonpartisan information on world events, programs, policies, educational methods and procedures, and organizational techniques.

Activities: Recommends to member organizations the adoption of principles decided upon by the conference. Promotes such programs of cooperative activity as may be agreed upon by the conference, working through member organizations which are best qualified to provide leadership in a specific program. Appoints committees on world community, national defense policy, neutrality, economics and peace, the Far East, military training in schools and colleges. The findings and reports are transmitted to the member organizations, some of which work directly with youth in an attempt to develop intelligent opinions on questions of national and international importance.

Publications: *National Peace Conference Bulletin*, 12 issues annually, $3 a year; *Washington Information Service*, 19 issues annually, $2 a year. Numerous pamphlets and booklets ranging in price from 5¢ to 75¢.

Staff: Full-time paid employees, 3.

Finances: For the fiscal year September 1, 1939 to August 31, 1940, operations were as follows:

Income

Gifts and grants	$17,507.00
Membership fees	2,044.18
Publications	1,433.79
Other services	75.48
	$21,060.45

Expenditures

Salaries	$ 8,416.00
Travel	590.36
Communications	723.06
Office supplies	125.46
Publications	695.80
Rentals, insurance, etc.	3,004.52
Commission on National Defense, and other purposes	4,092.89
	$17,648.09

WOMEN'S INTERNATIONAL LEAGUE FOR PEACE AND FREEDOM (1915); 1734 F St., N.W., Washington, D.C.; Dorothy Detzer, National Executive Secretary; Catherine FitzGibbon, Finance Secretary.

Membership: Individuals, 14,000, in 130 local branches in the United States.

Purpose: To unite women in all countries who are opposed to every kind of war, exploitation, and oppression and who work for universal disarmament and for the solution of conflicts by the recognition of human solidarity, by world cooperation, and by the establishment of social, political, and economic justice for all, without distinction of sex, race, class, or creed.

Activities: The work of the league is based upon the statements adopted and the resolutions passed by the international congress of the league. The primary objects remain total and universal disarmament, the abolition of violent means of coercion for the settlement of all conflicts, the substitution in every case of some form of peaceful settlement, and the development of a world organization for the political, social, and economic cooperation of peoples. State and local groups in the United States work for the attainment of these objectives by means of legislative and political action, through state and congressional representatives; conduct educational and publicity work, in the press, libraries, schools, churches, clubs, and radio and through study and discussion groups; sponsor community projects, caravans, and demonstrations. Especial attention has been given to education of youth for peace, by supplying teachers with literature on peace and war and lists of books on the question, and by furnishing suggestions to churches and clubs for peace programs.

Publications: Pamphlets: *How to Work for Peace*, 4 pp.; *First Twenty Years of the W.I.L.*, 12 pp. An extensive list of pamphlets at nominal prices.

Staff: Employees at headquarters, 8.

Finances: Contributions and membership fees constitute the only source of income. Value of equipment at national headquarters, $1,500. Approximate annual budget, $30,000.

TABLE XXV

STATISTICS OF ASSOCIATIONS ADVOCATING PEACE, CONSUMERS' COOPERATION, TEMPERANCE, AND HUMANE EDUCATION

Organization	Year Founded	Approximate Aggregate Membership (individuals)	Number of Members under 25 Years of Age	Total Employees on Head-quarters Staff	Aggregate Endowment of National Headquarters	Plant and Equipment (headquarters only)	Approximate Annual Budget (headquarters only)
Allied Youth	1931	10,000	10,000ᵃ	8	$ ...	$ ...	$17,400
American Humane Association	1877	8,000	...	16	...	...	66,700
American Humane Education Society	1889	5,000ᵇ	7,000,000ᶜ	11	434,117	...	16,800
Committee on Militarism in Education	1925	77ᵈ	...	2	...	10,000	7,800
Cooperative League of the United States	1916	1,041,000	100,000	11	...	...	17,500
League of Nations Association	1923	10,000	150	15	...	...	56,000
National Committee on Cause and Cure of War	1925	10ᵉ	...	4	none	...	15,000
National Consumers League	1899	15,000	...	3	...	...	...
National Council for Prevention of War	1921	26ᵉ	none	21	...	...	...
National Peace Conference	1935	65ᵉ	...	3	...	...	21,000
Women's International League for Peace and Freedom	1915	14,000	...	8	...	1,500	30,000

a Includes persons up to 30 years of age.
b Adult membership only.
c American and foreign membership in Bands of Mercy, sponsored by the society.
d Membership of executive board and national council; the committee also has a mailing list of 1,600 interested persons.
e Number of constituent bodies.

APPENDIX

Should Youth Organize?*

Most of the organizations which young people join are either sponsored or controlled by adults, or made up mainly of adults in their active membership. Almost every type of adult organization—political, fraternal, social, commercial, labor, agricultural—includes some members under 25, or even under 21. In some cases there are special junior sections in which the young members serve a kind of apprenticeship. The junior sections are often of great value as training schools and as a channel through which the younger members can express themselves.

The advantages of close association between young people and older members are so great that any organization devoted to a particular objective should normally provide for the inclusion of interested young people. For the actual accomplishment of results, as distinguished from practice in free discussion, it is common experience that youth can do more in conjunction with adults than in separate organizations of youth alone.

ADULT-SPONSORED YOUTH ORGANIZATIONS

In addition to distinctly adult societies with a minority of young members, there are two types of organization sponsored by adults that enroll large numbers of young people: the religious youth societies and the so-called character-building organizations for boys, girls, young men, and young women.

The importance of these groups can hardly be exaggerated. They include large numbers of young people, and because of their long history their former membership includes past generations of youth who are now adults, even aged persons. They have been a steadying influence, particularly in the recent years of stress when young people have had to face unusual problems. The religious and character-building organizations, which reach young people both inside and outside the churches, share a deep concern for moral values. They also provide a diversified program of leisure-time activity. Both types of organization afford opportunities for young people to exercise initiative on their own behalf. To be sure, it is usually so much easier and apparently safer for adults to make the decisions, that most of the programs are conceived, supervised, and dominated by adults. Yet the fact is recognized in theory, and sometimes in practice, that the only way for young people to learn to be responsible is by carrying responsibilities. Youth are quick to realize when "youth leadership" is unreal, and many of them react by losing interest and by looking for other associations in which more vital relations can be found.

* Reprint of statement adopted by the American Youth Commission, April 15, 1940.

In the adult-sponsored organizations that provide real opportunities for initiative on the part of youth, much of the most effective, stable, and valuable youth leadership is found. In such organizations, also, there is often much valuable discussion of public questions, with the participation but not the domination of interested adults. When conducted in cooperation with other races and other religious creeds, such discussions are particularly useful, building greater understanding and tolerance, a realization of the needs of youth as a whole, and a sense of the dangers of apathy in the face of social problems. The fundamental beliefs common to all religious faiths can be translated into living social advances only if there is freedom to learn the causes of unrest and to discuss possible remedies.

YOUTH-LED ORGANIZATIONS

In America, where the forming of organizations is a universal habit, young people for many years have naturally insisted on having their own clubs, fraternities, and associations, free from adult interference. It is equally natural that the older people have often been critical of these youthful activities, and in many cases have taken measures to control or suppress them.

Healthy young people are prone to rebel against the world as they find it. They gain some little freedom and in due time settle down to defending the *status quo* against the following generation. We may recognize this normal and immemorial conflict of the generations as a fact of human nature without being obliged to accept it as the sole basis of judgment on present-day youth organizations.

The current youth-led organizations, it is important to remember, are not so universally devoted to public questions as might be supposed. Actually a very large number of them are still the familiar social clubs and fraternities devoted mainly to personal enjoyment and campus politics. Their existence presents no problems that have not been equally pressing, in one form or another, for the past fifty years. An active interest in economic and political problems is not the most general characteristic of American young people, even at the present time.

Depressed economic conditions, however, brought an increasing number of youth associations devoted to the discussion of public affairs. Many organizations for this specific purpose are found in the colleges, though it is true that the membership is usually relatively small. In addition, there have been formed local youth councils in a number of cities, with membership drawn from a wide variety of other organizations. The American Youth Congress is a similar organization, on a national scale, with delegates coming from many organizations, though often not as official representatives.

In the local youth councils, representatives of the religious and other character-building organizations of youth have taken a prominent part. Social, political, labor, racial, and other societies having youth membership have been represented, together with student groups, community center groups, and various independent social and athletic clubs of young people.

The local councils have varied in their practice in regard to accepting as voting members the adult representatives of organizations serving youth, but in almost all cases such representatives have been welcomed and have taken active part in discussions.

The main service of the local youth councils has been to provide a forum for the discussion of community problems as they affect youth. Education, recreation, and employment questions can often be handled most effectively at the community level, where most of the pertinent facts are available to those participating in discussion. Young people coming from different backgrounds of experience can gain a balanced knowledge of community affairs, which is of great value as a preparation for their duties as citizens.

National meetings of young people for the discussion of public questions necessarily involve peculiar difficulties to which the local youth councils are much less subject. Meetings with the potentialities for publicity afforded by any national gathering are particularly attractive to those bent on protest and who therefore tend to be present in force. Because of this factor and also because of the expense involved in travel, the attendance at any national meeting under youth leadership may easily fall short of being representative geographically or in any other way. Difficulties of this kind were exemplified at the national meeting of the American Youth Congress a few months ago.

National organizations and local youth councils have all been retarded in their growth by the general suspicion and hostility that commonly attaches to any organization actively discussing controversial questions which is sponsored and directed by youth. In some cases this opposition has resulted in the abandonment of the enterprise or in the withdrawal of certain organizations that should be represented if the participants are to have the benefit of all shades of opinion. Doubtless connected with the same cause is the chronic scarcity of funds which has acted as a severe handicap to the work of all youth-led organizations.

DISCUSSION OF PUBLIC QUESTIONS

The Commission recognizes that youth organizations for discussion of public questions form a small part of the total number, and that social, religious, athletic, and other associations are of great importance and value. The chief problem of immediate interest, however, is the attitude that should be taken by adults and by youth toward these discussion organizations.

In the Commission's opinion, there is no effective way to train large numbers of competent citizens for participation in public affairs which does not include actual practice in the discussion of public questions. The tendency for such discussions to be one-sided and ill-informed is not a peculiarity of youth. This tendency is equally apparent and far more dangerous among adults who have, or may acquire, actual power over public policy. It is therefore highly desirable that young people who are not yet in a position to exert any great influence on the adult world should occupy themselves in learning how to lead their contemporaries and how to choose and reject leadership. This process is not different from other educational activities which are best carried on at an age and under circumstances that minimize the dangers involved in mistakes or false starts.

Like all educational activities that create a disturbance, youthful discussion may be irritating to many adults, but should not be suppressed on that account. The young people are learning what kind of public speaking is effective, what behavior will bring from the press either praise, silence, ridicule, or condemnation, what causes appropriations to be granted or withheld, which leadership wears well and which is ephemeral, and all the similar types of knowledge that they will find useful as mature citizens. It is not to be supposed that only the vocal leaders are learning, at the expense of the mass of their followers. Those who sit and do nothing but observe the proceedings may often gain more understanding than their more articulate fellows. Together they are in process of growing up.

Because of the importance of the educational processes to which youth-led organizations can contribute, the Commission believes that they can have major values. In any event, the violent and hysterical persecution of young intellectual radicals is in itself a childish procedure. No doubt there are organized foreign spy systems in this country, with which the authorities are bound to deal, but they should be distinguished from the normal exploratory activities of young people who seek to find solutions for our admittedly unsolved social problems. Moreover, the tendency to suppress youth by refusing to allow them the small sums needed for financing their societies, or by intimidating possible contributors, is unworthy of sensible adult attitudes toward the educational process.

Notwithstanding the difficulties youth-led organizations are now undergoing, the Commission is convinced that, in some form, they are here to stay. It therefore feels impelled to make some comment on ways by which such organizations may improve their standing in the eyes of the American people.

The practice of free speech undoubtedly includes the possibility of embarrassing one's friends and doing harm to one's own interests. A study of adult organizations as well as those of youth will readily confirm the truth of this observation. Young people who desire to influence public opinion should therefore give thought to one aspect of their situation which they sometimes overlook, namely, that while adults often do not appreciate youth attitudes, young people may have even greater difficulty in apprehending the attitudes of adults. Every adult has had the experience of being young, but no youth has had the experience of being an adult. To compensate so far as possible for this lack of experience, all youth organizations should take special care to avoid outraging the adult community through conspicuous bad manners and through gross failure to give a hearing to adult points of view. This is an elementary rule for any youth organization dealing with controversial topics which is interested in self-preservation and effective action.

Moreover, any youth group which presents itself to the public as a comprehensive organization should adopt policies calculated to result in fact in a diversified and broadly representative membership. Among other things, this means that when youth organizations select speakers for their public occasions, it is imperative to provide so far as possible a balanced representation of different points of view.

If some of the points of view upon presentation seem lacking in intelligence or honesty, they should nevertheless be heard courteously, a rule of conduct which may be commended to audiences of adults as well as of youth. A willingness to hear more than one view is essential to the maintenance of the American tradition of free speech.

CONCLUSION

Above all, it is imperative for each of us to recognize that the principle of free speech and assembly is established as the safeguard of democracy. It should not be mistaken for a menace. If events similar to those in the dictatorships were to happen here, they would not be the result of discussion or propaganda. They would be the end product of economic paralysis, uncontrolled monopoly, unemployment, and poverty. To distract attention from the real and dangerous diseases that threaten democracy by hysterical rejection of the curative though irritating processes of public discussion is un-American and might be suicidal.

BIBLIOGRAPHY

Directories of Organizations

ATWATER, ELTON. *Organized Efforts in the United States Toward Peace*. Washington: American University Graduate School, 1936. 47 pp. lithoprinted.

Lists and describes some 42 national nongovernmental organizations interested in the promotion of peace, classifying them into four major groups according to their respective attitudes and approaches to the subject. Brief history, membership, purpose, policies, activities, and finances of each are summarized wherever possible.

BAKER, PAUL E. *Negro-White Adjustment: An Investigation and Analysis of Methods in the Interracial Movement in the United States*. New York: Association Press, 1934. 267 pp.

Includes summaries of the history, philosophy, and programs of the ten principal national interracial agencies, a study of methods used by them in typical situations, and recommendations regarding their organization and administration.

BROWN, KARL (editor). *The American Library Directory, 1939*. New York: R. R. Bowker. 531 pp. $13.

A classified list of 10,253 libraries with names of librarians and statistical data.

COFFMAN, HAROLD COE. *American Foundations: A Study of Their Role in the Child Welfare Movement*. New York: Association Press, 1936. 213 pp. $3.

Appendices A, B, and C (pp. 157–62) list 55 foundations, 20 community trusts, and 32 child welfare organizations. The policies and interrelations of these agencies, and the significance of foundation support of child welfare activities, are discussed in the body of the book.

COMMUNITY CHESTS AND COUNCILS, INC. *Facing the Future with the Character-Building Agencies*. New York: Community Chests and Councils, Inc., 1936. 31 pp. 25¢.

Pages 24–28 contain brief summaries of the purposes and programs of nine leading national social agencies working with youth. Page 29 contains briefer mention of six additional "allied programs," including leading national governmental, educational, and recreational organizations and the research agencies maintained by them.

Educational Directory, 1940. U.S. Office of Education Bulletin, Bulletin 1940, No. 1. Washington: Government Printing Office, 1939. 233 pp.

Part I lists state and county school officers; Part II, city school officers and Catholic parochial school superintendents; Part III, all institutions of higher education; Part IV, educational associa-

tions and directories. This last part includes eight subdivisions as follows: American educational, civic, and learned societies; educational foundations and boards; church educational organizations; international educational associations and foundations; National Congress of Parents and Teachers; executive officers of state library commissions; state library associations; and educational and social directories and yearbooks.

EVANS, ANASTASIA H. (editor). *Directory of Social Agencies in the City of New York, 1940*. New York: Columbia University Press, 1939. 484 pp. $2.75.

Forty-third edition of this standard directory, now published for the Welfare Council of New York City. Alphabetic and classified lists of approximately 1,200 organizations, with subject index and personnel index. Many sections relate to different aspects of youth service. Addresses and telephone numbers are given. Directories for use to social workers are listed on pages 450–53.

HULSEMAN, BERTHA F. (compiler). *Directories of Social Agencies*. New York: Russell Sage Foundation, 1931. 11 pp. 20¢.

Lists many directories of general social agencies, national, local, and foreign, and directories of some 30 types of special agencies, including religious, educational, health-promoting, correctional, and recreational, both public and private.

INTERNATIONAL COUNCIL OF RELIGIOUS EDUCATION. *A Directory of Agencies Working with and for Adults*. Research Service Bulletin No. 13. Chicago: International Council of Religious Education, 1934. 71 pp. mimeo. 50¢.

Descriptions of 125 nondenominational national agencies in the United States working for the civic, social, moral, and religious education of adults. Purposes, activities, and publications are noted. An appendix classifies the organizations according to the areas of human experience within which their efforts lie.

KURTZ, RUSSELL H. (editor). *Social Work Year Book, 1939*. New York: Russell Sage Foundation, 1939. 730 pp.

Part III (pp. 593–708) is an annotated list of 982 social agencies, public and private, national and state-wide in scope. The section on national nongovernmental agencies is especially valuable, containing some 370 entries with notes on the membership, purposes, activities, and publications of each agency.

LINDEMAN, EDUARD C. *Wealth and Culture*. New York: Harcourt, Brace, 1936. 135 pp. $3.

A critical study of the policies and methods of 100 foundations and community trusts, in which 80 national foundations are listed. Includes a socio-economic study of 402 individual trustees of the several foundations and an analysis of foundation disbursements during the decade 1921–30.

LINDSAY, MARY RODGERS (compiler). *Directory of Youth Organizations*. New York: National Youth Administration, 1940. 293 pp. mimeo.

Data from 281 organizations, largely of the type having a majority of their membership between the ages of 18 and 25. Arranged to exhibit the following items: general character, officers, membership, purpose and program, activities, affiliations, and publications. Most of the groups included are national in scope, but some are local only.

MARSH, C. S. (editor). *American Universities and Colleges*. Washington: American Council on Education, 1940 (fourth quadrennial edition). 1120 pp. $4.

Part II (pp. 167–1018) lists 724 institutions of higher education and gives extensive and detailed information regarding each. In Part I, Chapter IV (pp. 100–52), professional schools in 17 professional fields are listed. Appendices contain several lengthy lists of institutions classified in various ways.

MOODY, MILDRED O., and ELVA M. WESTBROOK. *A Survey of Agencies Working with and for Children*. Research Service Bulletin No. 7. Chicago: International Council of Religious Education, 1929. 87 pp. 50¢.

Separate brief descriptions of the purpose, scope of work, and some of the publications of 120 organizations of national scope in the United States and Canada concerned with any and all phases of child welfare. Includes a brief preliminary analysis and an extensive topical index.

MOORE, HARRY H. (editor). *We Are the Builders of a New World: A Summons to Youth*. New York: Association Press, 1934. 165 pp. $1.50.

Appendix B (pp. 148–55), "Contemporary Social Movements," lists names and addresses of about 110 organizations in 14 categories, including public health, peace, crime prevention, civic planning, welfare work, political reform, temperance, protection of labor, education, "youth movements," religion, social and economic research, foundations, and the civil service.

"National Agencies in the United States Dealing with Refugee Problems." *Survey Graphic*, XXIX (November 1940), 591–92.

Lists 37 organizations. The address, names of officers, and a brief description of each organization appears.

NATIONAL CATHOLIC WELFARE CONFERENCE, Department of Education. *Catholic Colleges and Schools in the United States*. Washington: National Catholic Welfare Conference, 1940. 238 pp.

Lists seminaries, universities and colleges, normal training schools, secondary and elementary schools, and summer schools. Gives brief historical sketch and description of each institution.

NATIONAL CONFERENCE OF SOCIAL WORK. *The Conference Bulletin*, 43: No. 2. Columbus: National Conference of Social Work, January 1940. 55 pp.

Lists members, both individuals and organizations, of the National Conference of Social Work. Also lists the names and addresses of the 475 members who have continuously maintained their interest and support for a period of 20 years or more. A number of the organizations listed work directly or indirectly for the welfare of youth.

NATIONAL COUNCIL FOR PREVENTION OF WAR. *Organizations in the United States that Promote International Understanding and World Peace*. Washington: National Council for Prevention of War, February 1938. 31 pp. 15¢.

A directory listing a large number of organizations of four types: (1) national peace organizations, (2) organizations having peace committees, (3) organizations whose activities increase international understanding or which support peace organizations through affiliation, and (4) state and local peace organizations. Revised at frequent intervals.

NATIONAL INFORMATION BUREAU. *Giver's Guide to National Philanthropies*. New York: National Information Bureau, Inc.

Bulletin of national and interstate organizations engaged in social, civic, and charitable work endorsed on furnishing evidence that essential standards of financial and administrative policies are maintained. Lists approximately a hundred agencies, giving in each case the names of the three or four principal officers and a brief statement of the organization's purpose and work.

NEW YORK WORLD-TELEGRAM. *The World Almanac and Book of Facts*. New York: New York World-Telegram. 60¢.

Contains a list of approximately 800 "Associations and Societies in the United States," among which are many youth-serving organizations. Gives headquarters address, date of founding, names of principal officers, and aggregate number of members in most instances.

PENDRY, ELIZABETH R., and HUGH HARTSHORNE. *Organizations for Youth*. New York: McGraw-Hill, 1935. 357 pp. $2.75.

Accounts of 40 organizations, including history and growth, organization and administration, program and procedure, philosophy and method, motivation and rewards, and evidence of success.

Also lists an additional number of Catholic, Jewish, and Protestant youth organizations.

PUBLIC ADMINISTRATION CLEARING HOUSE. *Public Administration Organizations—A Directory 1938–39.* Chicago: Public Administration Clearing House, 1938 (fourth biennial edition). 183 pp.

Lists 558 national organizations, 1,342 state organizations, 80 regional organizations, and 87 Canadian organizations. Only the section dealing with national organizations is annotated, with information regarding the membership, finances, secretariat, activities, affiliations, and publications of the organizations.

ROWDEN, DOROTHY (editor). *Handbook of Adult Education in the United States.* New York: American Association for Adult Education, 1936. 423 pp. $2.25.

On pages 345–89 is an extensive annotated list of governmental and nongovernmental national organizations having adult education programs. The book contains information on the membership, program, and publications of each organization. Many other sections of the book contain similar lists of local and national agencies of adult education in specific fields.

RUSSELL SAGE FOUNDATION LIBRARY (compiler). *American Foundations for Social Welfare.* New York: Russell Sage Foundation, 1938. 66 pp. 50¢.

Lists 157 foundations and 31 community trusts in social welfare, health, research, international relations, and related fields. The brief descriptions of the foundations include the amount of the established fund and an outline of general purposes.

SEYBOLD, GENEVA (compiler). *American Foundations and Their Fields.* New York: Raymond Rich Associates, 1939. 218 pp.

The fourth edition of earlier studies published by the Twentieth Century Fund under the same title contains a survey of 243 foundations. Tabulates the capital funds and capital changes, 1931–37, of the 33 largest foundations. Shows data obtain-

able on foundation investments, and on classification and distribution of grants. Pages 39–128 carry a descriptive directory of American foundations, showing donors, trustees, officers of administration, purpose, year of establishment, direct activities, grants, capital assets, and publications, in cases where these data could be obtained.

STONE, WALTER L. *The Development of Boys' Work in the United States.* Nashville: Cullom & Ghertner, 1935. 188 pp.

Appendices A and B (pp. 179–88) list and classify 144 agencies "considered as part of, or related to, boys' work." The book contains probably the best extant history of the development of these types of agencies and extensive information regarding the membership and activities of half a dozen of the largest boys' organizations.

WICKEY, GOULD, and RUTH E. ANDERSON (editors). *Christian Higher Education—A Handbook for 1940.* Washington: Council of Church Boards of Education, 1940 (fourth edition). 342 pp.

Part I shows the history and organization of the council and the organization and function of the denominational boards of education together with their relation to educational institutions. Part II lists denominational foundations and student clubs. Part III presents information on 1,154 institutions of higher education. Part IV gathers together the educational standards of accrediting associations for educational institutions and lists educational and religious foundations and associations.

WILLIAMS, MARGUERITA (compiler). *Youth Movements Here and Abroad.* Bulletin No. 135. New York: Russell Sage Foundation Library, February 1936. 8 pp. 20¢.

An annotated bibliography of some 60 titles, followed by a fully annotated directory of more than a score of American "youth movements." The organizations listed are chiefly denominational, political, or student movements, and youth departments of agencies propagandizing for international peace or other reform movements.

List of Tables

List of Charts

Index

(An italicized number indicates the exhibit page)

THE AMERICAN COUNCIL ON EDUCATION

GEORGE F. ZOOK, *President*

The American Council on Education is a *council* of national educational associations; organizations having related interests; approved universities and colleges, technological schools, and private secondary schools; state departments of education; and city school systems. It is a center of cooperation and coordination whose influence has been apparent in the shaping of American educational policies as well as in the formulation of American educational practices during the past twenty years. Many leaders in American education and public life serve on the commissions and committees through which the Council operates.

Established by the Council in 1935, the American Youth Commission consists of the persons whose names appear on a front page of this publication. It operates through a staff under the supervision and control of a director responsible to the Commission.